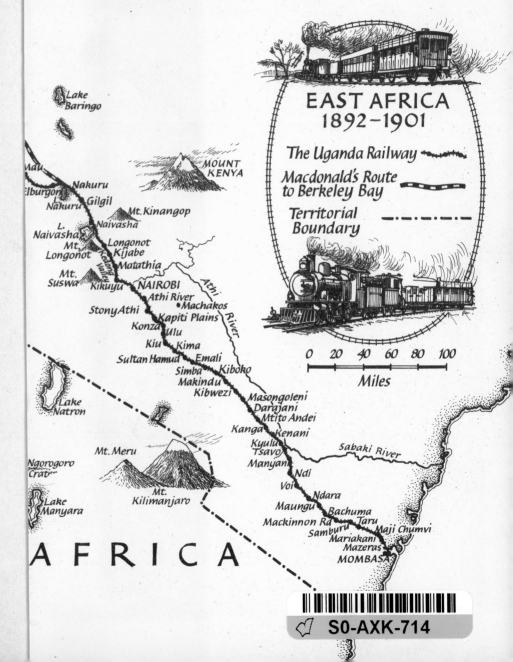

BRITISH EAST AFRICA

Lake Baringo

MOUNT KENYA

Mau
Nakuru
Elburgon
L. Nakuru
Gilgil
Mt. Kinangop
L. Naivasha
Naivasha
Mt. Longonot
Longonot
Kijabe
Matathia
Mt. Suswa
Kikuyu
NAIROBI
Athi River
Stony Athi
Machakos
Kapiti Plains
Konza
Ulu
Kiu
Kima
Sultan Hamud
Emali
Simba
Kiboko
Makindu
Kibwezi
Masongoleni
Darajani
Mtito Andei
Kanga
Kenani
Kyulu
Tsavo
Manyani
Ndi
Voi
Ndara
Maungu
Bachuma
Mackinnon Rd
Taru
Samburu
Maji Chumvi
Mariakani
Mazeras
MOMBASA

Athi River

Sabaki River

Mt. Meru
Ngorogoro Crater
Mt. Kilimanjaro
Lake Natron
Lake Manyara

EAST AFRICA 1892-1901

The Uganda Railway

Macdonald's Route to Berkeley Bay

Territorial Boundary

0   20   40   60   80   100
Miles

AFRICA

The Iron Snake

RONALD HARDY

THE IRON
SNAKE

'The two iron streaks of rail that wind away
among the hills and foliage of Mombasa Island
do not break their smooth monotony until, after
piercing Equatorial forests, stretching across
immense prairies, and climbing almost to the
level of the European snow-line, they pause
upon the edges of the Great Lake.'

Winston Churchill. *My African Journey*

COLLINS

ST JAMES'S PLACE, LONDON

1965

Contents

Illustrations

Acknowledgements

I have received much valuable help from Mr Trevor C. Colchester, C.M.G.; from Mr J. P. Lovegrove, Public Relations Officer of East African Railways and Harbours, and his successor Mr James Kibera; from Mr G. C. Whitehouse in respect of his father, the late Sir George Whitehouse, K.C.B., one-time Chief Engineer of the Uganda Railway; from Mr Ralph Preston and his sister Glynis in respect of their grandfather, the late Ronald Owen Preston, railhead engineer of the Uganda Railway; from Mrs Mary Gopal; and from Mr B. Cheeseman, the Librarian to the Colonial Office. I have also been able to consult, with gratitude, many old books (long out of print) from the shelves of the London Library and the Royal Commonwealth Society. I must add that none of these generous people is responsible for any part of the book. The opinions and the interpretations and (if any) the errors and the wrong conclusions are entirely my own.

Ronald Hardy

An iron snake will cross from the lake of salt to the lands of the Great Lake. . . .

Ancient Kikuyu prophecy

The railway is the beginning of all history in Kenya. . . .

Sir Edward Grigg

Prologue

Later, in the early year, the true dhows would come on the north-east trades, high-pooped and rigged for the ocean, and the lateens would fill the Harbour. Now there were only a few sardine-boats, the insignificant sails of local dhows from Lamu. The quays were bleak avenues of sunglare where nothing moved. There was a smell of stagnation, of sea debris. A sack of raw salt stood propped like some scrap of abandoned cargo, the contents spilling and the shadow of its hessian ears pricked on stone.

The Old Harbour lies on the east of the island of Mombasa. You can still catch the airs of antiquity; and, if you have a sense of past, hear tongues of silver, smell merchandise and spice. The caravans came here. They came announced by flags and drums. They brought ivory and produce from the Victoria Nyanza and beyond—and they brought it on the backs of slaves.

The railroad story begins with the caravans. There was a route; found and prospected by the Arab traders. It led from the north, from as far as Lake Rudolf, joined with the old Uganda track. It was beaten out by generations of naked feet; and, later, by processions of Kamba stock. Africa is a land of thirst: it is dominated by water, by the need and the search for water. The caravan track followed water, wound and deviated for it; from river to stream, from spring to well, from the dried beds of wadis to where sandstone pools evaporated in yellow heats. Then, later still, the railroad followed the caravan track: not without divergence (for there were convolutions of land, rivers to bridge, considerations of subsoil and gradient) but with approximation. The expeditions of survey returned again and again to the routes of the Arab and Swahili traders. Charts, the fruit of compass and theodolite, emerged in harmony with ancient trails of instinct and tradition.

But in the days before the surveys the map of tropical Africa was as bare as the surface of a new leaf. Little was known. Then the Great Explorers came and drew thin veins of discovery across the face of those ungiving lands. The name of David Livingstone entered and engaged the awareness of a nation. This was more than exploration, more than scientific quest, much more than the spectacle of bravery and endurance. (Britain, after all, had a plenitude of heroes.) Livingstone was Christianity embodied in its most pure and militant form. He walked alone. He was consumed with an evangelical fire. He was endued with that special quality which irradiates a darkness. He gave to the ultimate and placed his wife in the soil of an African river-grave. Livingstone was saintly.

His historical destiny was to re-awaken Britain to the plight of the enslaved African; to wander and to die and, in the dying, leave a kind of guilt. Before the wanderings slavery, as an issue, was either dead or quiescent. The British Empire had cleaned its own stable: it had been purged from the British system in 1833. Outside the Empire the trade still flourished and, for a time, the British exerted pressure beyond its colonial frontiers with all the terrible zeal of the reformed sinner. But the enthusiasm waned. Practical humanity was both costly and exhausting; a nation already throbbing with the first pulsations of a new industrial power could not afford such self-indulgence; and in any event this was surely the province of the churches and the missionary societies. The infamy was now confined, it seemed, to the negroid peoples of Africa's western coast: the passage of time, political change and humanitarian example would cure their afflictions. Britain and its Government had, in fact, turned away. It was left to Livingstone, through the testimony in particular of those last seven anguished years until his death in 1873, to re-orientate its gaze. An Arab slave-trade ran, and swelled, in evil rivers from the East.

On this eastern coast of Africa the old Portuguese dominion had shrunk as far down as Mozambique: north of that point Arab power (owing a nominal allegiance to Zanzibar) was supreme. There was, of course, nothing new in a Muslim Arab trade in slaves. Slavery in one form or another had existed since the earliest inland expeditions. But by Livingstone's time the trade had increased dramatically. It was organised with a fearsome energy. Funds flowed from Indian sources in Zanzibar. Fire-arms could now be bought and the caravans went further and further into the interior. Ivory was the goal. Those were the days of the great elephant populations and money hung, it seemed, from the heads of the tuskers in inexhaustible supplies. But there was no wheeled transport. Only men could carry it. The caravans penetrated even deeper, even as far as the Great Lakes. There, on the shores where the tribes were concentrated, was an abundance of bone and muscle. The arrangement was perfect in its simplicity. Both commodities, ivory and people, were obtained at little cost: both were valuable and were saleable on the coast. By the middle of the nineteenth century some fifty thousand slaves were passing yearly through the Zanzibar market. One half were exported. For each to survive the rigours of the long march down (Livingstone estimated) perhaps ten had died. These were the statistics of misery, these the revelations which were to rekindle in the British nation the dormant passion for philanthropic crusade. And, later, when Sir Samuel Baker revealed that another arm of the trade was reaching with greed and ferocity from the north into the equatorial areas of the Upper Nile the way was opened for a further chapter in Christian adventure.

These were, of course, dramatic times for missionaries. Livingstone's story—the wandering, the aloneness, the enormous compassion, the death and the epic march through the wilderness on which the body and the diary were borne to the coast—was almost theatrical in its impact. There was no lack of disciples. Within three years a new thrust of missionary endeavour had begun to pierce the lands of the caravans. Missions from the Church of Scotland and the Free Church infiltrated the regions around Lake Nyasa. The Universities' Mission to Central Africa (incongruously based in Zanzibar itself) pressed inward from the coast to the east fringe of the lake. A year later the Church Missionary Society entered Uganda, asserting in the court of King Mutesa the Anglican claim to exclusive divine representation; and, a year after that, the priests of the French Roman Catholic Mission of the White Fathers arrived (as you would expect) to contest it. Never had the great areas of Central and East Africa been so well served by the emissaries of Christendom. To the battle already joined between Islam and Christianity was added the bewildering sub-conflict of Protestant and Catholic.

Now Livingstone, for all the fervour of his beliefs, was a Scot and a realist. Like Wilberforce and Buxton before him he had never claimed that a glimmer of Christian faith pricked weakly here and there in that immense pagan darkness would diminish the volume of suffering. The Arab slavers were avaricious and unpitying; and, conveniently, the Koran did not proscribe slavery in general, it merely forbade the enslaving of another Muslim. Livingstone and, indeed, all the great missionaries, saw clearly that it was the emptiness of central Africa that was at the root of the problem. Anything could happen in that mass of unmapped territory, the strong were unchallenged and the meek could inherit nothing but sorrow. Africa had need not of the shrieks of martyrs but of lines of communication, of fruitful toil, food, goods and transport. Africa had need of trade.

Livingstone had called it 'commerce and Christianity.' It was a good phrase, coined in a time when business enterprise and a strict morality had seemed compatible. Five years after his death a group of Scottish merchants led by James Stevenson formed the African Lakes Company. The Company was based on Lake Nyasa and its primary objects were to victual and equip the missions and to develop trading links with the Africans. There, isolated and inadequately armed, exposed to the hostility of the Arab slavers and the Portuguese in Mozambique, began the first practical expression of Livingstone's dream. Much followed from that early, and precarious, foothold in 1878. The 1880s saw the emergence of the Chartered Companies. In the west the Royal Niger Company exploited the great waterways of the Niger and the Benue. In the south Cecil Rhodes had formed the British South Africa Company and, impelled by his Cape-to-Cairo vision, was moving up through that land of granite kopjes toward Lake Nyasa. In the east the Imperial British East Africa

Company ventured inland from Mombasa along the route to Uganda. These were new, exciting rhythms. Caravans of trade were on the move.

The Imperial British East Africa Company received the dignity of the Royal Charter in September of 1888. Modestly subscribed it was yet invested with considerable power. It could acquire territory from native chiefs, establish civil and judicial administration, levy taxes and customs duties, construct roads and other public works. It could even coin money. These were, in practice, sovereign powers. The Company's main object was to take over the mainland concessions granted to the old British East Africa Association by Barghash, Sultan of Zanzibar and, by that authority, develop avenues of trade.

The formation of the Charter Company was belated. Since the days of the first explorations British influence had grown around the great unappropriated area of middle Africa; in Zanzibar, in the western lands of the negro, in Egypt, in South Africa. Britain had only to move, to occupy, to plant the flag. And yet she did nothing. There were always reasons for inaction. Strategically the area had no significance. It was poor and likely to be unproductive (the country between the Indian Ocean and Lake Victoria was regarded by the Foreign Office as 'a sterile region'). Adventures in colonial expansion were apt to be expensive and, in any event, white settlement in such primitive lands was hardly a possibility. Annexation was an act of the future: in the meantime trade and development was the proper field for private enterprise.

But by 1884 the major European powers had begun to gather in covetous array. The fist of Leopold of the Belgians contracted around the Congo. Portugal sought to girdle the waist of Africa from Mozambique to Angola. France reached out from Senegal along the river of the Niger. And Bismarck's agents, grouped under the cloak of the Society of German Colonization and directed by the ruthless Carl Peters, pressed inward from the East African coast through the dominions of the Sultan of Zanzibar. Germany's appetite was predictably keen. At the end of the year Peters' caravan emerged from the interior with treaty rights (negotiated with native chiefs in defiance of the Sultan) to 60,000 square miles of territory; and by March of 1885 Germany had declared a Protectorate.

East Africa was now irreparably divided. It had been there for Britain's taking: she had turned aside. All that remained was formal recognition of the unseemly partition of the Sultan's empire; and in October of 1886 Germany and Britain defined, by agreement, their 'spheres of influence.' The German sphere (in rough correspondence to the Tanganyika of today) lay south of a line drawn from the Umbe River on the Indian Ocean to a point on the east shore of Lake Victoria. North of the line, in that territory which approximates to Kenya, was the British sphere. Both powers recognised the sovereignty (now sadly weakened) of the Sultan over the islands of Zanzibar, Pemba, Mafia and Lamu; and over a coastal strip of ten miles depth extending from Tunghi Bay to Kipini.

This, then, was the eroded inheritance of Sir William Mackinnon, first president of the new Imperial British East Africa Company.

Mackinnon was a Scot from Argyll whose ships, under the flag of the British India Steam Navigation Company, had plied to Zanzibar since 1872. He was devout, gentle and shrewd; a curious mixture of the philanthropist and the man of business. Later the Prime Minister, Lord Salisbury, leader of a Government bent on appeasement of Germany, was to censure him as having 'no energy for anything except quarrelling with Germans.' Now, in 1888, Mackinnon had already displayed sufficient energy to build a thriving shipping line, an integrity of character conspicuous enough to have won the trust of the Sultan of Zanzibar; and, it seems, personal qualities so exceptional that the Government was prepared to appoint him its virtual representative in East Africa. For this was the measure of the Company's authority. Ahead lay the primitive lands, raw and lawless terrains in which the trading stations must be set like stepping-stones, in which rivers of commerce must be made to flow; and, above all, in which the competition and rapacity of the Germans must be met. Ahead was Uganda.

Stanley, the explorer, had described it as 'the pearl of Africa.'

Certainly, to the contestant powers now matched in the great equatorial arena, it shone with an irresistible lustre. Here was an immense and fertile land running from the north-west shores of Lake Victoria (the source of the White Nile) to the Sudanese border. It was rich in ivory and in the fruits of the land. 'The position of that country on Victoria Nyanza (wrote a historian[1] of the period) formed a key to the Nile Valley beyond and the populous and productive provinces ruled by Emin Pasha. The power holding Uganda would exercise a paramount influence in the surrounding regions . . . There was no desire on the part of this country to annex Uganda, or to become responsible for its good government; but there would have been the strongest objection to its annexation by any other country. From a very early date the Government recognised this fact, and it was not, as may be readily supposed, without considerable uneasiness that the activity of the Germans began to be observed. Uganda was not likely to be left for long unapproached by people so enterprising who meant to make it their road—as it was already the road of commerce—to the Equatorial Provinces from the East Coast of Africa.'

Throughout 1889 Mackinnon and his associates sent their agents into the interior. Treaties were made in the tribal territories. Paths were beaten through the bush. Small outposts were built, the chain reaching in that year as far as Machakos, three hundred and fifty miles from Mombasa. A steamer, decked in the Company's colours, plied on the coast. In August a great caravan of five hundred men (led by Frederick Jackson, a hunter destined to become Governor of Uganda) marched inland from Machakos with instructions to explore, negotiate treaties and build further stations.

But these activities, adequate in any ordinary trading company concerned with nothing more than a first cautious consolidation, were derisory in an enterprise charged, in effect, with an imperial responsibility. The Company was desperately short of funds. It had begun its life with a capital of only £240,000. It was contracted to pay out of income an annual sum of £10,000 to Zanzibar in respect of the lease of the coastal strip. It was

<hr>

[1] P. L. McDermott: British East Africa or Ibea (1893).

expected to pay its way, make a profit and reward its share-holders; and, if anything were left, succour slaves, support the missions, defeat the Arab traders and compete successfully with the German East Africa Company.

Of course it could not do so. The German Company was an arm of German ambition. It was under no obligation to return a profit or even support itself. Its activities were directed openly by Major Wissman, the Imperial Commissioner in German East Africa. Funds and soldiers had been made available to it. Mackinnon wrote repeatedly to England for Government support. Strategy, prestige and the prize of Uganda demanded immediate state intervention. Incredibly, the British Government did nothing. Salisbury, who had once referred to 'the inconvenience of protectorates' apparently saw no reason to alter that assessment. The development of Britain's sphere of influence in East Africa was still the field for private enterprise. Another trading company in another place, the East India Company, had delivered India to the Crown through the power and ramifications of commerce: the British Charter Company would, no doubt, do the same for Uganda.

In the spring of 1890 the German threat to Uganda intensified. Wissman was preparing a large caravan, containing two hundred Sudanese soldiers, for the march to the frontier. Carl Peters had already reached the Kavirondo district on the north-east shore of the Great Lake. In Germany maps were in circulation which, arrogantly placing Uganda within the German sphere, revealed a clear intention. Annexation was now a danger. Even then British opinion was inclined to reproach the Charter Company rather than the Government. The Times of London wrote: 'It results from all this that the British East Africa Company must lose no time in putting its house in order, and in taking effective possession of whatever it hopes to keep on the shores of the Victoria Nyanza . . . British influence must either cut the route from German territory south of the Victoria Nyanza to Emin Pasha's old province, or German influence must cut the com-munications of the British Company with everything west of the Great Lakes. Neither nation can for a long time to come have so much at stake as to preclude peaceful agreement, but it is plain that just at present the German temper is one of uncompromising aggressiveness . . .' Then, grudgingly: 'The British Company is at a heavy disadvantage because, while it must conform to the laws of a commercial undertaking, it has to compete with what is practically on the part of Germany a scheme of imperial conquest. It is the German Government, much more than German traders, that is pushing forward the present attempt to secure the whole of Central Africa . . .'

The Times article also referred to the need for a territorial line (perhaps scattering one of the first small seeds from which would burgeon the project of the Uganda Railway): '. . . it would seem that in one way or another good communications must be rapidly established with the Victoria Nyanza . . .' Sir William Mackinnon had long nursed such a project. The building of a railroad from Mombasa to the Lake (the true route to Uganda) had lain in his mind like an unwritten clause in the Company's charter.

Eighteen-ninety was a fateful year.

It had begun, in Uganda, with the manœuvring of three men. These were Jackson, Carl Peters and Lourdel, leader of the French missionaries. At the centre of the triangle sat Mwanga, King since 1884. Jackson, suave, gentle and chivalrous, proffered the Company's flag and extolled the benefits of its protection. Peters, cruel and unscrupulous (his route to the capital had been scarred with bloody atrocity) uncoiled the whip of German aggression. Lourdel, cast in the classic role of priest-intriguer, whispered in Mwanga's ear the French case for a neutral Uganda. Mwanga, barbarous, stupefied from hemp and more interested in the pleasures of sodomy and spectacular public tortures than in political manœuvre, watched idly and listened with half an ear.

Nothing of positive value emerged from this confusion. Early in the year Mwanga accepted the Company's flag—and then rejected it. In March Lourdel and Peters, drawn into brief alliance by a common hatred of the British, inveigled the degenerating King into an agreement that Uganda fell within the German sphere. Peters sent copies of the treaty to Bismarck and to Leopold of the Belgians and, avoiding Jackson's caravan, fled from Mengo (the capital) to the coast. Jackson entered Mengo. Lourdel was hostile, Mwanga unreachable. Jackson had hoped for a treaty but (he wrote in desperation to the Company's Court of Directors) '. . . the King has little or nothing to say in such affairs, but is a mere tool in the hands of Père Lourdel and the Roman Catholic chiefs . . .' In May he began the long safari to the coast. Lourdel died of malaria. Mwanga sank deeper into the quagmires of barbarism and sensuality.

But Peters' treaty, gained secretly and without the approval of the Ugandese chiefs, could not be sustained. His own conduct, the record of cruelty on the march through Kavirondo, militated against him. Germany was not at war with Britain. The scent of burning villages had reached Berlin: it could not endorse so embarrassing an account of murder, brigandage and trespass within the British sphere. In July Salisbury brought his own patient and secret negotiations with Germany to a head: a new Anglo-German agreement was signed. By its terms Uganda was secured to the Company as an area of British influence. But Germany's withdrawal was bought at a price; the agreement conceding, among other things, great masses of the East African hinterland, the southern shores of Lake Victoria and, in another clime, the island of Heligoland. The German territory now commanded important routes. Strategically it lay in significant juxtaposition to the British sphere. Nothing had been annexed by Britain and, despite its ambiguous authority, the Charter Company flew merely a flag of trade. Failure could yet draw the hem of the German shadow.

During this time of Salisbury's negotiations many great maritime and colonial nations had been meeting in Brussels. Slavery, increasing even in the face of the wave of re-awakened sentiment, had brought them into conference. The European Powers, the Congo, America, Russia and Zanzibar were all represented. After eight months' deliberation a General Act emerged to coincide almost to the day with the Anglo-German Agreement. The signatories (they claimed) had been 'animated by the firm intention of putting an end to the crimes and devastations engendered by the traffic in African slaves.' Seven clauses were listed in Article One which, the Conference adjudged, were 'the most effective means for counteracting the slave-trade in the interior of Africa . . .'

Of these Clause Three provided a powerful and timely prop to the ambitions of Sir William Mackinnon. It advocated: 'The construction of roads and, in particular, of railways, connecting the advanced stations with the coast, and permitting easy access to the inland waters, and to such of the upper courses of the rivers and streams as are broken by rapids and cataracts, in view of substituting economical and rapid means of transport for the present means of carriage by men.'

Here, contained within an instrument of international force and, moreover, underwritten by his own Government, was an explicit reference to railways. The 'inland waters' could only refer to the Great Lakes of which Victoria Nyanza was the largest. Mackinnon, thus armed, was hardly the man to fail to use so potent a weapon.

On 6 August 1890 a large caravan left Mombasa. It was led by Captain F. D. Lugard,[1] a man whose name was to become illustrious in African history. Seconded to the Company's services by the War Office in the previous year Lugard had already taken one exploratory, but less ambitious, caravan into the interior. At this time he was thirty-two years old; a decorated soldier of the East Norfolk Regiment with service in the Afghan War, the Sudan and Burma campaigns, and a record of command in the Nyasaland campaign against the Arab slave-traders. A contemporary portrait reveals hollowed temples and haggard cheeks, a pair of deep, bright, almost fanatical eyes, thin dark hair and the melancholy droop of a mandarin's moustache. Spy's cartoon, drawn for *Vanity Fair* five years later, shows a face cadaverous from the West African campaign: the hair has receded and a finger-tip could sink under the frontal bones, the chin juts sharply and the eyes are darkly brilliant in the orbits. He has a prim, neat body, slender, putteed calves and small, meticulous feet. There is a sense of that ferocious and inexhaustible energy which always powered him: the dainty feet, you feel, will mince rather than plod through the miles of bush and jungle.

Lugard's instructions were to find the best and shortest route

[1] Later Lord Lugard of Abinger, P.C. G.C.M.G. C.B. D.S.O.

to Uganda, to build Company posts at selected points and to form alliances with the tribes. But, of course, the expedition, mounted within five weeks of the Anglo-German Agreement, was far more than that. The term 'sphere of influence' was meaningless without physical occupation: possession was, indeed, nine points of the international law. Before entering Uganda he was to await the arrival of Sir Francis de Winton, the Company's Administrator, or, in lieu of that, mails with further instructions. Lugard's expedition, in fact, would become political at that point in time at which he crossed the Nile. He took with him George Wilson as second-in-command; Fenwick de Winton (Sir Francis's son); William Grant; and Dualla, a Somali servant and interpreter. The caravan was guarded by seventy Sudanese soldiers.

The normal caravan route ran inland from Mombasa, through the Rabai Hills and across the Taru Plain. Drought sometimes stretched this great pan of heat and scrub into a desert sixty miles deep. The Taru was feared by porters. It was a place of sickness, desertions and death. The Company and Lugard believed (wrongly) at that time that the true route to Uganda must lie along the course of the Sabaki River. The Sabaki emptied into the Indian Ocean at a point seventy miles north of Mombasa. Lugard, accordingly, avoided the Taru and marched his caravan along the coast to the mouth of the river. Then he struck inland. He reached Machakos on 20 September. Wilson was nearly dead from illness and exhaustion. Only eighty of the five hundred loads of provisions they needed were stored in the post. Wilson's recovery was slow. Two weeks had passed before the caravan resumed its march.

Lugard reached Dagoretti on the third day. The land was high and the vegetation lush. North were the hills of Kikuyuland, south the Masai steppe. Here, at Dagoretti, he built a stockaded post; and it was here, on 18 October, that a runner brought him mails from Mombasa. These were the orders he had expected. He was to enter Uganda. De Winton's letter charged him with the urgency of the situation: Charles Stokes (a renegade ex-missionary employed by the Germans in the running of guns and gunpowder) was already marching along the German route for Uganda.

Lugard left Dagoretti. Wilson, again too ill to move, remained at the post. The caravan marched through the silent valley of the Rift to Lake Nakuru. There, Lugard planned the next stages of his route. Already the lands ahead had touched him with their sense of oppressiveness. 'To the north (he wrote) would lie the country of Nandi, whose people are reported to be excessively hostile and fierce, and no caravan, European or native, has ever yet dared to cross their hills. To the south the equally hostile and exasperated tribes of Lumbwa and Sotik. Between these two mountainous countries it was rumoured that a pass existed by which we might cross the giant range of Mau. This would be the prolongation of the direct line from Mombasa to the north of Victoria Lake . . . the shortest route to Uganda . . .'

But Lugard lost himself. The forests were thick and primeval. 'I attempted to cut my way due west through the pathless forest . . . Range on range lay before us, all clothed in the same interminable forest, and I saw that I had attempted the impossible . . .' He struck north-east for Lake Baringo, climbed along the flank of the Elgeyo Ravine and on to the Nandi plateau. Below the plateau lay the sweep of the Kavirondo plain. Rinderpest had brushed the land and left it unclean. 'Through all this great plain we passed carcases of buffalo . . . The breath of the pestilence had destroyed them . . .' He reached Mumia's (the village of the Chief Mumia) on 29 November.

Mumia's lay perhaps ten days' march from the Nile. Lugard's entries make it plain that it was not until after he had entered the village that he informed the caravan, its porters, soldiers and servants, that the destination was Uganda. The deception (six weeks had passed since the receipt of de Winton's orders) is a significant pointer to the evil of Mwanga's reputation. The King was unpredictable. The Company's flag was a gossamer protection against the blood-lusts and those terrible hemp-induced rages. But the caravan was three hundred and fifty strong. There was even a Maxim gun which had belonged to Stanley. And Lugard was a leader of strength and resolution. The caravan spent four days in revictualling and re-equipping. At dawn of the fifth day it left Mumia's. On 13 December 1890 Lugard crossed the Nile.

Mackinnon had not been idle during the four months of Lugard's march. In London the Company's case for a sharing of the Imperial burden needed constant pleading. In East Africa the Company had continued to deploy its meagre resources in the British cause. Expenses were rising. Trading revenue was almost static. The cost of porterage to supply Lugard's caravan was sometimes as high as £300 for every ton carried. On 17 December Mackinnon (estimating with some shrewdness that Lugard must by now have taken the flag into Uganda) wrote a letter to Lord Salisbury.

The letter was of great importance. It was the first public claim on the Government to discharge its obligations. Mackinnon listed many irrefutable arguments. The Company was now in occupation of no less than 750,000 square miles. It had secured to the Crown the headwaters of the Nile. It was no longer in competition with the German East Africa Company (now dissolved) but with its formidable successor—the German Imperial Government. And, impoverished though it was, it had 'already anticipated the engagements of the Brussels Conference to a certain extent . . .' A coastal telegraph-line now joined Mombasa with Lamu. Roads and stations had been built on the route to Lake Victoria. A steamer patrolled the River Tana: two vessels plied along the coast. But, plainly, none of this fulfilled the obligation imposed by the First Article of the Brussels Act, namely, that the Conference Powers construct 'roads and, in particular . . . railways.' Only a line from Mombasa to the Lake could destroy the slave-trade: only a railroad could hold East Africa. The letter concluded with a request that the Government guarantee the interest on the capital required. 'With such support and with two or three steamers afloat on the lake for police purposes, the Company believe slave-trading would soon disappear, and they would have no difficulty in finding as much additional capital as may be necessary for the general purposes of the administration, and the development of an enterprise of national importance, largely advantageous to Imperial interests, and those of the Equatorial provinces of East Africa.'

Mackinnon had chosen the time for his appeal with considerable sagacity; for within three days Salisbury had forwarded the terms of the letter to the Treasury with his personal endorsement. The year was drawing to a triumphant close. In Uganda, on the day after Christmas, Lugard obtained Mwanga's mark on yet another treaty. 'Light and Liberty' (the Company's motto) was not, it seemed, too ephemeral a dream.

The Company received a note of the Treasury's proposals at its offices at 2 Pall Mall East. The Government had estimated (with no practical foundation for even the most approximate of engineering estimates) that a metre-gauge line to Victoria Nyanza would cost one-and-a-quarter million pounds. On such a capital, to be publicly subscribed, it would guarantee a five per cent interest. Any profits remaining would be apportioned equally between the Government and the shareholders.

The offer was the first small puncture in the fabric of Mackinnon's schemes. The Treasury itself was the main beneficiary; and, on its own admission, would (with the eventual destruction of the slave-trade) be relieved of the cost of the naval squadrons which, as an anti-slavery measure, cruised permanently off the coast of East Africa. And, too, investors were not philanthropists. The 750,000 square miles of the Company's territory through which the line must pass were almost wholly unproductive. Africa was undoubtedly an exciting new field for the employment of money: but, plainly, the other two Charter Companies (the Royal Niger with its thriving trade or Cecil Rhodes' British South Africa with its promise of gold) were the greater entice-ments. The major weakness contained within the offer was, as Mackinnon and Salisbury knew, that Parliamentary sanction must be obtained.

Lord Salisbury's party, in power without a House of Commons majority, was hardly in a position to force a contentious measure. The railroad, although potentially capable of generating an impressive head of Christian steam, was still an Imperial adven-ture; and, as such, must inevitably invite opponents. Salisbury was neither timid nor turncoat: but he was vulnerable. In a speech at Glasgow in May of 1891 he was already at the point of retraction.

'There is no doubt,' he said, 'that the slave caravans across that territory can be destroyed by one method, and by one method certainly, if that method can be applied. Sir William Mackinnon is doing his best to lay a railway from the coast to the Victoria Nyanza. Now the peculiarity of a railway, which everyone may have had the opportunity of observing in this country, is that where it is once laid it kills every other mode of locomotion that formerly held the same ground. After a railway has existed some time there cannot be—except as a matter of luxury or caprice—any other kind of locomotion to compete with it. If a railway could exist from this lake to the coast, caravans could no more be employed as they are employed now to carry ivory, the produce of the interior, to the coast or back again, and it is by these caravans that the bodies of slaves are brought along. It costs two or three hundred times as much to bring goods by caravan as it would cost to bring them by railway. Of course, when once a railway existed, caravans would become a matter of antiquity, and if no caravans existed, there would be no means of carrying slaves from the interior to the coast . . .'

At this stage in the speech Salisbury's Scottish audience may well have assumed that the rails were about to begin their sinuous route to the Lake. But the Prime Minister, with a politician's deviousness, had merely withheld the bitter draught which, now, he was to present to Mackinnon's lips. 'Whether the Treasury will be able, consistently with the sound principles of finance which are always upheld, to give Sir William Mackinnon the assistance which he requires, or whether it must be deferred to a distant date, I do not know . . .'

In political parlance the term 'distant date' was invariably ominous. It meant, Mackinnon knew, that the Treasury discounted the Government's chances of obtaining House of Commons sanction to the guarantee and would now take refuge in inaction. The original offer, parsimonious and unrealistic though it was, had in fact represented the first significant sign that the Government was preparing to accept its Imperial responsibilities in Uganda. But, now, it was once more uncommitted. The Company could not hope to survive without the railroad link; it could not maintain its occupation of Uganda out of revenue or uncalled capital: it could not raise additional funds without Government guarantees. Mackinnon protested, pleaded, lobbied for support. But it was too late. The Treasury made an unenthusiastic offer of a sum of up to £20,000 to finance a railroad survey. Then, when it became obvious that even this small project would be opposed in the Commons, the offer was withdrawn. The Company, the Treasury suggested, might consider discharging the cost of the survey out of its own funds subject to a Government undertaking to reimburse it by the end of the fiscal year (eight months distant).

The Court of Directors met on 16 July. It passed a momentous resolution:

'That to give effect to a policy of retrenchment, rendered necessary by the financial position of the Company, all the Company's establishments at Uganda shall be temporarily withdrawn; (and) That for the present Dagoretti shall be the extreme point of the Company's occupation in the interior.'

This, in effect, meant (if implemented) the end of British influence in Uganda. Into the vacuum left by the withdrawal the German claw would almost certainly stretch. 'Such a withdrawal,' *The Times* said later, 'would be nothing short of a national calamity ... Whether we desire it or not, the British East Africa Company, working under a Royal Charter, must be identified for all practical purposes with national policy ... The whole slave-trade interest is fully aware that the matter is for it a matter of life or death. If the British East Africa Company can hold its ground in Uganda, the slave-trade organisation, powerful and ramified as it is, will surely be broken up. In the contrary case, it will establish itself more firmly and defiantly than ever ... We cannot now come away and leave things as they were. Our choice is practically between pushing forward the civilising work we have begun, and handing over all who have trusted us to a worse fate than would have been theirs if we had never penetrated to Uganda at all ... What the British East Africa Company needs to keep it going is the construction of a railway from Mombasa to the shores of the Victoria Nyanza. Such a railway would at once open up an enormous district around the Great Lake, furnishing a solid basis for operations from which trade and civilisation would rapidly permeate Central Africa ...'

The Times article was typical of the reactions provoked by the news of the resolution. The rest of the national Press (with the exception of the Liberal newspapers) was indignant. The literate element of the nation, for long nourished on a diet of anti-slavery sentiment and convinced of the righteousness of the Imperial cause, found intolerable this threat of abandonment. And the Church Missionary Society became immediately agitated at the prospect of unprotected missions.

The wave of feeling, violent and emotional in some quarters, was, without doubt, deeply gratifying to Mackinnon. That he was depressed by the plight of the Company is certain. That he was determined, in the absence of Government help, to evacuate Uganda is evidenced by the Directors' resolution. But, equally certain, the resolution was used as a weapon. It had been fashioned to evoke a particular response. Even the order to evacuate, sent to Lugard in East Africa on 10 August and which would take three or four months to reach him, was not, you suspect, entirely irrevocable. Some weeks after the passing of the resolution we find Mackinnon in the Scottish highlands, still energetically pleading the Company's cause; this time to the Anglican Bishop of Uganda. 'Uganda is costing us £40,000 a year (Bishop Tucker reports him as saying[1]). Help us to raise a sum of £30,000 and we will undertake to continue in the country for at least another year . . .'

The Bishop obliged. On 30 October, at a meeting of the Church Missionary Society, Tucker made a powerful and successful appeal. Within twelve days most of the money had been raised and, on 11 November, a telegram was sent to Mombasa for delivery to Lugard: the order to evacuate (it told him) was cancelled.

Time had been gained. On 24 November 1891 the Aden boat anchored off the island of Mombasa. Aboard the *Madura* was the first railroad survey party.

The party was led by Captain James Macdonald[2] of the Royal Engineers. There were three other engineer officers: Captain

---

[1] Tucker: Eighteen Years in Uganda.
[2] Later Major-General Sir James Macdonald, K.C.I.E. C.B.

Pringle and Lieutenants Twining and Austin. There were also a surveyor named Sergeant Thomas and forty-five Indians of assorted qualifications. All had had experience of railroad survey and construction across the plains and frontiers of India, a country where, perhaps, conditions were most nearly comparable to those in East Africa.

Macdonald at this time was in his thirtieth year: already the tropics had thinned back the hair to a sparse black tonsure. He was muscular, grim and humourless. The eyes were dark and cold, the moustache luxuriant, the lip pugnacious; the man himself impressed with the indefinable but obvious mark of success. Clearly this austere and autocratic soldier would march unerringly on a course to rank, prestige, dignities and civil honours.

Macdonald spent three weeks hiring for the caravan. More than three hundred porters, cooks, servants, gun-bearers, headmen and interpreters were recruited. Forty askari were enlisted for its defence. Sixty donkeys were bought. Two men, Jackson and Foaker, were attached by the Company. Then, mustering on paper his total force, Macdonald split it in half.

The first of the caravans left Mombasa on 18 December. It was commanded by Captain Pringle and it would reconnoitre the direct route inland across the Taru Desert, replenish its water from the pool which lay one thousand feet high on the Hill of Maungu and march from there to that place which was to become notorious in railroad history: Tsavo.

Macdonald's caravan left six days later. He was accompanied by the young Lieutenant Twining and Sergeant Thomas. The caravan would follow Lugard's old route, marching north and finding the Sabaki River at Makengeni. Then, trekking with the course of the Sabaki, it would rendezvous with Pringle where the Sabaki joined with the Tsavo River. The choice of marching date was characteristic of Macdonald's perverse and puritanical nature. Not for him (or his men) the Christmas fleshpots of Mombasa. He marched on Christmas Eve.

From Tsavo the expedition moved up-country. In the months that followed it divided, regrouped, divided again, pushing its exploratory feelers outward from a line that probed and lengthened toward the north-east tip of the Great Lake. It suffered all the hardships that were accepted by caravans in those days. It passed from the arid heat of the plains to the cold of the rain forests, through belts of fever and tsetse and regions stripped bare by drought and locust. There were hungry days. Smallpox burned intermittently and the graves of porters marked the route. Most of the donkeys died. But there were also streams of 'beautiful water, cold and clear as crystal'; and lands of abundance where 'peas, beans, sweet potatoes, cassava, pumpkins, goats, fowls, eggs, milk, and fish from the lake, are all procurable in exchange for beads, cloth and wire . . .'

At Mumia's (seventy-five miles from the inlet on Victoria Nyanza known as Berkeley Bay) Macdonald divided the caravan into three. Lieutenant Austin would remain at Mumia's with a small party of fifty men, most of whom were sick, there to draw maps and buy provisions for the journey back. Lieutenant Twining, commanding a section of one hundred, would scout the northern shores of the Lake for a harbour and a terminus for the railroad. The largest party of perhaps three hundred men, officered by Macdonald and Pringle, would cross to Uganda.

Macdonald reached Mengo[1] on 9 June 1892. There he met Lugard. Now Lugard at this time was a man ashine with glory and racked by disillusion. During the eighteen months since his entry into Uganda he had made his famous march to the west, securing for the Company great unappropriated territories as far as the Belgian sphere of influence. He had drawn lines of trade and communication and had studded them with garrisoned forts. He had defeated the Muslims and he had negotiated a new treaty between Mwanga, the Company and the Anglican and Roman Catholic Christians. The Company, in fact, had never been stronger. But, as Lugard knew, its year of grace must soon expire. At the end of that year it would (in the absence of reprieve) abdicate both power and responsibility. By the time of Macdonald's arrival he had already decided to return to England: only he, who had suffered and gained so much in Uganda, could speak with faith and passion for its retention.

[1] Mengo Hill (the site of the King's palace) was one of a group of hills now known generally as Kampala.

Macdonald spent one week in Mengo. Then, on 16 June, the railroad survey party, its pack animals and its soldiers, began the long trek to Mombasa. In its rear came Lugard's caravan of some two hundred Somalis, Swahilis, Sudanese and a number of women and children. The march was to be a period of bitter personal conflict.

The hostility had begun in Mengo almost immediately. The dislike was instinctive. They were both captains on the Army List. But Lugard was already distinguished in name and attainment. He had stripped off the corset of convention habitually worn by the regimental officer of those times. He was unmistakably a man of Africa: Africa had drawn him in its own clear lineament. He was, therefore, anathema to the correct and envious Macdonald. And Macdonald, humourless, dour, pompous and dedicated to the pursuit of fame and advancement, aroused a strong distrust in Lugard. Their mutual suspicion became open enmity in the court of King Mwanga.

It was Lugard's task to present formally Macdonald and Pringle at the palm-leaf palace on Mengo Hill; and it was for just such an occasion that the two captains had carried their regimental full-dress uniforms for more than eight hundred miles through the African bush. The uniforms had been sponged, pressed and lovingly preserved against the ravages of insects and mildew. Now at last was the opportunity to wear this splendour of sword, leather and insignia, to bring the dignity of the Crown to the court of a savage. But Lugard, knowing Mwanga's obsessional hatred of European uniform, had insisted they remove them. To Macdonald and Pringle this was an affront of the deepest nature. They did not believe Lugard. This, they thought, was Lugard's way of showing contempt for a uniform he himself had long ago abandoned. But in Mengo Lugard's word was law. They were presented in their patched and soiled bush-clothes and the King had grinned and fingered the buttocks of the pages and had shown them scant respect: this was humiliation.

Now, marching from Uganda, Lugard found himself the object of Macdonald's spite. He had left his rifles, his infantry and the Maxim in Mengo for the reinforcement of his deputy, Captain

Williams; and in doing so had delivered himself into Macdonald's hands. He had no choice but to attach his own small and defenceless band to Macdonald's heavily-armed caravan, no alternative than to submit to the command of a man who was his junior in Army service. During that seven weeks' trek to the Company's post at Kikuyu Macdonald heaped upon Lugard every indignity, insult and mortification that his bitter and vengeful personality could devise.

At Kikuyu there were mails; and it was from these that Lugard learned of the storm that had gathered in Europe around his name. He was charged (this compassionate and honourable man) with atrocities in Uganda. Missions had been sacked and burned, the French priests claimed; Catholics, both missionaries and converts, had been shot, enslaved, degraded. Uganda smoked with the ruins of schools, churches and orphanages. The protests were at French Government level. London seethed with rumour.

Lugard hastened from Kikuyu. He had obtained a few rifles from the Company's representative and a promise from Macdonald of an armed escort to follow the caravan and join it promptly. It was then that Macdonald performed a last vindictive act. 'On August 10th (Lugard wrote later) I marched, leaving 20 Somalis to follow next day, or the day after, with mails. They were to have 20 rifles from Macdonald, for he would no longer require his 230 now that we had passed Masailand. These 20 would form the escort to my unarmed caravan to the coast. They, however, were detained by Macdonald, and never reached me until I was within a day or two of the coast . . . Later I had, in consequence, to cross a dangerous Masai war-path escorted by six rifles from Wilson only . . .' Lugard reached Mombasa with a heavy heart. England, it seemed, was now to be the place of his arraignment.

On 7 September Macdonald's caravan marched into Kibwezi: at this point he was some two hundred miles from the coast. But despatches from the British Government were waiting. He broke the seals. He was charged to return to Uganda, to investigate the accusations against Lugard, to submit a report. He retained forty men for his personal caravan, handed the railroad survey charts into the keeping of Captain Pringle and turned again for Uganda. Six hundred weary miles must be recrossed. But, for all that, this was a not unpleasant task; one to which he could address himself with a degree of enthusiasm.

Lugard reached London in early October 1892. Politically the scene had changed. Salisbury had fallen from power in the mid-summer of that year and, now, a fading Gladstone sat in the Prime Minister's chair. Lord Rosebery was Foreign Secretary and in this man of strong colonial ambition Lugard found a powerful ally. Their aims, the control of the valley of the Upper Nile and the retention of Uganda, were identical. Lugard, about to face charges which could easily discredit him, was thankful to grasp a hand held out from the high places. Rosebery, whose African aspirations were not unopposed within his own Cabinet, was (in Lugard's words) 'glad to utilize me in giving effect to his opposition to the views of his colleagues . . .' Without doubt they had need of each other. Without doubt they collaborated in the propaganda campaign of the months that followed.

Lugard conducted his campaign with that same energy and resolution that had marked his travels in Africa: as in Africa he gained his objectives. Those were days when great audiences gathered to listen to the famous public figures. Lugard spoke; in London, in the Midlands, in Scotland, in city after city. He ate; with Mayors and Provosts and the Masters of colleges and newspaper proprietors. He read papers to the Royal Geographical Society and wrote frequent letters to *The Times*. He was not a flamboyant, or even a good, speaker: in none of his speeches will you find a striking image or a note of passion. But he was intense, quiet, devoted to a cause. Only the explorer Stanley could match his experience and knowledge of Africa; and indeed Stanley supported him and heightened the campaign with that glow of colour which Lugard lacked. By Christmas he had won a victory. Uganda was not to be discarded. Rosebery commissioned Sir Gerald Portal to prepare a safari and to report 'on the best means of dealing with the country . . .' Lugard had also won a smaller, personal victory. The two crowded months of the campaign had revealed him (through the modesty of his

words and bearing) as a man of dignity and humanity: the
French priests who, for political ends, had sought to traduce him
were shewn in contrast as obvious intriguers. During this time
Macdonald was assiduously gathering evidence in Uganda from
biased witnesses and marshalling the 'facts' into a Report which
he hoped would destroy a hated competitor. There is a sense of
retributive justice, even of pleasure, in the spectacle of this embittered man labouring to produce a document which was never
to be published. By the time Gladstone received it in June of
1893 the issue was already dead. 'Re Captain Lugard and Macdonald,' the Prime Minister wrote to Rosebery, 'Salisbury seems
to have blundered in appointing a personal enemy to report on
Lugard's acts . . .'

Sir Gerald Portal was Her Majesty's Agent and Consul-
General in Zanzibar. He sailed from the island on the first stage
of his expedition on New Year's Day, 1893. In many ways Portal
was one of the strangest of East Africa's administrators. He was
not eccentric. He was not bizarre. He did not wear a uniform
of idiosyncrasy like so many of the 'characters' of that time. He
was simply incongruous in that wild and torrid setting. To
describe the drawing of him, executed by the Marchioness of
Granby in the following year, is to use words more applicable to
the portrait of a girl. The hair waves softly, the eyebrows arch.
The neck is slender, the ears and nose are as delicate as coral.
The eyes are calm and innocent. The drawing somehow con-
trives an effect of pale luminous skin. Even the moustache, as
silky as a boy's, does nothing to conceal the effeminacy of that
full ripe mouth. But the fragile shell was the cover to an intellect
as hard and durable as a diamond. Portal was only thirty-five
when he landed at Mombasa; already knighted for distinguished
diplomatic services, still aglow with the bloom of an unfading
youth.

Portal marched from Mombasa at the head of a caravan of
four hundred porters. There were five Army officers (including
his elder brother Raymond); a doctor from the Scottish Mission
at Kibwezi; Berkeley, the Company's Administrator in Mombasa; Foaker the guide and a guard of askari. The Company,
given a three months' reprieve at the Government's expense, was

due to quit Uganda on 31 March 1893. It was Portal's urgent task to reach Kampala Fort before the evacuation.

The caravan entered the fort on 17 March. The trek had been exceptionally fast—over eight hundred miles in seventy-five days. But eight men had died. Dr Moffat's note-book recorded more than three hundred cases of sickness. Raymond was ill and Portal himself was faint from exhaustion. Only an immense effort of the will had brought that frail body from the coast to Uganda. He hated Africa; its terrible beauty, its violence, its taint of death. 'This beastly country . . .' he described it in a letter to his mother. Portal, characteristically, was dominated by the two women in his life: his wife and his mother. During the outward and return marches he wrote them many letters, confiding his problems, his loneliness and even affairs of state.

But Portal had come to Uganda to assess a situation; and although by the last day of March he had made no decision he was yet ready to perform a significant, and symbolic, act. On 1 April he assembled his men, hauled down the Company's flag and raised the Union Jack. This was the end of the Charter Company's power in Uganda, the beginning of the dominion of the British Crown.

Portal's strength was slowly ebbing; and, indeed, in those months of endings and beginnings, the end of his own brief road was already in sight. In the last week of May his brother was brought into the fort on a litter, gaunt and yellow from malaria. Portal watched him die, buried him in the shadow of Namirembe Hill. Africa, now, was turning a pitiless and deadly face. Time, Portal sensed, was running out; and, two days after the death, on 29 May, he led his caravan from the fort. Eight hundred interminable miles lay ahead. Macdonald remained in Kampala, dignified with the intoxicating title of Acting-Commissioner for Uganda.

Only Portal could describe the ordeal of that march. Rain beat the country into a quagmire, locusts descended on great regions of it and left it as naked as a bone. Food was short and the vomit of a host of nameless fevers marked the trail. Portal lost himself on the Tana River and reached the coast at Witu on 19 October. For nearly five months he had stumbled through a veil of exhaustion. He had drawn his maps and kept his diary. He had compiled notes and written a number of affectionate letters to his wife and mother. He had also sustained within himself the spark of vitality he would need for the writing of his Report.

He wrote it in Zanzibar, sent it to Rosebery in England on 1 November. It was a model of clarity and exposition. But Portal's signature thereon was like a douse placed over the last glimmer of a candle-flame. The effort was made. This was an end. Now he could let go. He followed it to England and died in January 1894; a flower too delicate to survive the hothouse of tropical Africa.

Gerald Portal's Report, presented to Parliament in the April of that year, was all that Rosebery (now Prime Minister in succession to Gladstone) required to ensure the retention of Uganda. Within two days of its presentation an announcement of immense importance to the future of East Africa was made:

'After considering the late Sir Gerald Portal's Report and weighing the consequences of withdrawal from Uganda on the one hand and on the other of maintaining British interests there, Her Majesty's Government have determined to establish a regular administration, and for that purpose to declare Uganda to be under a British protectorate. The details of the arrangement to be made are under consideration.'

Now there must be a railroad. Uganda could not be maintained without it. Portal had said, specifically: 'The whole problem of the development of East and Central Africa, the prospect of the creation of a profitable British trade, the suppression of inter-necine religious wars, the security of European travellers, the control of the lake district and of the upper waters of the Nile and, above all, I may confidently add, the only hope of really and definitely killing the slave-trade within a reasonable time— all resolve themselves into the all-important and overshadowing question of transport and communication . . .' The Report included a scheme for the laying of track, as a first stage, to Kikuyu (about 350 miles inland from the coast), and a provision for steam-launches which would cross the Lake and complete the connection with Uganda.

But the Report was also a nail knocked belatedly but effectively into the coffin of Sir William Mackinnon who had died in the previous June. It was strongly critical of the Charter Company. Portal, the perfectionist, had seen much to appal him in the Company's territories. He wrote caustically of 'the attempted administration of the country . . . and the publicly acknowledged failure of the attempt.' He asked, unjustly, whether the possession of 'two small posts within 340 miles of the coast is a sufficient result for the five years which have elapsed since the Charter was granted to justify the Company in retaining that Charter any longer . . . ?' He recommended 'in the interests of British commerce and of the whole of East Africa, from the Indian Ocean to the Nile Basin, that some arrangement should be arrived at, without further delay, by which the Imperial British East Africa Company shall cease to exist as a political or administrative body, either in the interior or within the limits of the Sultan's territory.'

Portal's suggested 'arrangement' was inevitably the Company's funeral. In June the Court of Directors invited the Foreign Office 'to negotiate for the surrender of the Company's rights and interests in East Africa . . .' For six months the Directors pleaded for a just settlement, for a fair price for its property and assets, for a reasonable compensation for holding Uganda in trust to the Crown. But the Treasury was in too strong a position: the undertaking was defunct, the obligation merely moral. It offered a sum, derisory in the circumstances, of £250,000; and this the shareholders of the Company accepted in March of 1895. In July the Company's territories, its power and its authority, passed to a British Protectorate.

So ended the Imperial British East Africa Company. Sir William Mackinnon, perhaps, would not have been displeased. The Company had died, but the death had been honourable. No-one had made money from it: its bequest was a deficit of £194,000. It had been a caretaker in the wild lands and, now, a powerful master was come to spread a cloak of benevolent protection. Steam, too, must come; and men would follow the rails and grow their crops and build their enterprises and the last slave caravan would march and disappear into the vault of history. That, after all, had been the dream.

The railroad was moving now into another dimension, from the pages of Hansard to practicalities. The time had come for tenders and appointments, for track instead of words. But the emphasis had shifted. The clichés of anti-slavery sentiment still fluttered to the floor of the House like leaves: it was still the great crusade which would bring black Africa from darkness into light, still the urgent field for the rays of the torch of freedom. But the political and economic motives were less emotional and at least as strong. The Government had changed once more and Salisbury was again in office. Curzon, his Under-Secretary of State for Foreign Affairs, told the House in August: 'Government have decided that the railway is to be constructed the whole way from the ocean to the lake, a distance of 650 miles . . . This railway has been commonly and justly called the Uganda Railway, and the application of that name itself suggests the truth as to the principal object of the railway, viz. that it is to bring down to the coast the resources, not only of the Uganda Protectorate, but of all those countries in the upper waters of the Nile and of the Congo, both in the British and German spheres of influence, which surround at no very great distance the Victoria Nyanza, resources for which the railway will be the natural outlet . . .' He concluded with a warning: 'Nothing is more certain than that if we do not construct a railway to the lake the Germans will.'

Curzon announced that day that the Government would itself build the railroad. Without doubt its experiences with the Charter Company had soured its vision of private enterprise; and, moreover, the construction would be dependent on Indian reserves of labour. No other country could provide so deep a pool of engineers, artisans and coolies, men already conditioned to the heat, rains, fevers and terrain of the tropics. (Macdonald had written in his survey report: '. . . the bulk of the labour would have to be imported from India . . . Natives from Madras and the south of India generally would be best employed on the coast between Mombasa and Kibwezi; while Punjabis, Pathans and natives of northern India would do well at the higher altitudes . . .') All this meant an approach to the Government of India, an amendment to the Indian Emigration Act, a political interweaving between the two Administrations. Only the Crown could embark on such a project.

The speeches would continue and the committees would sit and there would be all the predictable noises of political opposition until the Uganda Railway Bill was passed through the Commons and the Lords in August of 1896. But on 11 December 1895 a quiet man came to the island of Mombasa. There was no deep-water harbour and a lighter brought him from ship to shore. The ship had moved through the narrows under the long white shape of the Jesus Fort and the walls had glared in sun. Now the glare had gone and the Fort was greyed and the groves of mango, palm and banana began to merge with the dark of the water. The man was George Whitehouse and he had been appointed Chief Engineer of the great new railroad. There had been many other railroads, ribboning on the plane of memory through Mexico and India and south of the Zambesi and South America and fused by a trick of time into one long and indistinguishable line. Now another road must begin; wind from this place of palms and dhows and make its joint with the other, older roads and run its steels across a wilderness, across a changing century.

1. Guns and Axle-Grease

I had long been intrigued by this building of the railroad. It seemed to me to contain all the ingredients of the epic; men had toiled, endured and prevailed against enormous natural obstacles. They had laid track through bush, scrub and forest and they had laid it in the face of thirst, disease, privation and marauding wild beasts. They began it in 1896 and they brought railhead to the waters of the lake in 1901. It cost lives—and a million pounds for every mile. These were big men: the nature of their task and its accomplishment made them big. Who were they? What were they like? Where had they come from? What were their strengths and their weaknesses? their doubts and convictions? A heroic story needs heroes.

Not very much had been written about the railroad. There was plenty of data. You could find the dates and the routes, the number of rupees paid to a headman or an askari; the loco-motives used and their tractive power, accurate details of the mortality rate among the coolies and the animal transport. You could also find a few names: of engineers and doctors and veterinary officers and Indian jemadars. But these were names; names affixed to figures so lacking in dimension and substance that they were like shapes cut from grey paper.

There were contemporary publications which touched the railroad story obliquely; browning copies of Blackwood's with contributions from District Officers and officials of the trading companies who had been witness to the building of it; the records of missionary-societies and of their priests and pastors; the books and anecdotes of the hunters who had destroyed the predators and provided the meat. All of these gave the feel and flavour of the country. None of them was the personal record

45

I needed: that daily narrative which would follow the line until the last key was driven in on the shores of Lake Victoria.

Eventually I found it.

The search in Nairobi proved fruitless. If the library of the East African Railways and Harbours owned documents of that nature they were not revealed to me. I suspect they had nothing: history in the making is seldom recognised. They will put a Treaty in a frame and reverently hang it on a wall—and throw away the records of the men who worked to make it. 'There is an Official History,' they told me proudly. 'The development of the transport system in Kenya and Uganda. Surely——?'

'No,' I said. 'I do not want to know how the transport system developed. I want to know about the men who laid the track.'

'But they must all be dead.'

I agreed. It had happened sixty years ago.

'Many of the grandsons of the Indians who worked on the railroad are with us now.'

'No,' I said. 'That wouldn't do.'

They were polite—and suspicious. They gave me a Caltex Road Map of East Africa, a time-table, a folder indicating the port dues and the pilotage for shipping entering Kilindini Harbour in the Port of Mombasa, showed me a film about the railroad in which a circus-lion impersonating a man-eater dragged an obvious dummy from a railway carriage; and sent me on my way.[1]

The newspaper libraries were equally barren. It was all in the Official History: the book weighed four or five pounds and must obviously contain everything a reasonable person could want to know . . . But novelists are not reasonable; they like to know the significant things about people . . . No: there was nothing. It was a long time ago. There had been a fire. The nose crinkled as if the smell of burning paper could still be detected. I left.

The periodicals had nothing. It was all in the past. They liked to look forward, they said, not backward. In any case records did not go back that far. And in these days of Uhuru wasn't the colonial story best forgotten? I returned to my hotel. There was

[1] Later I received much valuable information.

a message from the first of the papers I had visited. I telephoned. No, the voice said, nothing new had been unearthed: but, it recalled, a woman named Tuck had offered a diary some years ago. She was a Goanese, the wife of one of the men—an Englishman—employed by the railroad. He had written the diary and she had preserved it. No: Tuck wasn't alive. The woman lived behind the Old Harbour in Mombasa. She had wanted money for the diary and she had offered it around Nairobi. Nobody would buy it. The Official History had already been published. It was all in the past. She had even offered it to the Museum: but, as everyone knows, Museums like to be given things. The voice gave me an address and a Box-Number in Mombasa, warned me not to pay good money for it—diaries were never what one hoped, they were usually indecipherable, they were monuments of triviality.

I drove to Mombasa. I had no faith in the existence or the value of Tuck's diary but I wanted to see some of the terrain through which the railroad had passed. Most of it was scrub. The motor-road followed the track: you peered through an explosion of red dust thrown from the murram surface. The spirit of the wilderness had long died. But there was an area where the road bisected the Tsavo Royal National Park: if you stopped the car a sense of illimitable distance came on the wind and there was only bush, silence and the acrid smell of wild places.

In Mombasa I wrote to the address. The reply came quickly. It was written by the woman's daughter, a Mrs Gopal. Her mother, she explained, was very old. She, the daughter, would negotiate anything that required negotiation. And the name was Turk—not Tuck. She suggested a time and a day. Mrs Turk lived in Abdul Suleiman Road.

Abdul Suleiman Road ran parallel to Vasco da Gama Street. I had twenty minutes to spend. I watched the sardine-boats and the scarf of enmeshed light when the nets were cast. Beyond was the quadrangular shape of the Fort. A quality of somnolence overlay the scene. The fishermen waited. Even the reflections seemed unmoving. I left the jetties. To the west of the island a ship's siren lowed in Kilindini Harbour.

Mrs Turk lived at the end of a row of squalid shops. They were half-shuttered to exclude the sun. Asian faces peered like rodents from brown glooms: it was hot, it was afternoon, a sale would be resented. There was nothing to sell in Mrs Turk's shop. Trading had been abandoned. The window was boarded, the door padlocked. You reached the upper rooms by a wooden stair and, pausing on those splitting treads, saw the water in the harbour like dull-blue oil, waves of heat standing on the wharves.

A painted sign was nailed to the lower rails of the stair. It was very old. The inscription was faint and some of the lettering had to be guessed:

ROBt. TURK
Gunmaker, Arms & Ammunition Merchant
Contractor to Imperial & Colonial Govts.
TURK'S CELEBRATED AXLE-GREASE

Turk moved one step nearer to life. He had existed. But there was no elation. The disintegrating sign-board with its archaic letters was like an old tomb-stone found in a churchyard: it left the taste of melancholy.

Mrs Gopal opened the door at the head of the stair before I reached it. She stared for a moment. I had the feeling that the contents of my wallet had been accurately assessed. She was a large woman with plump, sweating arms. I judged her to be sixty. She had light-brown hair dressed in a European style—and the sallow skin and pigmented eyeballs of the Asian. She murmured: 'Mrs Gopal.' I followed her into the half-light of a passage that smelled of wormy wood and urine: then from the passage to a large square room, blinded, with the same dismal wash of light, the same unpleasant scent.

She shut the door. I felt imprisoned. The harbour and its sterilizing sun was an enticement. 'Sit down,' she said. I sat.

The room was full of Victorian furniture which Mrs Gopal felt with her fingers when she moved about the room as if she would avoid its protruding angles. A calendar and a Landseer reproduction hung on the walls. The walls were rough and grey, speckled where the bodies of mosquitoes had been crushed. A large cane chair was positioned in the centre of the room of the kind once used by the English for reclining in the conservatories of country mansions; you expected a potted palm. In the chair sat a woman with dulled eyes sunk in the taut, glazed skin of the very old. The skin was dark and stained and revealing of the bone-structure. Soon it would split: there would be a skull. She was cocooned in black calico which had gone green with age: it partly covered her hair. The hair sprouted, yellow-white like the fibres of hemp. Mrs Gopal did not introduce her. Perhaps the old woman was beyond contact with the living. The daughter moved about the room, feeling the furniture. She paused. 'There is tea,' she offered.

'Thank you. No.'

'Or beer.' She went to the sideboard, brought out a tumbler and a bottle of Tusker. She poured it. 'I got it specially.' The glass was filmed with dust, the beer warm.

She sat, stared at her mother. 'She is enormously old—for one of her nationality.' She spoke with an air of disclaimer; as if nothing of that nationality could possibly reflect in her own bone and blood. She touched her European hair. Goa was immeasurably distant. 'This business of Turk,' she said. She waited. The Asian eyes gleamed. The buyer must reveal himself.

'It's quite simple,' I said. 'There is plenty of material about the railroad. But nothing much about the men that built it.'

'But Turk didn't build. He wasn't an engineer.'

'But he was there?'

'Oh, yes. He was there all right.' She hesitated. I drank some more Tusker. Mrs Turk pulled a stick-like arm from out the calico; it was mottled with age, shiny. Mrs Gopal said: 'You are actually going to write a book about the railroad?'

'Yes.'

'But there is already a book. I have seen it.' The hands lifted a large, imaginary object. 'A great big book.'

'Yes,' I said. The Official History was becoming ludicrous. 'A great big book about a great big railroad. But there is nothing about the great big men that built it.'

She stared without smiling. Then, flatly: 'Yes, you could call Turk that. He was a big man. Too damn' big . . .' She leaned over, touched Mrs Turk. 'Would you like some tea?'

The brown skull nodded and Mrs Gopal went through a doorway into the kitchen. She spoke above a gush of water. 'I was eighteen when he died. I don't remember much about him . . .' The water stopped. 'He was never with us. Always away.' Accusation touched the voice. The voice, dissociated from that body of sallow fat flesh, was pleasant to the ear. 'Hardly ever here . . . Always off on some trip or other . . .'

She fell silent. Mrs Turk watched me from the depth of calico like a turtle peering from its carapace. She seemed aware of me for the first time. The limbs moved on the wicker of the chair and the calico parted. One of the legs was bandaged. A red sore disfigured the ankle-bone.

Mrs Gopal asked from the kitchen: 'Are you going to buy the diary?'

'I don't know.'

'But you have some money, haven't you?'

'Yes.'

'It's a very big diary. It must be worth something.'

I sipped the beer. 'You offered it in Nairobi. Nobody would buy it.'

'You don't have to have it.' The voice was harsh. Mrs Turk turned her head abruptly as if the change in tone had alerted her. The movement brought a slightly fetid odour. I set down the beer. This old woman awaited death. It was there beside her.

Mrs Gopal asked: 'Do you make a great deal of money from books?'

'No.'

'Ah . . .' There was a silence. The mouth had probably twisted in disbelief. 'Do you know what I asked them for the diary?'

'No.'

'A thousand shillings.'

'That's a lot of money.'

'Is it? I don't think so. After all, you can't write your book without it, can you?'

'Easily.'

'How? What would you use?'

'Imagination.'

She repeated it: 'Imagination . . .' I heard the accent of doubt. Imagination, it seemed, was a poorer currency than fact. Mrs Turk smiled with a kind of recognition, as if some familiar fantasy had crossed her blurring mind. A lizard, pink like a thing never exposed to light, came from behind the Landseer, was transfixed in a coin of sun, retreated. Mrs Gopal brought a tray from the kitchen, filled a vegetable-dish with tea, milk and sugar. She gave it to the old woman. 'She likes to hold the handles,' she explained. 'It's easier like that.' Mrs Turk nodded, began to suck tea. The eyes stared at me through a wreath of steam. The daughter sat.

'Tell me about Turk,' I said.

'He was English,' she said. 'A Cornishman. A sailmaker by trade.' She grimaced. 'But he didn't stick it for long. Naturally. He left his ship at Mombasa.'

'When was that?'

'I've made a note of all these dates. It's in one of the diaries. He'd have been about twenty then. Or near enough.' She touched the teapot. 'Tea?'

'No.'

'You haven't finished your beer.'

I drank it.

She said: 'He must have gone up-country. We don't know much. All this was a long time ago.'

'Yes.'

'He married *her* . . .' she gestured at the calico bundle: for some reason the word 'mother' would not pass her lips . . . 'about ten years later. That was in 1896.' She hesitated. 'There is no existing record of the marriage, no *official* record, you understand? But we know it was 1896 because it was the year in which they started the railroad.' She poured tea, sipped it. I heard the lizard. The place was crepitant with tiny noises. She said, defensively: 'They *were* married.'

'Of course.'

'She was about eighteen at the time. We don't even know *her* birth-date. Turk was . . .' She reflected. 'Turk must have been thirty.'

'What happened in the ten years?'

'Before the marriage?'

'Yes.'

'It's very vague. I can remember only what *she* herself has told me.' She leaned over, wiped a dribble of tea from Mrs Turk's chin. 'He served with the Zanzibari troops—that's where he got his taste for guns. Then, later, he got involved with Peters —Carl Peters the German tyrant. Peters had marched along the Tana . . . you must have read about him?'

'Yes.'

'There was fighting and burning. Many people were killed. Turk, it seems, ran into him at Korokoro.' She pursed her lips. 'Naturally. Wherever there was violence . . .'

Mrs Turk put down the vegetable-dish. The constant repetition of Turk's name had engaged her: the brown bone of a head moved from side to side as if on a pivot. But the eyes were dull; you could not assess the degree of intelligence, of understanding.

Mrs Gopal said softly: 'She is very old. Soon . . .' She shrugged. The vulturine shadows around Mrs Turk moved nearer. 'Anyway, it was there, at Korokoro, that Turk joined the Company.' She saw the question in my eyes. 'The Imperial British East Africa Company. He had helped protect their property against the Germans . . .' Her lip curled. 'Of course, they would not understand that it was only the fight that interested him. They gave him a job.'

'What kind of a job?'

'With the caravans.'

I showed surprise.

She said impatiently: 'Not the slave caravans. There were plenty of those, of course. No: these were caravans of trade. They followed the same routes. They endured the same things. But they carried produce, trading goods, ivory. There were Mission outposts to be fed and clothed, the coastal ports to be served. That sort of thing. Turk became a caravan-master. His job was to lead, find trails and water and food, protect, bring the caravans to the coast.'

I must have alerted.

'Yes,' she said shrewdly. 'That interests you, doesn't it? Turk was a big man. The country was wild in those days. It needed a big man for a job like that.'

I relaxed. The price of the diary had advanced perceptibly. 'Didn't he make money?'

She waved at the room. I saw the bracelet of fat on the wrist. 'Does it look like it?' She finished her tea. 'That sort never makes money. They live to the limit of youth and strength. Then there is nothing.' She repeated the word as if it were an epithet: 'Nothing.'

'What happened then?'

She shrugged. 'Caravans, expeditions—anything that would keep him moving through the bush. That was his life. He was half-wild, I should think. Later they began to lay track—and that was when he met and married . . .' she looked sideways . . . '*her*.' Mrs Turk grinned at her private fantasies. She had two gold teeth. They gleamed. They were like ornaments hung in a cavern of decay. Mrs Gopal said cruelly: 'She doesn't look very marriageable, does she?'

We were silent. We heard the sirens in Kilindini.

'After they finished the railroad,' she said, 'he came back to Mombasa . . . here. They hadn't built the deep-water harbour then and this side of the island was the place for trade. Or so it seemed. He set up as a gunmaker. He loved guns. When I remember him it's usually with guns—weighing them in his hands, stroking them . . . And the smell of them, too, the smell of metal and gun-oil.' She smiled. 'It's silly to remember a smell, isn't it?' The eyes retreated for a moment. She was raising Turk: you felt his presence move through that resinous place of shade and lizards. 'He did well for a time. Many of the famous hunters came here. There were Army contracts. But it didn't last. A few good years and trade, *his* kind of trade, began to move to Nairobi. There was nothing there until the railroad came—just a swamp. But it grew. Turk, in a way, had helped to make it. And it broke his business. That's . . .' she searched for a word.

'Ironical?'

'Yes. Ironical. He hadn't the vision to see what Nairobi would become. Naturally . . .' Contempt touched her voice.

53

'You haven't told me what he did for the railroad.'

She reflected. 'I can't put a word to it. He knew nothing of railroad construction. He knew only guns, the tribes and the dialects, the country. There were a hundred ways, I suppose, in which they would use a man like that. There were coolies to be disciplined, miles of bush to be prospected ahead of the track, water to be found, game . . . That sort of thing.'

'When were you born, Mrs Gopal?'

'That's nearly a rude question. It was 1907. But I wasn't the first. There were two before me. Two boys. They died of the smallpox. Both of them.' She spoke without feeling: it was a long time ago.

'Does he mention them in the diary?'

'Yes. He mentions them. It cut him up.' The eyes were vindictive. Turk's pain was something to be savoured. 'It cut him up all right.'

Mrs Gopal said: 'He could never settle. Naturally. When the first German War started he was off—just like that. He didn't care. He put an Asian into the business . . .' She spoke with immense distaste. 'An Asian. They are no good, you know . . .' Her own Asiatic eyes stared at me. 'Quite a lot of trade passed through the Old Port during the war—but he wasn't here to take advantage of it. He was in the bush—fighting and killing like the barbarian he was. He'd hated Germans since the affair with Peters. The war gave him an excuse to do things . . .' She shook her head as if in rejection. 'He wasn't civilized, you understand?'

'He kept a diary.'

'You know what I mean.' I sensed her hostility. 'He was solitary. He couldn't stand towns, houses, people. He needed space.' Then, viciously: 'He didn't need a wife and a family.'

Her face was sullen. She had been a poor substitute, it seemed, for Turk's two dead boys. 'After the war,' she said, 'he came back here.' The carmined lips pursed again. 'He was always coming back. Life went on without him, years sometimes, and then—there he was. He was usually tired or ill or suffering from some wound or other. And, of course, older.' She smiled, taking

54

pleasure in the thought. Her face hardened. 'They always know where to come, don't they? But it didn't last. He tried his hand at one or two things . . .'

'Axle-grease?'

'You've read the board. Yes, axle-grease. Thousands of tins of it. He bought it cheap from the military. But nothing's cheap if you can't sell it.' Her voice shook. 'Axle-grease . . .'

I watched her. Turk's memory could still arouse emotion. She got up, opened the left door of the sideboard, found something and brought it over to me. It was a large, round tin. The label was stained, tattered. 'Turk's Celebrated Axle-Grease,' it read. 'Save your horse Labour.' There was a diagram depicting two Woolwich-carts one of which had collapsed on a broken axle. The other cart was passing at a fine pace and a bubble floated above its driver's head enclosing the words: 'My friend, you should use Turk's Axle-Grease.' I tried to remove the lid but it would not shift.

'You can have it if you like,' she said.

'Thank you.'

'——for fifty cents.'

I gave her fifty cents.

She began to laugh. The brown eyes filled. 'That's more than Turk could do.'

'What?'

'Sell it.'

She could not stop the laughter. There was no humour in it. 'He was a fool,' she said. 'Even the caption is wrong. Why should anyone want to save a horse labour?'

'I see your point.'

She sat, wiped her eyes with a twist of cambric. 'Later, he dumped the tins in the harbour. Thousands of them. They're probably still there. Then he went up-country. Naturally.'

'Why did he go up-country?'

'Ivory. Elephant-hunting. He didn't like it, though. He had a sympathy for animals. But it was the only thing he knew— how to track, to live in bush, to hunt with efficiency. There were no caravans to lead. The railroad had killed all that.' She stood again, returned to the sideboard, opened both its doors.

A smell of ants and stale perfume came into the room. Dust-motes revolved where sun escaped the shutters. She produced a package: things wrapped in a copy of the *East African Standard*. She removed the paper, folded it carefully. Then she put the contents on the table. There were six oblong books, a smaller packet from which she peeled tissue. 'Would you like to see a photograph?'

I took it. It was a monochrome portrait; it had been taken at the Photographic Emporium, Railway Road, Mombasa. Robert Turk's sepia face and upper body were outlined against a painted backcloth of palms, dhows and mosques. He wore a tight jacket and a high white collar. They had given him a book to hold: it had a tooled leather binding and a fragile lock. It sat in large, big-knuckled fingers. He was posed, self-conscious and brilliantined. He was a dummy. Only the hand was a living thing. I put down the portrait.

'Don't you like it?'

'No.'

'What about this?' She gave me another.

Turk stood in underbrush. You could not see his lower legs. He looked exceptionally tall. One hand buttoned his shirt and he stared sideways so that you saw him in three-quarter face. The jaws and lips were shaven but the hair hung very long and slightly-curling on the nape of the neck. He had a good chin and high temples and a predatory nose. The skin seemed swarthy. He was alert: you felt that the beaked nose sniffed the wind.

'Is that better?'

'Much.'

'Try this.'

Turk sat on a folding-chair in front of a hut with a papyrus roof. He was cleaning a rifle. The face was intent. He was entirely concentrated. The gun was important: it lay easily across his thighs. He was not a heavy man. The shoulders were high-boned, neither narrow nor wide; perhaps the long hair, falling in two waves on either side of his downturned face, reduced their width. But there was a sense of power: this man would endure and survive. He would move with grace.

'There is nothing to measure his height against,' I said. 'Was he tall?'

'Yes. He was tall.'

'And the hair and complexion?' I picked up the first of the photographs. 'He seems dark.'

She shook her head. 'No. These old prints always give that impression. Actually he had light hair. Perhaps it was yellow when he was young. I don't know.'

'Is there another?'

She handed it to me. It was cracked down the centre. Turk's face filled it. He was middle-aged. You could see the furrows of experience, perhaps of suffering. The jowls had developed. A tension afflicted the face—as if the jaws were clamped: a knot of muscle disfigured each of the cheeks. The eyes were deep and lustrous; the photograph had fixed them in a fractional second of time but you felt they were unstill: they searched, they watched, they were completely alert. I remembered her words: 'He was half-wild . . .'

The old woman stirred, licked her lips with the tip of a small leathery tongue. She held out her hand and I put the photograph into it. She did not examine it immediately. She held it on her lap, the weight of her hand across it.

'He died when he was sixty,' Mrs Gopal said. She jerked her head. 'In that room there. Don't ask me what he died of. I couldn't tell you. He'd just used himself up, I guess. He'd been hurt in the war by a mine on the line at Maji Chumvi. Later he lost several fingers of his hand when a rifle exploded in it. He'd had malaria and dysentery and blackwater. He'd once spent seven days at the bottom of a game-pit. He'd lived in the bush like a wild beast.' The voice gained intensity. 'You can't live like that. You have to pay. You always have to *pay*.' The brown eyes were lachrymose. '*Pay*,' she repeated savagely.

Mrs Turk lifted the photograph, stared at the contours of Turk's face. I watched her. Mrs Gopal said harshly: 'I remember him when he stripped to wash. It was all written on his body—the scars, the wounds, the illness, the life of wandering. There was a hole in his side and you could see something beating in it like a heart. And his legs were pitted from bush-ulcers.

I remember that very clearly.' She turned to me. 'Why should I remember a thing like that?'

Mrs Turk raised her eyes. They were no longer vacant. Some old emotion had unfilmed them. Her face enlivened with an infinite contempt. 'Turk . . .' she said. 'Turk . . .' The thin voice was envenomed. She dropped the photograph and Mrs Gopal retrieved it, studied it for a moment, shook her head. 'That Turk . . .' she said.

They stared at me. I felt their hatred. It was a tangible thing. It had never died. A few words, a few old sepias could revive it. They had hated Turk: hatred had sustained his memory, kept the focus fine in a way that love could never do. He had had freedom. He had taken life at its fundamental. He had drunk his youth until there was nothing left. He had fled all softness, the prison of house, trade and family. He had kept hard as steel. He had brought them unease. And he had died at sixty when they might have expected protection. They could not forgive him. They hated him.

We were silent. I heard the insects in the walls. Mrs Gopal gave me the diaries. 'Six of them,' she said. The voice was pleasant again. 'Covering about five years.'

I opened the first of them. The books were annual diaries with two days to each folio. The writing was large and impatient. There was a little punctuation and many exclamation-marks; the important nouns were graced with capital letters. Many of the passages which Turk had deemed significant were underlined. The margins had been used and you had to turn the book slowly in order to read. A stalk fell out leaving its black seeds spread on the page. The book smelled sour. I continued to turn. Some emanation from those yellow pages touched the membrane of my nostrils. I thought, irrationally, of black-water, of strange diseases. I did not look up but I knew that Mrs Gopal watched me for reaction. 'I don't know . . .' I said. I wanted the diaries.

I opened the second of them. This one smelled of eucalyptus. Little red insects scurried. Perhaps they liked eucalyptus. A leaf of quarto revealed itself.

'That's the paper with the dates on,' Mrs Gopal said. I looked at her, into the Indian face and those deep eyes of commerce. The Jews of Africa, they were called. I felt vulnerable. 'I'm not sure,' I said. I could hear my own accent of deceit.

'Oh, come,' she said impatiently. 'You know they're what you want.'

I read one of the entries to gain time. 'July 4th, 1897: All the camels dead and God knows how many mules and bullocks. Haslam has ordered them burned! I want Sumitra, want, want, want her. It is like a fever on me . . .' I shut the book. Mrs Gopal stared.

'What is your mother's name?' I asked. I saw her lips open to frame the answer and I felt an incomprehensible fear. I did not want her to reply. But the word came.

'Sumitra,' she said.

The old woman stirred at the name. The ankle moved into sun and I saw that it was cratered. I caught her sick-sweet smell. This evidence of time was suddenly unbearable. Time was a destroyer. It took things of beauty, desirable things, and turned them into decay and ugliness.

'Well?' Mrs Gopal asked.

'I'd like the diaries,' I said. 'But I couldn't pay a thousand shillings.'

'Why not?'

'It's a lot of money. If the book doesn't sell . . .'

'Don't you expect it to sell?'

'We hope it'll sell. But you never know.'

She stood, walked around the room; the fat hands touched lightly on the points of furniture. She lifted the blind and sun striated the floor. 'What would you pay?' she asked.

'Two hundred shillings. I couldn't pay more.'

'That's absurd.'

'It isn't really. You've had it a long time and you haven't sold it.'

'I could try again. Perhaps the railroad . . .'

'No. They wouldn't buy it. They wouldn't even offer me a concession on my fares.'

She laughed, dropped the blind and turned. 'Would you pay five hundred shillings?'

59

'No.'

'Four hundred?'

'Look,' I said. 'Why don't you lend them to me for two hundred shillings? I'd undertake to return them. And if the book becomes famous they'll be worth a lot of money.' I felt an immediate guilt. How many books become famous? A decimal fraction.

She hesitated. The eyes narrowed. Then: 'Will you give me a receipt?'

I left her at the head of the stair. The sun was low and there were red lights in the water, in the sails of the dhows. She closed the door and I went down the stair, read Turk's signboard again. It was pathetic. A few more years of sun and it would disintegrate. The board and the diary were all that remained of Turk. And the diary? Was it genuine? I felt the beginning of doubt. Perhaps the daughter had bought it in the bazaar. Turk had been half-wild: and things of the wilderness do not commit their thoughts to paper.

I turned from the sign. But he had also been a gunmaker. He had led men, assumed responsibility. He'd had a good face and good broad temples and intelligent eyes. He had been solitary. Perhaps something had denied him communication with other men: he had written the diary—a small, positive act of expression. I heard the door open. Mrs Gopal's head appeared. For one moment I thought she had reconsidered, was about to reclaim the books. 'You forgot your tin,' she said. She came down the stair. The treads yielded under her heavy feet. She gave me the tin of axle-grease. I thanked her. I knew the diary was genuine. We shook hands again. I looked at her.

I said, on impulse: 'Mrs Gopal, what was the name of the Asian? the one Turk put into the shop?'

'Gopal,' she said. Then, sullenly: 'I am a widow. It was a long time ago.' She climbed the stair. I walked toward the wharf. The sardine-boats were coming in.

2. Tea-and-Whisky

Robert Turk returned from Uganda in August of the year 1896 at the head of a large caravan of three hundred Zanzibari porters. The rains in that year were exceptionally heavy and the trek had been prolonged. Normally a caravan of that nature, professionally led and using professional porters, would take ninety days. Turk arrived at the mainland of Mombasa on the one hundred and twentieth day. He had received a leg-wound in a skirmish with Kikuyu. He had lost eleven hundred pounds' weight of ivory to Swahili raiders. He had suffered bouts of dysentery. He was weak and dispirited and thankful for a respite from the bush. At that time he was thirty-one; a man already pared by the years of rigour.

Turk crossed to the island and went to his quarters at the rear of the coffee-shop on the fringe of the Old Port. He had left his tracker (a Suk from the north-west) bivouacked in a fold of the Rabai Hills. Later he would rejoin him. Now there would be rest, hot water, tobacco and the mixture of tea and whisky to which he was addicted. A note awaited him. It invited him to present himself at the Grand Hotel on a matter of importance: the handwriting was bold and peremptory, the signature that of George Whitehouse.

Turk rested and bathed, combed water through the long hair which had grown to his shoulders and drank draughts of tea-and-whisky until the dysentery pains abated. Then he hired a ricksha, leaned back and watched the Arab doors and grilled windows of Mombasa flutter behind the hoops of the slender wheels. The dhows had gone with the south-east winds of April and the harbour was empty of sail. But there was great activity. The wharves were high-stacked, the warehouses filled. There were Sikh policemen, gesticulating groups of coolies in white cotton dresses, equipment under shrouds of tarpaulin painted with Bombay stencils. Already, it seemed, the railroad had begun. These were men and stores from India, this swelling island the reservoir; from here the track would grow.

He stopped the ricksha, put a few annas into the palm of the coolie. Then, on impulse, he left the Old Port, walked the two miles through the narrow streets that would lead him past the Customs House and across the knuckle of the island to Mbaraki Creek. The sun was quartered, the light red.

When he saw water its texture had already begun to deepen with night. The plantations of coco-palm beyond the creek were black serrations against the sky. There were three lighters on the water, a steamship, many longboats. He could see moving cranes: and the wharves and jetties and trolley-lines they had built as far as Kilindini. The island had changed. There was something immensely purposive in this concentration of ships, materials and installations. He heard the pulse of the steam-engines to the cranes and the noise was febrile in the August dusk.

The Chief Engineer received him in an ill-lit lounge of broken bamboo chairs and bead curtains. There was no hotel in Mombasa other than the Grand. It was Greek, dirty and ant-ridden; as noisome as the streets that ringed it. Whitehouse at this time was a man of thirty-nine. The pictures surviving from the days of those other, earlier railroads are curiously alike. In Mexico, South Africa and India the stalwart body poses proudly against an unvarying background. Rails curl into distance. Locomotives pant. Gangers lean on keying-hammers. The face in these old sepias is shadowed by the same huge topi: the chest strains against the same tight tropical-tunic. In the later pictures sun has darkened the skin and cut deeper grooves, the shoulders are wider, the moustache longer, the topi and the tunic shabbier; but these are the only noticeable differences. In each of the pictures there is an air of achievement. Sometimes a heavy bush-boot rests triumphantly on the rail like that of a hunter on the neck of a trophy. In portrait the face is more revealing. It is strong-boned, handsome. The forehead rises, broad and meditative, into short, light-brown hair. The mouth is generous and shapely but the jaw is aggressive, the eyes stubborn and resolute. This is plainly a man who has measured great, natural obstacles of mountain, forest and river, assessed them—and met their challenge.

But Whitehouse, that night, was weighted with responsibility. The Lake, that sea of water as big as Scotland, lay six hundred miles away. It would be years before he saw its waters reflected in the sky. Now it was like an unattainable mirage. It washed, blue, deep and inexhaustible, in the crevices of mind. He had summoned Turk to make him an offer. But, too, Turk was a breath, a scent, a living part of that wilderness he was charged to cross. Turk was a communication.

There is no account of his reaction to Robert Turk. He was no diarist. He was an engineer and it would not occur to him that human relationships are worth recording. But he must have been uneasy in the presence of this tall, fever-yellowed man with the long hair and the big hands who had brought the smells of gun-oil and bush into that decrepit lounge.

He sent for tea and, when it arrived, watched Turk take a flask from his pocket, splash whisky into the dish and then drain it. It was German whisky, Turk told him. They were dumping it in East Africa and you could buy a dozen Imperial quarts for 5s. 6d.; the same price as British soda-water.

Whitehouse had risen from his chair at that. Water, he told Turk, was one of his problems. He began to talk, pacing the room, a hunter watch swinging, characteristically, from thumb and forefinger; pacing in and out of pools of sallow light and sometimes shivering the Moor curtains when he turned. Already, he said, he had bought land on the island in the name of the Government. And already they were complaining at the purchase price. But he needed the land. There were depots and stores and warehouses and workshops to be built, places for the Administration. He had built jetties, excavated channels. Before that, he explained with incredulity, cargoes—*his* cargoes—had had to be dumped in the sea offshore, recovered when the tide ebbed.

Soon there would be four thousand Indian coolies. What else

could he do? The native labour was shiftless: it could not even use a spade: it worked badly in the heat: it would not take payment in coin. But it was the problem of water which occupied him. It would not leave his mind. There was barely sufficient to support the island. Water. A failure of rain, thousands of men labouring in unendurable heat in that nameless bush: they had to drink, keep clean. To say nothing of camels, mules, donkeys and bullocks . . . And had he, Turk, any conception of the quantities of water a construction locomotive used? Water. The danger was not appreciated. Lack of it could defeat them.

Turk listened. Always the talk returned to water. Men spoke of it as they spoke of ivory or gold. Crisis was never far from the springs and wells and courses.

Now, Whitehouse told him, he was erecting a distilling plant. He had had to beg to get it. It would distil twelve thousand gallons of fresh water from the sea each day. Water would be transported along the track already laid. The Indian Ocean was their reserve. How could they fail? Theoretically it was perfect. But nothing in Africa was ever simple; and he was still worried about water.

Turk records: 'I told him he would need water-trains for a hundred miles until he got to Voi. He had to cross the Taru Desert. And God help him if his precious Trains were late . . . Then I asked him how wide is the Taru Desert? He considered. From Taru to Maungu, he answered, the distance is about 37 miles. Taru is the beginning of the desert. And at Maungu there is a pool. I smiled and I told him he was right about the 37 miles. But sometimes the pool on the Maungu Hill dried out. And then his 37 miles stretched as good as 50. There are other pools, he replied. Yes, I said. But you cannot rely on them. They are dry or they are fouled by game or caravans . . . He listened with great attention. The Rail was charted to follow Captain Macdonald's route, he said, but already there were serious doubts. Then he stopped by the beads where the Greek was listening and he said very humbly: I have no men of quality around me, no-one I can trust. Will you join me?'

Robert Turk's entry for that day ends with the interrogation-mark on the evening of 20 August 1896. It needed no further embellishment: he had a fine sense of dramatic sufficiency. The entry, in fact, is the first in the diary.

It is significant that Turk decided to keep a record. He had led a life starred with danger and excitement. He had seen strange lands. He had followed, crossed and recrossed the routes of the Great Explorers. He had seen action and incident of so vivid and violent a nature as to provide irresistible compulsion to an habitual diarist. But there is no evidence of an earlier diary. Mrs Gopal did not mention it or produce (with that gleam of cupidity) so saleable an article.

The probability is that Turk had never kept one. Perhaps his way of life seemed unremarkable. Danger was the norm, the thread of romance was submerged in that wild loom of plain and forest. He had gone to Whitehouse out of curiosity: or he wanted information about a project which affected him; or he scented a commission. He had stayed to listen. It is easy to picture that humid room and its strings of trembling beads, its yellowing bamboo furniture and the yield of warping boards as Whitehouse paced, Turk sitting and the predatory nose turning slightly to the other's restive motion.

Turk had agreed. His reasons may have been prosaic. He was sick. He was tired. The bush had taken from him. He needed change or a long employment. The caravans would die and it was prudent to join the railroad. He was about to marry the daughter of a Goan merchant and the track would return him speedily to Mombasa, to the comfort of her flesh. Any or all of these considerations may have motivated him. He had agreed.

But he had begun a diary.

He had gone to the coffee-shop that night and he had begun it. Or, later, he had written of that night. He had known or sensed its importance, that he was to be in the van of an immense undertaking. There had been magic words and phrases, esoteric sounds of railroad lore; lines and locos, fishplates and fireboxes, buffers and boilers, sidings and sleepers. These were dangerous sounds; the sounds of boyhood. They evoked pictures which lay luminous on the imagination. Perhaps, when their talk ended, Turk and Whitehouse had already seen the rush of a great engine under an African night.

The next day Turk went to 'the weighing of the teeth,' a ceremony performed in the trading sheds in the shadow of the Jesus Fort. He was not an ivory-trader. He did not then hunt elephant. He was a caravan-master and, among other things, he delivered ivory. It came from lands as far as the Lake Rudolf basin, Karamojo, the plateaux of southern Abyssinia. It was a commodity of great value.

In those days Mumia's, a small outpost which had grown at the skirts of Mount Elgon, was the safari centre. Nairobi did not exist. A caravan could be stocked with ivory at Mumia's; and it was still profitable to transport it down-country to Mombasa. The caravan-master sometimes received a fee or commission calculated on the weight and quality of the ivory safely delivered. 'There was more than 12,000 pounds weight,' Turk writes. 'A tidy fee—but spoiled by the ivory lost in transit . . .' At that time Turk's delivery, if of the first quality, would fetch over £7,000 in the London market.

After the weighing Turk went by gharri to the depot at Kilindini. The gharri ran on metal lines the length of Vasco da Gama Street: it had painted woodwork and a bright canopy and it was pushed by two Swahili boys. At the depot Whitehouse gave Turk tea-and-whisky. Then he offered him a formal contract. Turk disdained it. He was there if Whitehouse wanted him. And he had given his hand on it. Whitehouse was insistent. Everyone had a contract; the Europeans, the Punjabis, the Pathans . . . everyone. Government was bound. It was better like that.

Turk would not agree. Contracts worked two ways. It was true that he had given his hand; but what if the railroad needed twenty years to reach the Lake? Whitehouse was silent. Turk's question had touched a nerve of anxiety. What was the cost of a good caravan-porter? he asked.

Turk considered. A Swahili porter received ten rupees a month. There were rations of flour, rice, a little meat and oil, ammunition for the best of them: in all say fifteen rupees a month.

Whitehouse had repeated it with a trace of envy: fifteen rupees. The official costing of the coolie labour was thirty rupees a man. This was the burden that had been placed upon him. Estimates were already derisory. Parliament had actually been told that the railroad would reach Victoria Nyanza in under four years, that it could be built for three million pounds. They were political animals; few of them had the slightest conception of the expenses, the difficulties. They would look for a scapegoat. They would take fright, halt the railroad in the middle of the bush. There would be no trains, nothing but track disappearing under secondary jungle.

Turk listened, drank the draughts of tea-and-whisky which were essential to him. 'He is a fine Engineer with a fine record,' he comments. 'But he has caught a strong stink of Politics. And he does not like it.' George Whitehouse was not the first idealist to catch that scent.

The first few miles of track were laid slowly and with reluctance. Mombasa and the sea were pleasantly near. Pay was generous. To expect haste was clearly unreasonable. The track crept from the littoral through patches of cultivation to the Rabai Hills. These hills rose from the coastal strip. They were steep and forested. They achieved a rise of almost six hundred feet in fifteen miles. Thereafter the hills flattened into a plateau of scrub jungle. Beyond this lay the Maji Chumvi Valley; and, thirteen miles from the valley, the Taru Desert—another name for thirst and privation.

Taru was a small camp left by the survey expedition on the fringe of the plain. It was impermanent. It would disintegrate in sun, rain and wind. In the dry season water could sometimes be drawn from the rocks. There were holes therein (like those formed by ancient geysers) of inexplicable shape and depth. You could drop a pebble and hear it leap faintly, the gulp as water received it far below.

But beyond Taru was the desert. In appearance it was not as a desert. There were no wind-ribbed dunes of sand, no unending vistas of erosion. It was red. It was grizzled with scrub like the grey-brown Karroo-bush of the South. It was spiked with aloe. There were trees of thorn acacia. Sometimes when the light changed there was a bloom of greenness; like a hint of fertility.

But this was illusion. It was a place of deceit. There was no water except within days of the finish of the rains; after that it dried. It concentrated heat. There was no game, nothing to sustain a man. Many had been deceived and many had died. The Taru was feared by the caravans; and respected. Most of them marched at night. They carried water in calabashes and tins from Taru-camp (or from Maungu Hill on the down-country trek) and men were whipped to the bone for the theft or waste of it. The professional deserters—those who joined at Mombasa with the intention of fleeing with rifle, provisions and advance pay—knew well their meagre chances of solitary survival in the Taru; they stayed with the caravan for the desert march.

Joseph Thomson, the explorer, described it: '. . . an apparently dead level plain, parched and waterless as if no drop of life-giving rain refreshed the iron-bound soil. The dense jungle, the grassy glades, the open forest disappear, and their place is taken by what may be called a skeleton forest. Weird and ghastly is the aspect of the greyish-coloured trees and bushes; for they are almost totally destitute of tender, waving branch or quivering leaf . . . To heighten the sombre effect of the scene, dead trees are observable in every direction, raising their shattered forms among the living, unable to hold their own in the struggle for existence . . .'

This, then, was the Taru Desert. This was the prospect. It grew in the minds of the construction gangs. It gained in reputation. The fear of it communicated itself to the limbs of that regiment of coolies, inhibited effort. Every foot of track brought them nearer to ordeal.

Turk married the Goanese on the twentieth day of September 1896. She was nineteen years of age: by name Sumitra, the daughter of Chandra Baksh. He left the coffee-shop in the Old Port and took his bride to new quarters in Vasco da Gama Street; this was then the main street of Mombasa and afforded a direct route to Kilindini. Whitehouse had moved from the Greek's hotel to a hut above the harbour. This hut into which stores had already overflowed and the walls of which were pinned with maps, schedules and surveys was to be the nerve of the operation until, at the end of the month, the new 'F' Class engines arrived from England.

Whitehouse had awaited them with impatience. He hated the 'A' Class engines. They were prematurely old (construction work aged an engine): they had burst their hearts in the valleys and ravines of India. They had come to him like fading crones; scarred and neglected and with voracious appetites. And they were insignificant. They aroused not awe but contempt.

Whitehouse loved railroads. His was the brain which assembled all that marvellous paraphernalia, sent power like a live and vibrant thing across the breadth of continents. But he had learned that the permanent way must be charged with life. Only one agency could consummate the months of toil in the sun; and that was the passage of a new and mighty locomotive.

Three engines came. They were unpainted. They were sleek with grease. They smelled of oil and new metal. They were off-loaded at night and their great iron corselets gleamed orange in the light of flares. To Whitehouse they were things of beauty. He had gone across to touch them, sensuously stroking the curves of their boilers as if the fingers felt for the reserves of heat and motion which would be generated there. One of these he immediately appropriated to his own use. This was his invariable practice. This was to be the invigorating force.

Robert Turk spent two weeks with the Goanese. There is a single entry in the journal during that period. 'I met Whitehouse and we walked to the middle of the Macupa Bridge where I chewed twist and spat juice into the Water and listened to his worries . . .'

There is no record of the manner in which Turk passed those fourteen days. He had money in his pocket from the ivory sales and a desirable wife. Presumably he made love to her (for a man of Turk's strength and primitive habit the expression seems too delicate), consumed quantities of tobacco and tea-and-whisky, waited for the leg-wound to heal, took an occasional

69

gharri or ricksha; and, perhaps, rode with Whitehouse down those pitiably few miles of track. Certainly a great deal of organisation occupied the latter part of the fortnight: for, on the fifteenth day, he left Mombasa at the head of a caravan.

This was the first of his assignments for Whitehouse. It was a small caravan by Coast standards. Its purpose was survey. Whitehouse had conceived a deep distrust of the official route; it had been charted, he knew, as much by dictates of economy as by considerations of terrain. He had been charged to drive through to the Lake at the minimum cost, the Treasury allocation must not be exceeded. Later, when the railroad was a matter of history, it could be re-routed.

Whitehouse, to his credit, had rejected that timorous policy. This, above all, would be his monument. He would be judged by it. It would open up a wilderness to trade and cultivation. From that thin metal line a colony would grow and there would be settlers, towns and cities in the sun. He was not a devious man and his mind did not move in circuits of expediency like those of the politicians whose plaints in the House had almost aborted the project. He had seen a vision. He would follow it.

Evidently he was drawn to Robert Turk. They were opposites. They moved in counterpoint. Turk was wild and taciturn, physically powerful, long-haired and unkempt, a creature of the bush who craved space and natural rhythms. Whitehouse, in contrast, was urbane and civilized; already enmeshed he could not flee the city like Turk. He was accountable: he accepted responsibility. Yet they were alike in directness. Each had seen the quality of the other. Whitehouse, isolate, turned to Turk like a man in search of truth. And Turk would give him this; he was entrusted to reconnoitre the route as far as Nzoi Peak. To this end he was allotted the technical support of a surveyor named Walter Herne.

Herne was a man in the late twenties; rotund, sedentary, red of flesh, heavy in the shoulders. He had been blistered by sun on the British-India ship from Bombay. Already the face, neck and forearms were lumpy from the bites of mosquitoes. He came with a Crown appointment and letters of introduction. He had little experience of tropical construction, but Whitehouse did not know this. 'He is soft,' Turk wrote contemptuously. 'He is a cold fish. The country will spit him out.'

The caravan assembled on the fifth day of October. Like most safaris moving into the interior it carried mail and stores for those posts and mission-stations it would encounter on its journey. It was joined by three Salvationists: Captain Muldoon, Mrs Heather and Miss Dolly Grey. Their destination was Taru-camp.

Captain Muldoon, for all his cavalier name, was a small, elderly, sun-dried man, browned and wrinkled like a raisin, bald of head but richly-endowed with eyebrow hair. He had served in Tanga and then in Mombasa. The seaport and its island fascinated him and he had written an article called 'The Isle of War' which appeared in *The Field* and of which he was immensely proud. He protected the cutting in an old tobacco pouch, carried it everywhere and showed it to Turk within an hour of meeting him.

Both women were young and new to missionary work. Mrs Heather was a widow. Turk's normal felicity of expression appears to desert him. 'She is gypsy-faced and thick in the leg ...' That is all; but in the case of Miss Grey he is more eloquent. 'A bright-eyed girl, with nice fair hair which she bundles up under her cap and a fetching way of laughing prettily when she talks. She is as fresh as new paint ... I envy the blessed natives ...'

On the inner cover of the journal Turk itemises the caravan in some detail. There is an inventory of stocks and provisions, a note of the complements of men and animals, an account of currency. The inventory is not exhaustive. Caravans carried a variety of stocks and equipment which Turk would regard as basic; medicines, chop-boxes, collapsible baths, surgical instruments, Cochrane water-bottles, water-tanks, knives, compasses, matches, tobacco, field-glasses, footwear and clothing, water-filters, brandy.

Maximum weight had to be carefully reckoned. The regulation load for a porter was sixty-five pounds. Foodstuffs were consumed on the march and deliveries were made at posts and missions; so the weight grew less. On the other hand porters became sick, died or deserted. Flour stocks could be replenished at certain stations *en route*. And game could be shot. It was almost incalculable.

The list is chiefly remarkable for its reference to Cape waggons. These were not in general use in East Africa and Turk (or the railroad) must have imported them from the south. They were heavy Afrikaaner waggons with iron axles and they carried four tons' weight. They could be arranged half-tented and they were drawn by at least two oxen. Perhaps it was an experiment. Oxen would not normally survive the tsetse belt which ran two hundred miles inland; and there was certainly insufficient water between Mazeras and Kibwezi.

Turk took the caravan inland along the swath which had been cut. There was a debris of brush and tree-root; odours of disturbed earth, of sap and burned vegetation came to the nostrils. Forest birds had come to pick in the scars. The line overlaid the old caravan route, deviated and returned again.

The landscape had altered. In that vastness of land this thin line of parallel steels, a metre wide, was nothing. Yet it had subtly and irrevocably altered. Something had come and something had gone. The line gleamed, was lost in the enfoldment of the hill, emerged, gleamed again and ran below the tree-line. He had felt irritation: now it was supplanted by an emotion he could not rationalise. The track was the beginning of change. It was the hand of man taking possession. He knew this, recognised it somewhere; but could not bring it to the surface.

Behind him the caravan straggled. The Cape waggons had already fallen to the rear; they could not be controlled and, now, the traces were tied and askari led the oxen. Mrs Heather and Miss Grey marched primly in their high-laced knee-boots, skirts swinging and the hands fanning little puffs of air. Muldoon walked rapidly on his short legs under a halo of mosquitoes. Herne followed sluggishly in the dust of the donkeys. Six Wasoga tribesmen had enlisted. Later, at Nzoi, they would leave the caravan, trek to the Lake and beyond it to the White Nile. Turk had agreed to give them food, water and protection in exchange for porterage.

In the Rabai Hills he was joined by the Suk tracker. The man had come from the woods like a shadow, a breach in the flow of yellow sunlight. Turk felt his presence before he appeared: then the thin dark legs fell into harmony with his own. They did not speak.

Two miles before the ravine of Mazeras Turk heard the whistle. The sound was distant. It lay outside the pattern of bird-call and the Suk turned his head so that the pigtail of mud and dung swung across his shoulders. It came again, three shrill notes like a signal, lost immediately.

Turk left the caravan, clambered up the embankment into sun-glare, on to the line. The Suk stood unmoving behind him. The shank of the spear threw an oblique shadow across the creosoted sleepers. He felt vibration in the lines.

The track had climbed from the coast. Below him were the palm-leaf roofs of villages, squares of cereal and cassava, a belt of woodland and, then, the curvature of the track and a long perspective which diminished into a single point of light. He waited and the vibration came again: a small white flower quivered in the haze of distance. The flower grew, broke in trees, reformed and effloresced and, now, they saw the separate convolutions of steam and the breast of the engine growing from miniature into a thing of power and majesty.

The locomotive stopped. It was immense. It awed and dwarfed him. He had seen nothing like it. It threw a great shadow and the cowcatcher was as high as his chest. He reached up and touched, feeling the pulse of latent power behind the visor. He smelled hot metal and the thick scent of hot new paint. The funnel seemed as tall as a man. The metal was cleaned and burnished and there were twin lamps above the cowcatcher and a huge, central lamp at the base of the funnel whose brasswork gleamed yellow-white in sun.

He walked down the length of it. Jets of steam were disgorging on the track. He peered through the wheels and pistons into the iron viscera, touched it again. He went past the footplate and tender, past the two carriages and the brake-van, back on the other flank. Whitehouse watched him from the cab.

He went down the embankment to get distance. The train was brilliant in a livery of yellow, red and green. The letters U.R. were painted gold on the gun-metal armour of the tender. There was even a triangular flag: it had begun to curl in heat. He returned to the footplate. Whitehouse was like a boy awaiting praise. He had named it the Uganda Queen, he said with pride. The carriages were divided into a travelling office and personal quarters. Now he could be mobile, always at the heart of things. He reached and the whistle blew again. Birds flew from the tree-line. The train began to move. Turk turned to the Suk. The man was grinning and the ivory lip-plug danced on the chin.

The caravan reached Mazeras by nightfall. This was railhead; ten and one half miles from Mombasa. There were six hundred men at the ravine and already the trestle bridge and its intricacy of timber had achieved two hundred feet of span.

Turk made camp, watered the donkeys and the oxen. There were fires to kindle, food to cook. With night Mazeras had become a place of fires. They pricked the depth of the ravine like garnets. The smells of cooking came. Rain was near and wind enlivened the fires. Turk had set his camp apart from the railroad coolies. Each of the porters had a sleeping mat and a small cotton tent; he arranged these tents to encircle the four carts and the two waggons. Then he posted askari sentinels. High in the ravine were the six Wasoga.

That night by the fire he listened to Captain Muldoon. The Salvationist spoke of Africa; of Livingstone and Speke and Joseph Thomson; of Mombasa and its Portuguese dominion and of the Arabs who came a thousand years ago from Oman; of the Mission at Frere Town; of the forest between Mombasa and Malindi which, he said, disturbed him and opened up dark places of the soul; of a man named Gregory who, three years before, had found things at Olorgesailie which suggested that here—*here*—was Eden and the beginning of man. His voice was rich and deep for so puny a frame. Mrs Heather and Miss Grey listened in silence. Turk puffed smoke into clouds of mosquitoes. Walter Herne sat slightly apart.

He hoped to die here, Muldoon told them humbly. This

country had awakened him, given him a kind of rebirth. So it was right that it should use him—and take him. But one man could accomplish little. He had a capacity for smiling at himself. A man of God could gird up his loins and smite divine sparks from the Christian anvil, he said with deliberate parody; but they would soon expire in the darkness of the pagan mind.

Herne sat sullenly. He was exhausted, unused to marching. The soft thigh-muscles still quivered from reaction. When he spoke it was with a note of injury. Why had he had to walk from Mombasa? he asked suddenly when Muldoon paused. Ten miles in all that heat and flies and dust . . . The Chief Engineer's Special Train had come to railhead that very day. Surely he could have ridden on it? He had kicked disconsolately at the embers of the fire and the colour of flame leapt into the walls of the ravine.

Turk headed the caravan out of Mazeras at first light of the second day. The swath of cut underbrush, trees and earthworks continued for three miles beyond the ravine. At that point he passed the last of the coolie-gangs; and at mid-morning reached the watercourse of Mwachi.

No water ran. There were depths of mud and sediment which he had to bridge with stone, trees and bracken. The sun climbed. Herne complained of fever, made no attempt to survey the gully or assess its hazards. 'He was afraid,' Turk said later. 'Afraid to venture without escort, afraid of long grass, of snakes, of insects, of the food and the water and the sun.' Fear was Herne's inseparable companion. He looked for hostility and inevitably found it.

After Mwachi the caravan made slow progress. The terrain rose. It needed six days to reach the ravine of Maji Chumvi. Turk crossed the bridge which had been built by the defunct Imperial British East Africa Company, replenished the caravan from the heavily-salted water of the river and led it into the valley. They were then thirty-two miles from the coast: and it was in this valley of Maji Chumvi that they suffered the first of the misfortunes.

Two oxen died and four sickened. Muldoon had spent three

years in Natal and diagnosed it as 'lung-sickness.' It was common in the South, he told them; and there, where everything was known about oxen, it was the custom to inoculate them by binding a sliver of diseased lung into the slit tails of the healthy beasts. 'He did not offer to do it,' Turk notes caustically. Within three days all of the oxen were dead. Muldoon was no veterinary and it is reasonable to assume that the tsetse had killed them.

Turk abandoned the Cape waggons. 'I found that the so-called iron axles had split. They had been painted black but were, in fact, of greenwood . . .' The loads were distributed and the caravan moved on to Samburu.

There were water holes at Samburu, a little game. Turk made camp and waited for Herne's fever to abate. On the first day he took the Suk and six Swahilis on a search for meat. He killed four small antelope and three teal 'which must have strayed from the river.' On the second day the six Wasoga stole water, meat and copper wire from the stores, and deserted.

It was at this point, it seems, that Robert Turk alienated himself from Muldoon and the others. Until then he had been quiet, withdrawn and courteous. He had drunk cheap German whisky (in hot tea) in quantities which must have alarmed the missionary captain: and he had chewed tobacco-quids and spat juice with a liberality which certainly offended Mrs Heather. But eccentricity was expected in a master of caravans. Africa, as everyone knew, produced characters.

But with the desertion of the tribesmen they saw another facet. Desertion accompanied by theft was a major crime. It could not go unpunished. The Taru was near and the idea of flight from its rigours lay in the minds of many of the porters. It was a matter of discipline. 'It was known that I kept a tight hand.' Turk left the caravan in the charge of the senior headman, slung his Winchester and a bandolier of shells, and went with the Suk tracker on the trail of the Wasoga. He took no askari.

Turk returned after two days. It was sundown and Muldoon saw the figures reel black out of a red mist. There were four Wasoga and they were tied the one to the other: the Suk pricked them intermittently with his throwing-spear. Turk was dirty, sore-eyed, the long hair and clothes thick with dust. Two of the

Wasoga were dead, he announced: these others would be punished.

Miss Grey, Mrs Heather and Herne had come from the fires to stare at this stranger of a man with the dust-red skin and the pitiless face. Muldoon went with a calabash of water to the Wasoga but Turk stopped him. Muldoon protested: the men were in need of water. Turk shook his head: they were in need of punishment. How did they die? the missionary asked him. Turk lifted the rifle, tapped it significantly. Then he assembled the camp. The Wasoga were tied to one of the carts and the offences recited. They were cruelly flogged. 'He came and preached to me later,' Turk wrote. 'Two lives, he asked me, was it worth it? For a pint or two of water, a pennorth of copper wire . . . ?'

The caravan returned in the middle of November. Sickness and rainstorms had stopped all platelaying and the track had gone no further than Mwachi. By that time three thousand Indian coolies were encamped at railhead and at points along the line. They were wet, mutinous and apathetic; afflicted with jungle-ulcers, the suppurations left by the eggs of chigger-fleas, malaria, a host of ailments. In those days relatively little was known about cause and prophylaxis, of the connexion between tropical disease, food, water and sanitation. When Turk reached railhead he learned that one half of the complement of coolies, native labour and Europeans was sick.

Whitehouse was there. He received Robert Turk in a carriage of the Special Train. 'We talked of this and that and of the progress of the Railway. We smoked a pipe and he gave me some real Scotch whisky which he insisted I drink without adulteration (he meant tea). We looked at the Rain which was falling in torrents and then he gave me some English newspapers and a copy of *The Field* which he said had come on the same Ship as the whisky. I picked up *The Field* and I said that reminded me. Of what? he asked. Of Muldoon, I said. Both Muldoon and Walter Herne are dead . . .'

This casual interpolation toward the end of a conversation in which they had 'talked of this and that,' in which the caravan-master had had time to smoke a pipe and drink a glass of whisky, is revealing of Turk. The deaths were unimportant. This was a country in which life was merely a tenant. Muldoon and Herne were dead: that was all. The journal itself is hardly concerned with the ordeal of Herne, with Muldoon's final act. The entries are terse to the point of indifference. It was left to the Sub-Commissioner's inquiry, to the evidence of Miss Grey, Mrs Heather and of Turk himself to clothe the bones of the story.

Walter Herne, it seemed, was better connected than White-house knew. He was the son of a Senior Collector in the Indian Central Provinces, a nephew of an Indian Army soldier of General rank. Within a week the Administration had sent its representative to Mwachi and the inquiry was held in the second carriage of the Uganda Queen.

Mrs Heather was plainly hostile to Turk. Muldoon, a man she had admired, was dead. Turk had caused it. 'He drank bottles and bottles of trade whisky,' she told the Sub-Commissioner. 'He chewed tobacco and spat like an oaf in a tap-room. He thought more of that half-naked savage (the Suk) than he did of us.' Later, she described the affair of the Wasoga. 'They had taken no more than any Christian would have given them for the asking. They were simple, timid men, a thousand miles from their home. He pursued them as if they were dangerous animals. He murdered two of them. The other four he brought back roped like cattle and had them lashed until they bled . . .'

It was his duty to pursue them, Turk replied. He could allow no man to succeed in desertion and theft. And if he had wanted to murder he would have murdered them all. In fact, the two Wasoga had thrown spears: he had shot them and the others surrendered. They had been punished, he said, in the manner common to such an offence.

Mrs Heather had interjected: 'You mean in the manner common to slavers.' She went on to describe the distress of Captain Muldoon. He had wept over the plight of the Wasoga. He had washed their wounds. He had even formed a liking for Robert Turk. But then they had seen the other side of Turk. 'He had not an ounce of forgiveness, he wanted vengeance . . .'

Turk replied, laconically, that Africa was now a land overflowing with Christian charity and that he could safely leave all that to the missionaries; further, that he could not afford to wait for the Lord to exact vengeance—he had a caravan to discipline.

Miss Grey said little. She was subdued, perhaps deeply shocked by the deaths, by this excursion into a land which had bared its teeth, shewn its savagery. 'She is a sweet girl,' Turk entered in his diary. 'The matter was over. She would not add to the bitterness.'

Walter Herne, Turk told the Sub-Commissioner, was immature, unsuited to the tropics, 'ever-fearful as if something were about to spring upon him . . .' He was a laggard. Also, he had done very little survey work. Even he, Turk, could see that his reports were a mass of surmise. For that reason the caravan had gone no further than Ndara.

At that point the Sub-Commissioner must have looked to Whitehouse for corroboration. It was true, Whitehouse agreed: Herne's work was valueless. In a report prepared at Taru-camp Herne had concluded, negatively, that Macdonald's map was suspect and that 'the projected route has merely been drawn to the shortest distance between various trigonometrical points, many of them very widely separated . . .' But, Whitehouse said, this was already known. This was precisely why he had sent Herne and Turk into the interior. He had wanted a survey in those very terrains where the density of jungle had confined Macdonald to the Swahili caravan road.

After Samburu, Turk said, they had marched to Taru-camp. Herne constantly complained; of fever, diarrhoea and sore feet. The camp, he found, was in the charge of 'a Portuguee and two lazing Swahili.' They remained there four days. The three Salvationists were installed, he left them stores, food and fire-arms and a guard of two askari; then at dawn of the fifth day he and Herne led the caravan into the Taru Desert.

The march began on the twentieth day of October. Maungu was thirty-seven miles from Taru-camp: Turk reached it in two days. From the beginning of the trek across the desert to the death of Herne the journal is curiously uninformative. Herne is scarcely mentioned. The folios for the period seem naked compared with those that precede and follow it. The Sub-Commissioner referred to the 'paucity of information in the caravan Log.'

The journal merely records that, *en route* across the Taru, the water-holes (always perverse and unpredictable) at Maziwa Matutu and at Ziwa Buchuma were dry. They reached Maungu, climbed the thousand-feet hill and found that the crater 'contained only an inch or two of fouled water. It had been spoiled by an Arab caravan.' Turk marched a further eleven miles to the region of Ndara. Here he found water. And it was here, he told the Sub-Commissioner, that 'Mr Herne declined to go further on account of his Condition.'

Turk decided to return. The survey was over. He spent one day at Ndara, hired a dozen Teita tribesmen to carry water in calabashes and turned the caravan for Taru 'at the early light.' Two days later, within ten miles of Taru-camp, Walter Herne 'decamped by night into the desert.' The phrase is Turk's. There is no further allusion.

'Did you not search for him?' the Sub-Commissioner asked.

Turk had hesitated. Then: 'I imagined he had gone on to Taru.'

It was noon when the caravan reached Taru-camp. There was no sign of Walter Herne. Muldoon and the two Salvationist women had gone by donkey-cart in the direction of Samburu. They returned one hour before sundown. Turk reported Herne's disappearance. 'Muldoon was horrified,' Turk said at the inquiry. 'He wanted an immediate search-party. I said no. The light is going. The sky is full of rain. And Herne might yet come in.'

Herne did not come in. At dawn Turk assembled the caravan. Muldoon was astounded to learn that Turk had no intention of organising a search in the Taru Desert. 'He pleaded with Turk,' Mrs Heather said. 'He begged him not to abandon Herne in that terrible plain. But Turk refused—as he had refused mercy to the Wasoga. He told the Captain that Herne had no hope of survival without water, that if he wanted Herne's body he had better go out and find it. And that,' Mrs Heather concluded grimly, 'was exactly what the Captain did.'

Robert Turk then led the caravan on the thirteen-mile trek to

Offloading railway material at Mombasa

The first train to leave Kilindini

of the hut. [?]sons servant made a can of tea. we did no
talk much because everyone had one ear cocked for lions **5**
I told them they would not hear much of them when
20th April, 1898
they did come + they would most
likely come from the river where we had seen prints _al
over the sandy banks_. Later on I went off to his blessed
water-tank + we gave Brock a gaurd to the sick-Tent
which was a fair way off from the main camp because
the danger of spreading the pox. These coolies have gone
down like ninepins with everything you can think of.
After seeing Brock alright we went down to Ibrahims
tent which was right by the river. but he was not in
it — strange because all the Indos and the askari were
scared stiff and would always be tied in for the night
as soon as it was dark. A bad omen for somebody.
It was now raining really hard and the Tzavo was
filling up — not a good night for lions! but you can
never tell. We went back from the river + through the
coolie tents and around the thorn hedge — it was now
raining + thundering and we could not hear much with
all the rain drenching on the leaves and tents. the[re]
was not a sign of Ibrahim and his gang — if he w[as]
out on the rampage there was not a blink or a s[ign]
of him! There was not a sign of the lion or lion[s]
21st April, 1898
but later on we spotted his _fresh_ print
in the mud + once we saw his eyes! or thought we
did. There was quiet a storm blowing up + it was
very difficult to see anything but rain — all the
fires had been washed out, nowhere to dry out —
worse luck! We saw the lions eyes again and
mistake this time — I think he was following +
doubt looking for a meal. It was a job to keep the
breech dry in the pouring rain. I had a drink of
whiskey + then we went through the lines again
+ sudenly the lightning made it as bright as day
+ we saw Ibrahim between the tents with his gang
there were two of them holding some poor devil, they
had done for him by slitting his throat. I shot him
like a mad dog and Ibrahim threw the weapon (it
turned out to be a claw fixed to a glove like a leg
or a lion would be) where it stuck in my side
am writing this a good deal later after it all happ[ened]
There were a lot of screams coming from the sick-T[ent]
and we went over + found that the lion had torn t[he]
canvas away + had dragged out one of the coolies +
the tent to the hedge! He was found half-eaten
next morning — Brock said it was a smallpox case +

[left margin, vertical:] likely + the lion had done us all a good turn!

A page from Turk's diary

the valley of the Maji Chumvi. Muldoon, it appears, went into the desert with the Portuguese, a donkey, water and provisions.

Turk testified that he had gone half the distance toward Maji Chumvi when it occurred to him that Captain Muldoon 'might really venture into the desert—perhaps even with the ladies.' The possibility would not leave his mind. He put the caravan in charge of a headman and sent it on its way. Then, accompanied by the Suk, he retraced the path to Taru.

It was past noon when they reached Taru. Muldoon and the Portuguese had been gone five hours. 'I was relieved to find Miss Grey still there . . . (Mrs Heather was also there). We did not stop. We went straight on into the desert.'

Twenty-four hours later Turk found the Portuguese wandering in the scrub. The man was delirious from thirst and heat-exhaustion. An hour later he found the donkey nibbling at a patch of aloe flowers; and an hour after that the dead body of Muldoon.

It sat upright against the bone-white wood of a petrified shrub, three miles off the caravan track. Although the breast-pocket of the jacket was buttoned over a small Testament Muldoon's fingers held only the cutting from *The Field*.

That night the rain came.

Herne was never found. His death was presumed. The Sub-Commissioner, Miss Grey and Mrs Heather returned soberly to Mombasa.

Certain conclusions can be drawn. Robert Turk and Walter Herne were of different clay. The caravan-master, a man fashioned by that land of wild rhythms, had nothing but contempt for Herne. Like many of the strong he despised the weak. He had already prophesied: 'The country will spit him out.' Perhaps he had wanted that.

The incident of the Wasoga tribesmen had crystallised this contempt. It became positive. Captain Muldoon and Dolly Grey (two people he had liked) had turned from him, left him in isolation. He reacted. Compassion was the currency of the Salvationists: Turk debased it. Herne was the obvious target: Turk forced him to breaking-point.

Herne was ill; certainly unfitted for a march across a waterless plain which even the strong and the seasoned treated with respect. He could not endure it. He 'decamped'; a bald and callous word for the act of a man who, desperate from heat and sickness, had found irresistible the night of the desert: a place in which to go out and die.

There is nothing censorious of Whitehouse in the Sub-Commissioner's Report. Africa in those times was a land which claimed the health and lives of many men. Whitehouse had entrusted Herne to Robert Turk: and Turk was a man of exceptional calibre.

But Herne had come with letters of introduction from high places. He was young, inexperienced, not endowed with the quality of courage. His death distressed Whitehouse. It was pitiable. It was a waste. And there would be echoes in the halls of power.

The affair is important to the railroad story. Understandably, it eroded Whitehouse's confidence in Robert Turk. It led him, later in the Taru, to question Turk's judgment. It contributed, indirectly, to the calamities in the desert.

3. No Epitaphs for Coolies

Turk went to Mombasa after the inquiry. The malaria which had enfevered him at Samburu had returned and he spent six weeks with Sumitra at the house in Vasco da Gama Street. He was estranged from Whitehouse and he saw nothing of the Chief Engineer until the last day of December. Perhaps the emotions of the final hours of the ebbing year caused Whitehouse to relent. They talked, smoked, and came to an arrangement.

Railhead was at Mile 23: a shameful performance, Whitehouse confessed. At this rate he would need fifteen years to reach the Lake. The Germans would never miss such an opportunity. Already there had been an intensifying of their survey operations. The trade of Uganda was there for the grasping. The Crown might lose it; and a great deal more.

Turk listened. The Uganda Queen, Whitehouse said, had had an inspiriting effect: but only for a time. Whatever the gain from the sight of that splendid locomotive, it had been lost to rain, cold, sickness, discontent—and the news of the affair in the Taru. That, of course, had been magnified by rumour. The Taru was impassable. Not even a reptile could live there. How could a man labour in that place of bones and survive?

But the Taru was only the beginning. The difficulties would not diminish. What of the extending line of communication? the victualling of this swelling army? the permanent way? the Masai? the escarpment of the Rift?

Whitehouse liked to raise his obstacles to an impressive height, and then demolish them. There was nothing insuperable, he said. He needed men of quality, of strong faith; and a system of continuous survey. Then, without enthusiasm, he asked Turk to lead another expedition.

Turk left the island of Mombasa late in January of 1897. He took no pack animals and the whole of the caravan went by train to railhead. From there it would trek to Kikuyu in the region of the valley of the Rift. There had been no drums or flags or sense of occasion. They had simply climbed into a train. Steaming through the plantations of the littoral and into hill-forest Turk must have reflected on the nature of change and the passing of things. Sumitra was already pregnant.

When Robert Turk returned from the Rift toward the end of April the line had reached Taru-camp. There were many new faces, a great concentration of men and equipment, rashes of corrugated-iron, tents and dumps, a large timber hut. The Uganda Queen was there. Its brilliant liveries had been refurbished: the woodwork was titivated with coloured scrolls and flourishes. Turk had felt the beginning of dislike. 'She has a carnival look to her,' he wrote. 'Men are already dying of Disease and she is much out of place. She is like a painted Trollop come to a funeral.' The phrase was prophetic.

Turk and his surveyor, a man named Hoad, saw Whitehouse in the carriage in which the inquiry had been held. They were ill at ease. The presences of Herne and Muldoon stood between them. Whitehouse did not at once examine the reconnaissance and survey reports. The Rift was a long way ahead. It was the problem of the Taru which occupied him. But he was confident, he told them. There were some first-class men at railhead. He was no longer alone.

One of them was Ronald Preston, a man with whom Turk felt an immediate affinity. He judged him to be about thirty years of age. He was slender, handsome, restless of eye and limb. He had a thin, carefully-scissored moustache—foppish in a man less obviously masculine. Turk recognised him at once. He was an adventurer. This man would go wherever lay space, freedom, danger and challenge.

Later, after nightfall, they drank German whisky in Preston's tent. Rain had begun. A hurricane lamp had been placed in the opening and water ran down its glass, throwing a movement of oleaginous red whorls on to the canvas. The atmosphere was humid. A gramophone played somewhere in the camp: the phrases came on squalls of wind.

Preston talked of an early life in India. His father had been an insignificant Government officer. He could not remember his mother. Then the father, too, had died. They were alone. They? Yes, there had been an elder sister. They became orphans. They were immensely privileged. Only orphans could get into an orphanage.

Preston spoke with a kind of bitter humour. Men revealed themselves in the dark of tents with a glass in the hand. There was something about tents; the proximity, the smell of canvas, an alien world outside. Intimacy came quickly. In the morning the words, the delvings, the confessions were regretted or forgotten.

He became an engineer. There had been eleven years of construction work in the states of India. He had worked on the harbour at Madras, the bridge at Godavari. He had learned; about concrete and steel, coolies, the Hindustani tongue. In 1891 he had married Florence Daly. Two children were born. Then Government had asked him to go to East Africa. He had accepted: the opportunity was too good to refuse. He and Florence had come to Africa, leaving the children in the care of his sister. He had not liked that but, later, he would send for them. Florence[1] was in Mombasa. He had been in East Africa three months. He would never go back. This was *his* country. He had known it the moment he came ashore from the *Nowshera*. There was something elemental here. It beckoned. It took possession. It would never release him.

In the morning there were other men. Turk went with Preston through the camp, aware now of the respect in which the engineer was held. Preston had already earned a reputation. He had thrown a forty-foot girder-bridge across one of the Maji Chumvi

[1] Like many of the wives of engineers Florence Preston spent intermittent periods under canvas with her husband, returning to the Coast or to Army garrisons when the track ran into conditions of exceptional hardship or danger.

streams without benefit of tackle, blocks or derricks. The feat had impressed them.

There were four hospital-tents and two railhead doctors. Sanitary-trenches had been cut in the earth around the tents. They were fly-infested. They overflowed with rainwater. Turk stared in disgust. Wherever men came they brought refuse and soiling. Three of the tents were occupied by coolies, the fourth by Europeans and headmen. He went into the first of them, into the stench of sickness. Coolies in dirty cotton were arrayed like mummies. A man came forward. He was a grey man; he had grey, pompous eyes and wisps of grey beard on the cheeks and lips which added only weakness to the face. The flesh was grey and etiolated. 'Dr Willem,' Preston told Turk.

In the second tent he met Dolly Grey. The skin under the eyes was dark with fatigue. She did not laugh in the way he remembered. Dr McCulloch, she said, had begged her to come from Frere Town. How could she refuse?

He did not enter the third tent. Two women held a vomiting coolie over a pail. The man hung suspended on arms as thin and bone-yellow as celery. Outside the tent eight men on stretchers were prepared for transport. The bad ones were shunted back to Mombasa, Preston told him.

In the fourth and largest tent he met Dr Orman. Orman was a small, volatile man, burdened with the face and presence of a clown. He had soft, dismal eyes, a lugubrious mouth, brows which arched in perpetual amazement. The moustache was black, thick and mournful. He wore a cloth cap absolutely straight on the head. Turk had smiled. Later he found that Orman was alert, widely-read and obedient to conscience, scrupulous and direct. He could not offer an aura of professional airs and graces: instead he gave skill, learning and compassion. The voice was high and piping: it, too, robbed him of dignity. He had worked in Southern India, he told them, where subtertian malaria was endemic. Most of the coolies came from the malarious regions. And this was what Willem would not understand; that blackwater fever was only a sequel. Expose them to sun, cold, rain and exertion and you had all the right conditions for it.

Preston and Turk went from the hospital tents to the animal transport lines. Rain was falling. Parts of the encampment were morass. Steam rose from the soil and the animals seemed to paddle in pools of whiteness. The smells of hide and urine came. There were mules, bullocks and donkeys: the shapes of camels loomed gaunt against the whiteness.

Captain Haslam greeted them in a hut with a sloping iron roof from which rainwater leapt. He had been seconded from the Army Veterinary Department, he told Turk against the drumming of the roof. He was a squat man with a deep chest and thick thighs and jaws carefully shaven around a postage-stamp of bristle under the nose. He had an aggressive lip and bright eyes. He hated camels, he said. He went to the door of the hut to stare at arches of necks swinging in mist. Hated them; he would do his duty but he hated them. And they would surely die. Camels were always the first to go. Pugnacity thrust out the lip. He had asked for Cyprus mules, nothing but Cyprus mules. And *this* was what they'd sent him; including, unbelievably, two beautiful white Muscat donkeys with flowing tails.

There were others.

A face, large, red and glistening, had stared down from the footplate of one of the 'F' Class engines, across a forearm matted with ginger hair. This was Shutt, Preston announced; a driver of engines without peer. Shutt's tonsured head with its ginger fringe seemed to rock behind wreaths of steam. The chest swelled against a striped flannel shirt. It was sodden with sweat. Shutt was short, wide and muscular. A cheroot was stuck like a spike in big stones of yellow teeth. Turk watched him reverse the locomotive into mists of rain.

Then, oilskinned, they had gone through the coolie lines; through avenues of wood and canvas and saturated cotton. Turk, a man attuned to the significance of smell, turned his head from side to side. These were elusive scents that had no part of Africa, scents of cloth and flesh, of cooking food corrupted by alien spices.

A Muslim, gross, bearded and turbaned, came from the head-men's hut, emptied a pail of slop into the mud, glowered at them, spat and went back in. Turk had sensed the enmity of the man. Something smouldered there. It alerted him. This, Preston told him, was Ibrahim, the Chief Headman; a man as strong as a bull, a ferocious master with a great enjoyment of beating. Ibrahim, Preston said, claimed to have marched for Joseph Thomson.

Turk makes no further reference to the claim, neither accepting nor discounting it. Obviously, he had never before seen Ibrahim. But it is of interest. Thomson, who had led the Royal Geographical Society's expedition of 1883-1884, described in his 'Journey of Exploration among the Snowclad Mountains and Strange Tribes of Eastern Equatorial Africa . . . to Mount Kenia and Lake Victoria Nyanza' a headman named Brahim, or Ali Ngombé (Ali the bullock).

Thomson wrote: 'It was a somewhat risky step on my part to put this man in the position of a head-man. In my first expedition he was a porter, who, while he was without exception one of the best men in my caravan as a worker, was yet the ringleader in all the troubles with the men. He it was who led the mutiny in Uhehè when every man deserted, and at all times he was a thorn in the flesh. Powerfully built, with a ferocious expression when angry he was the very beau-ideal of a savage . . .'

Thirteen years had passed since Thomson crossed Masai-Land. Ibrahim was older. Those years, it seems, had been a crucible. Whatever the annealing process he had emerged a brute.

At this point in time the bush-clearing parties had gone eleven miles into the Taru. There were four gangs of two hundred men, each attended by a headman and three armed askari. Bush and scrub were cut by panga to a swath one hundred feet wide. The gangs worked in intermittent rain, encamping at nightfall and moving forward at dawn. They were victualled by porter from the supply-camp.

Whitehouse had now abandoned his time-schedule. In Kilindini it had all seemed measurable. A mile of metre-gauge could be expressed in terms of steel rail cut into thirty-foot lengths and handling at a weight of fifty pounds to the yard; steel transverse sleepers at a weight of seventy pounds and spaced at thirty-two inches; allow for laying and the coupling and adjusting of joints and aligning, the effect of loop, gradient and curvature. There was surely an optimum rate of progress which could be calculated; India and Mexico had proven it.

But it had not been like that. These men, of Madras and southern India, the Pathans and Punjabis and the men of the north, had brought indolence and apathy. They were prone to accident, a prey to zymotic disease. They were a long way from home. They moved slowly into inertia. And certain things were not predictable. He could not know that bubonic plague would erupt in Karachi and put replacements in quarantine; or that the animal transport would die with enthusiasm; or that the Supply Department in Kilindini would collapse from incompetence; or that the salt water from the Maji Chumvi would corrode the boilers; or that the cut scrub and timber along the permanent way which was supposed to fuel the engines would be inadequate and that they, the ones in Kilindini, would organise the coal out of existence.

Or that rain would fall with unseasonable strength.

'You should be thankful for it,' Turk told him. 'Rain and cold is better than heat and thirst.'

Whitehouse was not convinced. He was an engineer. He knew the effect of rain, the unique hazard of it. He waited for abatement. The anxiety grew. The skies were dark with cloud and it seemed that a mountain of water hung poised above the Taru. It oppressed him. Humidity came down and the rain was warm; they sweated but the rain brought no refreshment. Then, watching the cloud, its development and the failure of light and the evil green texture of the sky and the land he waited; not for abatement but for deluge.

When it came, in that month of May, it came with ferocity. It scoured, beat and eroded the land. It washed through the wadis, broke in red-sedimented flood across the savanna. Whitehouse watched with incredulity. This was no land of thirst. It was opening, bursting into flower. It seemed he could hear the growth of liana and the movement of sap, smell the awakening of new and ravenous life. This was an inexhaustible reservoir. The earth was filling.

Whitehouse called a meeting in the Uganda Queen. Hoad, Preston and Turk were there, Willem, two bridge-foremen, a road-engineer and a man from the Supply Department. The carriage trembled under the impact of rain. Paraffin-lamps threw sallow light: oilskins, the flesh of hands and faces were orange in it.

The news was bad, Whitehouse reported. Ten miles of track were now unsafe. Storm-water had undermined embankments and earthworks. Cuttings were collapsing. Already a trestle at the Maji Chumvi ravine had gone. And there had been derailments. He paused, stared out at the rain which runnelled from the roof: it came in sheets, came at the carriage on the gathering wind.

Railhead was now at Mile 51, he told them. Platelaying had gone six miles into the plain from Taru-camp. Out there in the scrub (he pointed to the night) were a thousand men. Only God knew the miseries they endured. Willem, here, was getting a casualty return of fifty men a day. The gain in track-miles was negligible: the daily bush clearance was now measurable in yards. Behind (he pointed in the direction of the coast), the permanent way was in evident danger. They had to decide; to continue or consolidate.

There had been a silence. Then Preston asked: 'What would that mean?'

'It would mean withdrawing from Taru.'

They had talked. Charts and surveys were examined. Then Whitehouse asked for views.

The bridge-foremen wanted to withdraw. One bridge had been destroyed; that was a clear pointer to the strength of the torrent. The official from the Supply Department supported him: the demand for food, fuel and material had already strained his department's resources and he could not guarantee supplies and victuals if the line went further. The road-engineer was non-committal. Dr Willem said, drily, that from the medical viewpoint the railroad ought to be abandoned altogether: these men were low and debilitated, ripe for epidemic. Hoad sought compromise: surely there were sufficient men to restore the permanent way *and* to press railhead onward?

Whitehouse rejected him. There could be no half-measures. He had turned to Preston for support but Preston was silent: this was not withdrawal, it was retreat. Robert Turk had sat there in the grip of dysentery-pain. He was in no mood for temperate expression. He confesses that 'I expressed myself strongly. You are a fool, I told him, the rain is your ally and you do not know it. By the time the rain is finished you could be half across the Taru . . .'

Whitehouse had flushed. '. . . He said very quietly that the rainfall had been the heaviest since the keeping of Records. There would be enough water in the Taru for a twelve-month. Every rock-hole, bed and well must be full of it. Rubbish, I said, a week of sun and it will be as dry as a bone. Then he stood up. Rubbish maybe, he said, but I will trust my own judgment. He stared at me and I knew he was thinking of Herne and Muldoon. He looked very stubborn. I have made my decision, he said. I am going back.'

Whitehouse withdrew the whole of the labour-force from the Taru, spread it back toward Mombasa. Viaducts were strengthened, embankments shored; and track, slewed by flood-water, re-aligned. The coolies worked in downpour, shifting earth, rock and timber in the task of consolidation until those forty-five miles of permanent way were stable for the passage of engines and rolling-stock. At the end of three weeks Whitehouse said: 'I am satisfied. Now for the Taru.'

That accent of complacency must surely have seemed justified. The track was secure. There was no impediment to supplies. The flow of water from the distilling-plant at Mombasa and the streams at Maji Chumvi was assured. The rain had almost stopped and he could reasonably expect an improvement in health, in the rate of chest disease and blackwater.

In the middle of June Whitehouse sent his parties into the Taru; and Robert Turk to Mombasa on an errand for the purchase or hire of mules. Now there were more than five thousand coolies, mainly Punjabis; two-thirds of them would be used in one intensive effort to push rail across the plain to the Hill of Maungu. They needed water, grain and rice. These were the elements of survival: failure or delay could be disastrous. Human porterage with its load of sixty or seventy pounds was clearly inadequate.

Mombasa was stirring. There had been centuries of sun and somnolence, Islam and the Portuguese and the monsoon dhows, leisurely trades in honey, wax and ivory. Nothing much had changed. Now it had the air of a city. Already the Asian merchants had come in the wake of the railroad; the rituals of buying and selling had brought their own currents of urgency. Life had quickened. There were British, Norwegian and Zanzibari freight-vessels in the crowded port, a ship of the German East Africa Line. The quays displayed cargoes of grain and livestock, dates and cloth, rubber and kerosene, steel for the track.

Life, also, had quickened within Sumitra. Turk spent a week in Vasco da Gama Street. He drank tea-and-whisky, took an occasional Arab coffee from the copper pots in which it was always infused, watched the flutter of colour in the streets and the pageant of human commerce; and enjoyed, perhaps, the warmth of rainless skies.

At the end of the week he entered into an agreement with an Italian trader from Genoa. The Genoese had already begun to ship mules from certain ports of the Red Sea; he had considerable quantities of very fine animals on hand (all bred to maximum loads, tropical heat and desert voyages), he was confident that these superlative beasts could be hired at a gain to both himself and the railroad.

Turk left Sumitra in the care of the merchant Baksh, entrained for railhead. The child would be born before he again saw Mombasa. He hoped for a son. 'I have no interest in daughters,' he wrote with open contempt; and underlined it. Turk's values must be judged by the locale and the period and his own wild temperament. Sons, if not actually proof of masculinity, were contributory to it. The caravan-master, bound on that narrow track for the rim of desert, perhaps looked indolently into the mirror of future, saw the reflection of himself.

Heat was building when Turk reached the camp, the mud of

the rains already encrusted. Soon the crust would break, crumble redly into dust. He reported to Whitehouse. The Chief Engineer seemed buoyant. His anxiety had gone with the last of the storms. He had devised a crossing of the plain.

There were thirty-four miles between the camp and Maungu. Speed was the essence; and that meant perfect co-ordination between material-trains, water-trains, railhead and the advance parties. He had stipulated two trains a day; the first to arrive at daybreak with fuel and materials, the second at sundown with food and water. This water-train would carry the minimum daily requirement for men, animals and locomotives. The forward parties would be supplied by mule from railhead. He would shift railhead camp on the completion of every eight miles of track. The goal was eight thousand feet a day; and that, he said with ebullience, assured a comfortable train-ride across the Taru in perhaps three weeks' time.

Turk had stared; at the optimism in Whitehouse's eyes, then at the immense plain and its horizon of scrub and its pale tones of aridity. Whitehouse saw his disbelief. Three weeks, the dry voice said with resentment. And during that time a permanent camp at Tsavo River must be prepared.

Tsavo River ran into the Sabaki at a distance of one hundred and thirty-two miles from the Indian Ocean. The line would bridge it. Turk planned for a trek of eighty miles from railhead. To this end he enlisted the aid of Preston, who gave him porters, carpenters and labourers; and Haslam, who supplied twelve camels and a score of donkeys.

Turk used the next three days to equip his caravan. Then, at sundown of the third day, he left Taru, marched through the night and into the plain. He avoided the swath which had been cut, preferring trackless scrub to that bristling road of stumps. Distant he had seen the fires of the bush-cutting gangs, pears of light elongating in the caprices of wind. There, crouched or sleeping, would be the regiments of coolies. The disbelief returned. These men had crossed an ocean. They were rootless. They had no point of contact with this land of Africa beyond fear of it. They waited in darkness for the first flush of dawn light, for the pressures of sun and glare and the labours of a new day. Why should they care? Whitehouse and the others would work with faith and pride: but not these. They had left family and homeland for a better rate of pay; for no more than that.

The caravan crossed the Taru in two marches. Turk made camp at the foot of the Hill of Maungu. The sun was dying. The last of the marches had been bad. They had used their water. There were stragglers somewhere in the desert; twenty or thirty men who would rejoin when the water was drawn and the food prepared and the fires kindled. Anger supplanted his weariness. They would be punished; these and the headmen who had failed to keep the caravan tight.

The saddle of Maungu lay one thousand feet above. The water in its depression was reputed to be permanent: but Turk knew this to be untrue. At one time Teita villages had clustered on the hill within reach of its water. Then, in a year of great heat, the reservoir dried. The tribe had moved to the Sagala Hills.

Turk assembled a party. This ascent of the hill was always an ordeal after the desert march. They had taken tins, calabashes and pails and filled them from the crater and, standing there on the edge of the saddle in the last of the sun and above the plains, already grey, he had looked across this ravine of greyness to the mountain of Ndara. Its ridge was caught in an oriflamme of light and he felt the beauty of this land, which was his, clutch him and reclaim him. He went down to the crater.

The pool was inexplicably shallow. The rains had been heavy but the water was low. If there was an explanation he did not know it. He led the party, water-burdened, down the path of the hill. The stragglers were coming in, stupid with thirst and looking for water. Later, in the light of the fires, he punished them with ten strokes of the cane. They were Asians and they were in contract with the Government and there would be trouble. But he did not care. The headmen, he decided, would lose a week's pay.

Turk built the camp on the bank of the Tsavo. The river ran fast and it was good to work and sleep within sound of flowing

94

water. This, too, was wilderness: wastes of scrub, lava and wait-a-bit thorn drew the eye through distance to encirclements of hills and conical peaks. To the north-east was the ridge of the N'dungu Escarpment.

The river revived him. It was one of the good rivers, always swift and clean, with none of the stagnation of the other rivers. The work had gone well and, impelled by the need for solitariness, he left the camp on the fifth day, followed the fringe of palms to where the river joined the Athi. There were rapids between the camp and the Athi and he had walked alone and through this engulfment of water-sound, which was sensuous and restorative of the spirit.

There, between the reefs, he had fished. The fish were poor and could not be eaten and he had no great interest in fishing: but he had fished because this sitting on a rock in the shade of fronds and the plying of an improvised rod was a contact with water. He could enjoy it with all the senses; hear it, taste it and smell it and feel it on his flesh when he dipped his hand or broke the fish from the hook, watch it whiten on the points of rock.

On the fifteenth day he began the return march from Tsavo, leaving twenty men and most of the animal transport. The caravan made good time to the Hill of Maungu. The base of the hill was deserted. He set up camp. Then, in the sun of evening, he climbed the path to the saddle, walked to the ridge and stared out across the Taru.

There was no sign of the railroad. He glassed the plain, taking the binoculars carefully from where the slant red light began and through a parabola of greying scrub. There was nothing; not the glint of a line or the scatter of a railhead camp or the smoke of a fire, not even the scar of cleared bush. He turned, examined the crater. The water was lower than he had ever seen it at this period of the year. The light had already gone from the basin, it was full of shadow and he could not gauge its depth. He stood there in disquiet, watching the rock change colour. Then he went to the ridge, glassed the plain again. A guinea-fowl crossed his field of vision and the wings beat noise against that silent hill, seeming to emphasise the stillness and the empty plain.

At daybreak he took the caravan into the desert. The heat was already fierce. This was the peculiarity of the Taru. Heat filled it like a liquid. It lay there, as in a bowl, with a consistency of its own. The legs and the body thrust against it. It parted and there were further, illimitable thicknesses of heat. Soon, Turk knew, the caravan would fall silent. Each man would be cocooned in his own sheath of effort and there would be only the rasp of breath and the scuff of feet, the creak of the mules' harness.

After ten miles he saw the first of the bush-gangs. They were miniatures trembling in heat-waves, bent under ellipses of light which were the sweep of pangas. There were many hundreds of them. They moved jerkily in glare, the flesh of face, arm and calf black against the cotton dresses.

When he neared them he saw their distress. They were agape with thirst, saturated with sweat. They could not co-ordinate their movements. Many of them knelt before the thorn-boles, slicing in desperation at the stubborn wood. Others bent in the immobility of exhaustion and spittle hung from the mouths in glutinous laces.

'I was appalled by their condition,' Turk wrote in pity. 'They begged me for water but I refused. They were not my responsibility.'

Turk marched parallel to the hedges of cut scrub. The road had been left with an embroidery of sharp white spines. A procession of coolies trailed back to railhead. Their feet, torn by the spines, had bled to leave a spoor. Three miles on he reached the track. The lines, terminating there in the middle of desert, aroused a curious sense of futility. Who would use this railroad? Who would cross these wildernesses? Preston and a gang of platelayers were there.

The holes had dried at Taru-camp, Preston told him: there was no water. The voice was weak from heat and dust. Turk gave him water from his own bottle. There were trolleys on the line and tanks on the trolleys. He went to the nearest of the tanks and looked into it.

It contained three feet of discoloured water. It smelled evil. Nothing would make them keep it clean, Preston's voice com-

Ronald and Florence Preston at Tsavo

Plate-laying gang shifting camp

A cutting near Voi

Temporary bridge between Elburgon and Molo

plained behind him. The mussucks were dipped into it; and with the mussucks those hands of cuts, sores, iodoform and bloodied bandages. He had gestured tiredly at the coolies. They moved in that ferocity of heat like men without equilibrium. They lurched. The fingers fumbled. The limbs were slow. Their strength and their resolve had gone. The white turbans rocked in sunlight. This was the ordeal: it would end with night. The rails and the plates were too hot for the flesh and they had learned to gather the heated metal in the stuff of their dresses.

Railhead camp was at Mile 65; that is, twenty miles into the Taru. Turk reached it one hour after noonday. It was strangely quiet. There were many tents, huts and men; but no man moved with urgency. The Uganda Queen and two 'F' Class engines were there; but no steam broke on the still air of the plain. Men, sickened with sun, sat or squatted or leaned in the shade of coaches. There were now seven hospital tents. On the perimeter of the camp they were burning the carcases of pack animals: the flame had no brilliance in the glare of day. Smoke rose in pillars and the stench of smouldering hide touched the nostrils.
He dispersed the caravan. Then he went to the Uganda Queen. Whitehouse lay on the truckle-bed. He was yellow with malaria. He got up when Turk entered and gave him a thin lemon hand. Then he had begun to talk. The heat in the carriage was oppressive and sweat came from his pores with the effort of speech. Everything had gone wrong. The finger pointed to where the sun hung white and implacable in a sky pale with heat. *That* was now the enemy. It had sapped the strength from their bodies, sucked the water from the holes and wells. The land was dry. He repeated it in wonder: dry. How could that happen after those torrents of rain? Even the wells at Taru were dry. He had relied on them to water the camp. And he had expected water from the holes at Maziwa Matutu and Ziwa Buchuma. But no: they were dry. The word obsessed him.
Turk recorded: 'He began to shake with the Malaria and he sat down on the bed. The sheet was soaked. I told him the Crater of Maungu was drying out, that there was very little at Ndara, but he appeared not to hear . . .'

Five or six thousand men were now absolutely dependent on the water-trains, Whitehouse said. Already there had been a derailment. A material-train had closed the line for eighteen hours. What if that happened to a water-train? How long could men go waterless? A man lost a lot of fluid working and sweating in the desert sun. Men were collapsing from heat-exhaustion, from dehydration, from the effects of malaria. A few hours in the sun and they became careless, they tore their feet on the stumps left by the panga-parties. Soon the soles ulcerated. They could not walk. He had sent hundreds back to Mombasa. More than fifty men had died; from disease, from heat, from simply lying down and giving up the ghost. A gang of twenty men had deserted into the plain. Perhaps they too were dead. There had been fighting between the Hindus and the Mohammedans: six men were stabbed, a dozen heads broken. The animals were dying off. Haslam could not keep them alive. Even the mules and the donkeys were dying. And the heat went on and on and on . . .

Turk left the train, went to Preston's tent at the head of the coolie-lines. Preston had built a thatch of grass and brush about the tent to repel the heat. He showed Turk a dirt-encrusted foot with two inflamed toes. He held a needle and a bottle of turpentine.

Turk took the needle, knelt, ran his finger over the pea-like elevations. He squeezed the first of them and the sac of eggs burst out. While he worked Preston talked; of the obstacles, the heat, the fear of water-failure, the air of crisis and the mood of ugliness which had prevailed since they had left Taru-camp. Every day there had been an incident which had run like a flame through those ranks of fevered men. The sun was in their brains like (he held up his foot) the maggots in these toes. Ibrahim had brought them slowly to the point of mutiny, feeding them stories of the Taru, of death and disease and Masai barbarities.

An Arab caravan was at this time less than a day's march behind Robert Turk. It was a large caravan and it had come from the upper reaches of the Congo, harvesting the shores of Victoria Nyanza and marching down-country through Mumia's. A great burden of merchandise and ivory was carried now on the backs of one thousand slaves. The caravan was led by an Omani trader named Saleh-bin-Amir. It reached railhead camp at sunset of that day, building its tents and fires within five hundred metres of the camp.

That evening Saleh, properly attended, came to railhead. He was a slaver of dignity and fame: it was his custom at such fortuitous meetings to present himself for the rites of hospitality. Whitehouse joined him. The fever had not left him and he sat close to the fire, the shoulders blanketed and the flame enlivening his face. Preston lay stretched in the radiance. Turk sat on a folding-chair, apart from them, the Winchester across his knees and an unstoppered bottle of rifle-oil in the breast-pocket of his shirt.

Saleh had brought Whitehouse a small gift. The Chief Engineer received it coldly. This notorious Arab, this enslaver of men, had come with a gift; to drink coffee and murmur politenesses, to talk as an equal. Yet out there, where the fires reddened the darkness, was a multitude of slaves. They lay there yoked, half-dead from privation.

Saleh was a fat and ageing man of exquisite manners. A turban of green-and-gold swathed his head: it was pinned with a ruby. He was heavily bearded and the beard curled, grey-threaded, from a round, yellow-brown face. He had hung beads and tied a sash for the occasion. A small, red cherry of a mouth which seemed plump with blood glistened in the beard. He was sensual, shrewd and ceremonious. The voice was rich and vibrant: when he spoke the beard jerked and thrust like a live thing.

He had come to talk, he admitted. It had been a long safari. He had had enough of loneliness and meditation, deserts, swamps and forests. He was too old for such enterprises. He had made money, he had sons and property. This was his last caravan. He would retire to the breezes of Zanzibar, live by the sea and devote himself to the pleasures of life which, as all truthful men conceded, were food and fornication.

Dr Orman came to the fire, bringing an odour of disinfectant. Later they were joined by Haslam and Willem. Saleh became expansive. He loved an audience. He presided. The small fat hands lifted in expressive arcs. Some inherited instinct reacted to firelight and faces and the shapes of burning wood. He was a storyteller. They listened.

He spoke of great caravans of slaves and ivory. He had marched as a youth behind the blood-red flag which signified the Sultan's protection. Those were the days when Zanzibar was the most important market of them all and its square of orange sand had fluttered like a peacock's wing with the colours of the merchants' robes and the slaves had come in their thousands to be felt, measured and assessed, to be shipped to the ports of Arabia. It was said that four-fifths of them died, that they were treated with barbarity. But that was not true. A slave was an article of value. He had to be purchased. And does not a man protect that which he has purchased?

Whitehouse listened with an admixture of distaste and fascination. The voice, with its elegant phrases, its depth and its pleasant modulations, was hypnotic. It engaged the ear, then seduced the mind. Its beauty was transmuted into truth.

There were many slave-routes, Saleh said (the hand flowed through firelight to encompass the breadth of darkness behind him); along the Nile to Khartoum; from Pangani to Tabora and from thence to Ujiji on the Lake of Tanganyika; from Kilwa to the shores of Lake Nyasa. A man in prime condition could be sold for fifty cloths; a girl—young, healthy and nubile—for as much as two hundred cloths.

But, Saleh said drily, times were changing. The British had received no share in the riches of the African slave-trade: so they disliked it. They would build this splendid railroad (the fingers opened in disdain). They would stop the trade. Already, the legal status of slavery in Zanzibar had been abolished. What would happen to the clove plantations? Who would work them?

Orman had laughed suddenly at the note of resignation in the slaver's voice. What right have you, he asked, to come to this black man's country? to take him from his tribal lands? to *steal* him?

Saleh turned to stare at the doctor. The eyebrows lifted in surprise. Had this piping sound come from the throat of a man?

He had answered with seriousness. He followed the Prophet: he must abide by the Koran. And the Koran forbade a Muslim to enslave another Muslim. But it did not proscribe slavery itself. So, obviously, the Arab traders must cross the boundaries of their own country. For a thousand years the Arabs had come to the lands of East Africa. Contrary to legend they did not steal the bodies of the blacks. The blacks were, in fact, sold to the traders by the chieftains themselves. Slaves were money: their lives and health must be preserved. He gestured behind him to the fires of his camp. During the whole of the march there had been one death, only one; a sickly Andorobbo who could not stand the yoke and had died at the Hill of Maungu.

He had stood. The audience was over. Whitehouse thanked him, held the plump, beringed fingers for a moment. He could not reconcile this imperious man with the role of slaver. Saleh was suave and civilized, enormously wise. Whitehouse walked with him to the fringe of darkness. Water was his problem, he confessed: it was said that there was good water at Maungu and at Ndara . . . ? Saleh had nodded. There was an abundance of sweet water at those places. He himself could confirm it.

Later, in darkness, Turk walked through the scrub to Saleh's camp. The slaves lay or sat in sighing columns. There was much good ivory and a great quantity of merchandise and grain. The water-supply was under heavy guard. No man washed or drank or cooked with water or infused coffee. He saw no water issued. Three headmen came with cups and were refused. Turk had led many caravans: he knew the signs of scarcity.

He reported to Whitehouse. 'Saleh lied,' he said. 'He is short of water. He got nothing much from Maungu or from Ndara.

Whitehouse, alone by the fire, had gathered the blanket at his throat, then turned away his head in that mannerism of obstinacy which Turk had come to recognise. Why should Saleh lie? Whitehouse asked: he had nothing to gain from lies. And in any case they were not entirely reliant on Maungu and Ndara. The pools and courses there would be used as a supplement to the water-trains.

They had stared across the firelight, aware of disharmony. Turk had wanted to speak, to tell him that Saleh hated the

British and the railroad, that the hatred was concealed behind the beard and the flamboyant tongue, that he had lied for a purpose.

But he had not spoken. Whitehouse was unreachable. The shapes of Herne and Muldoon were there, still accusing.

Fourteen miles of desert now lay between railhead camp and the Hill of Maungu: not a great distance in terms of railroad engineering or to those preparing multicoloured progress charts at the headquarters in Kilindini.

But to Whitehouse, weakened by sickness and tenuously linked to the coast by sixty-five miles of slender track, it seemed insurmountable. The telegraph line had not yet reached railhead. He was isolated by failures of communication. Between him and the coast, its stores of equipment and reserves of food and water, lay a wilderness.

Until now he had been careful never to permit the bush and platelaying gangs to work more than eight miles in advance of railhead camp. Beyond that point the dangers grew; and at that point he had made it an inflexible rule to move forward the camp. But now, the project foundering and the men sunk in apathy, he broke it. The camp must remain at Mile 65. He would stock, victual and man it, use it to provide the impetus for the final lunge across the Taru.

In the closing days of that month of July 1897 Whitehouse marshalled his men and resources, checked his water, arranged (reluctantly) an inducement for Ibrahim and his henchmen; and thrust his division into the territory ahead. At that precise phase of the month the sun bared, suddenly, to its ultimate ferocity. Where, before, it had been a dispassionate enemy it now became malevolent. The desert seethed. Even Turk, inured to heat, was moved to write: 'It was like being in a pan of something molten . . .' And, expressively: 'Around us the Taru shivered in heat like waves of Chinese silk . . .'

Into that heat, goaded by the headmen, went the Punjabis. Behind them came the platelaying gangs; the sleepers placed and the rails laid on the sleepers and the rails coupled with bolt and fishplate and true into the lugs of the sleepers and the track levered and hammered and settled and slewed to the contours of the way and still the heat and the swing of keying-hammers and the concussion of them which came into the brain with the heat and the moving forward into greater envelopments of heat and acrid wastes and ahead, blue and undefined on the rim of vision, the Maungu Hill.

At this time Major James Macdonald (that same captain of Royal Engineers who had led the survey expedition) was about to leave Mombasa. Salisbury had asked him to lead another expedition; to explore the frontier lands of East Africa and Uganda, to pacify the tribes, to carry the flag to where the Juba River rose and beyond to the Italian field of influence.

To this end he had assembled an impressive caravan. The expedition, its men, animals, officers and equipment, were loaded on to a train at Mombasa to the accompaniment of martial music and solemn ceremonies. It was, after all, an occasion: the first on which the Uganda Railway was used to convey passengers and freight. But one train could not possibly accommodate the expedition and the huge water-tanks consigned to Whitehouse. Half the men and equipment were offloaded. The men stared lamely. Macdonald glowered from a mask of injured dignity. The train steamed from a silent station for the interior.

James Macdonald's safari-train is significant in the Taru story. It was bound for railhead. The march to the frontier would be reduced by sixty-five miles. Two-thirds of the dreaded desert trek would be avoided. But to Macdonald the absurdity of the departure was an omen. He believed in omens: if a safari began badly it was bad throughout. He was not confounded. At Mile 54, nine miles into the Taru, the train was wrecked.

Preston was at railhead camp when the news came. It had travelled by telegraph as far as the wire reached, and then by runner. The runner, a Kamba youth, reported casually. There had been a derailment, the finger pointed into shimmers of heat. The face and voice showed no sign of urgency.

Preston received the news, fed the runner and sent him on his way. There had been many derailments. Usually it meant that a wheel had jumped the rail; an hour's work and the locomotive, the waggon or the carriage was re-aligned. He loaded tackle and a dozen gangers. Then he, Turk and Shutt climbed up to the footplate of the engine and steamed slowly down track.

Shutt was the first to see it. At distance in that empty plain the train was like a toy scattered by a child's foot. A miniature engine with fragile wheels and pistons thin as needles lay over-turned under a curl of steam. Tiny carriages stood on end and the couplings hung like snapped thread. Then, nearing, they saw it grow from miniature into the dimension of reality and they were awed by the sight and sound of disaster, this rending of steel and timber. Men were coming from the hazes of heat and steam; torn, bloodied and grimed, appealing for succour. Macdonald, the powerful neck rivuletted with congealed blood, came slowly to the footplate.

The silence of the plain obtruded. There was only the escape of steam, the voices of men muted in the presence of catastrophe. The embankment had collapsed under the seventy-five tons of the locomotive and liquid rust sloughed redly from its boiler into the red sand of the Taru. They went the length of the train. Thirty yards of permanent way had been torn into a debris of rail and sleeper. They counted the pinned bodies of twenty dead and injured. The water-tanks had split and the soil was a mire into which wreckage sank. Beneath the last of the open trucks they saw a dead Swahili, the head wedged immovably and the face wetly glistening under a gush of water from the ruptured casing of a tank. How could a man drown in this waterless place?

With the wreck the situation in the Taru became complex. Macdonald's original caravan was now divided. One half was steaming from Mombasa; the other half had been disgorged in the desert with an effective loss of twenty-six men and eleven animals. Out of more than eight thousand gallons of water only four hundred gallons remained. The permanent way was im-passable and Preston, unprepared for a disaster of such mag-nitude, had neither the heavy tackle nor the men to clear and restore it. Beyond railhead camp Whitehouse had spread working parties totalling four thousand men who toiled through unre-lenting sun toward the Hill of Maungu; a daily minimum of four pints of drinking-water was needed to sustain each man. At railhead itself Whitehouse held a water reserve equivalent to only half of one day's ration.

Such was the situation: when the second train arrived at the scene of the wreck bearing the remainder of Macdonald's caravan but without supplementary water-tanks it moved from an area of complexity to one of peril.

Major Macdonald paraded his re-united caravan ('. . . like a blessed General on the Horse-Guards,' Turk observed), satisfied himself that the safari was in good marching order, replenished his men with water from the single tank and told Preston, imperiously, that he was prepared to march the eleven miles to railhead camp: the train must be used to carry his equipment, food and pack-animals ahead of him.

Preston hesitated. He had resented Macdonald's use of the precious water-tank, his assumption of authority. He had wanted to object, to stay, to make some effort to open the line to traffic and desperately needed water. But Macdonald had turned away; his authority, it seemed, was absolute.

Events now moved toward a climax. Preston obeyed, reluctantly, Macdonald's order. The major led his men into the scrub and reached railhead camp in under three hours. Preston instructed the driver of the second train, that is the train on the Mombasa side of the accident, to steam for Maji Chumvi, to take on water and return without delay. He, Preston, would deliver the caravan's gear, its injured and its beasts at railhead camp, load the heavy tackle and available men and rendezvous at the wreck.

Maji Chumvi was at Mile 32, twenty-two miles back. Railhead camp, at Mile 65, lay eleven miles on. Within three to four hours, Preston calculated, he should rendezvous with the water-train and save the situation. In fact this train, which was of such immense importance to many thousands of thirsting men, steamed straight through to Mombasa. It did not return until twenty-four hours had passed.

No-one knows why Preston's order was not obeyed. Perhaps the driver misunderstood; or, understanding, saw no ground for urgency; or, inflexibly, decided that he could not diverge from the scheduled run to Mombasa. Perhaps he was uncaring or negligent or spiteful. Perhaps he craved a speedy return to the fleshpots of the coast. All that is certain is that Preston made the rendezvous, set the gangs to work on the wreck and the permanent way; and, through the heats of day, searched the line and the perspectives of distance for a train that never came.

In that time of waiting Whitehouse's reserves of water fell perilously low. Macdonald, fiercely defensive of his own command and indifferent to all considerations beyond personal success, impressed sufficient quantities of water to sustain the caravan at least as far as Ndara. Whitehouse, like Preston, had yielded. There was something in Macdonald, some recognisable aura of power which transcended the solitary crowns on the epaulettes. Whitehouse measured his water, felt the onset of alarm—and immediately cut the drinking ration to a third.

By nightfall of that day the water had almost gone. The temperature dropped with sundown and the multitudes of coolies bivouacked ahead of camp found a measure of relief. The water was late: but it would come. Now the hill had grown, reformed in sun-enfevered brains. The crater was as cold and deep as a sea and the hill brimmed over, ran white with streams.

But at dawn the water had not come and the sun climbed, its ferocity renewed, and, soon, they were immersed again in the glare of day and there was no respite or escape from this torment of sun, toil and thirst. At an hour before noon the headmen in charge of those parties lying relatively near to railhead decided, properly, to abandon work and to return the men to camp. And at about that time Ibrahim, who commanded the forward gangs (those engaged in clearing bush and preparing the permanent way) reached the same decision. But these men of Ibrahim lay nearer to Maungu than to railhead camp; and the slaking of thirst was now their urgent need. Without water they would die. Some seven hundred men began the trek to the hill.

The sun was still vertical when they reached Maungu. The hill seemed to smoke in heat. This was the hill of legend, the great natural calabash of water which would restore them. They swarmed up its rocky path.

At the crater they fell silent before a few feet of malodorous slime. In it floated the body of an Andorobbo. The cord of the slaver still looped the neck and Ibrahim leaned forward, found its end and pulled the body through a thickness of vegetal matter. He turned it with his foot and stared down into the noduled face of leprosy.

Turk writes of the sequel: '. . . that night hundreds of blabbering Indos staggered into Camp from the plain. They came out of the night like a lot of scurrying ants. Some of them were almost done for. We gave them 2 cups of water each from what we had left and for which they cried thanks like babies. Seven died in the night, Our Chief was much upset. We buried them in the morning. Then we took a Tally and held an Inquiry . . .'

Nothing much came from this inquiry. Ibrahim, eight Muslim headmen and about eighty Punjabis were still missing: it was not until the second of the inquiries, after the remaining miles of track had been laid to Maungu, that the facts emerged. By then Ibrahim had rejoined railhead.

The seven hundred had descended the hill, he reported. The pool was poisoned and nothing would overcome their fear of that leprous body. He, Ibrahim, had gathered them at the foot of the path. He had pointed to the hills of Ndara. We must go on, not back into that terrible desert. He had led them through ten miles of wilderness along the old caravan track to Ndara.

Ndara was dry; and those parched and weary men had wept, torn their clothes in frustration. Now, he told Whitehouse, the situation had changed. He could not conjure water from the earth. You must go back to railhead, he ordered them. It is your only chance. Time has passed and, who knows? the water train has arrived. They had obeyed him. He himself had followed the track to Voi, where he and his headmen found ample water.

Whitehouse dismissed him. Then he stood, asked Preston to minute Ibrahim's statement, left the carriage.

Turk followed. The sun had gone and the aridity of the plain came strong to the nostrils. Whitehouse walked to the periphery of the camp, away from the light of hurricanes and the coolie tents to where the line gleamed faintly and ran into the darkness of the desert. Turk stopped. Whitehouse needed solitude: he understood that need. And there was nothing to say. Fifty men had wandered, died of thirst or heat-exhaustion or hopelessness. Ibrahim had known there was permanent water at Voi and that Voi lay only eleven miles on from Ndara. But he had sent those reeling men back into the Taru. Why? What kind of senseless evil had motivated him?

He watched Whitehouse, a silhouette against the night-sky. Then the figure turned, turned from the Taru. The Taru was behind. Whitehouse seemed to be looking, now, above and beyond the camp and the Hill of Maungu to where the Tsavo River and its palms would lie, to Kibwezi and the plains of the Athi, to where the soil was red with fertility and the land rose and the air was sweet: to where the track would go.

4. *The Camp at Tsavo River*

In those pioneer days nearly every hunter, missionary, Government servant or explorer whose work, greed or lust for killing took him to British East Africa wrote a book about it. Never was so marvellous and pristine a setting served with such conspicuous lack of talent. Most of these men walked through an Eden with their eyes shut.

Joseph Thomson was an exception: he was deeply affected by the sight of Kilimanjaro. He confesses at the outset that 'I shrink from the task of attempting to convey any idea of this colossal mountain. I feel that the subject is beyond the power of my puny pen . . .' The puny pen then consumes fourteen pages of description. Written in the extravagant idiom of the time it is still an impressive piece of writing. For him the mountain was, indeed, the Masai 'House of God.'

From that deluge of print little survives which is not dull, pompous and arid or which does not sicken the mind with the interminable rituals of game-killing. If these men felt wonder they did not communicate it: if they felt ecstasy it was at the sight of kicking beasts and the end of things of grace. They came home to write their books, to recount shikar stories, to adorn their walls and floors with those trophies which, it seems, were necessary to sustain the legend of their own doubtful masculinity.

The railroad produced its authors. By 1897 Major Macdonald, anxious that his efforts should not pass unnoticed by those in the higher echelons, had already published an enormous book which (unspoiled by excesses of modesty) described his experiences 'as Chief Engineer of the preliminary survey for the Uganda Railway' and his achievements as Acting-Commissioner 'in the stirring times that heralded the advent of our Uganda Protectorate.'

Preston, who remained to love, live and die in East Africa, later wrote a short, privately-printed book named *The Genesis of Kenya Colony*. He, too, had no gift for words. It narrates in pedestrian style his part in the building of the railroad. It is poorly produced (you suspect it was set up by an Asian compositor), disproportionately burdened with advertisements, and does less than justice to the value of his contribution. There is a Foreword written in a fine flush of patriotic fervour and, beneath it, a verse from 'Land of Hope and Glory'.

Preston's ardour for things Imperial was to be sorely tried. On 8 March 1898 an incredible figure arrived at railhead camp: a man who was the very personification of the British Flag, a member of the Distinguished Service Order, an engineer holding an impeccable Foreign Office appointment. This formidable figure was Lieutenant-Colonel J. H. Patterson.

Patterson, who is more renowned for his persecution of man-eaters than for the building of the bridge over the Tsavo, wrote, at the passing of the century, a short account of the episode of the Tsavo lions; it was printed in *The Field*. A copy was sent by Selous (another notable extirpator of big game) to President Theodore Roosevelt who wrote in reply: 'I think that the incident of the Uganda (his geography was lamentable) man-eating lions described in those two articles you sent me is the most remarkable account of which we have any record. It is a great pity that it should not be preserved in permanent form.'

Inevitably, Patterson wrote a book. It was called *The Man-Eaters of Tsavo* and it was published in October of 1907. This was an age of solemn Forewords and, as you would expect, Patterson's Foreword was written by Selous.

Patterson reached Tsavo at dusk. The journey from Mombasa had been hot, dusty and tiring: he presented himself to Whitehouse, stacked his gear and went to a palm-thatch hut. He slept until dawn. Then, refreshed, he reconnoitred the camp and the terrain and the river-bank, stared with a professional eye at Preston's temporary bridge and returned to the hut.

There he found that four servants, a cook and a Sikh jemadar named Ungan Singh had been assigned to him. He paraded them, fastidiously examined the cook's hands, then addressed himself to Singh. He had spent many years in India, he announced; he understood the Sikhs, the Pathans and the Punjabis. He demanded respect, cleanliness and obedience. He then gave a rupee to the jemadar, a few annas to each of the others.

That, he said, demonstrated that he was a man of generosity: virtue would be rewarded. Contrarily, any lapse would bring severe punishment. He was also a man of unvarying ritual. At dawn he would require a pint of hot, unsugared tea and a breakfast of cold meats and dry bread. Water must be heated and the indiarubber bath, which had accompanied him across the seas of the world, be two-thirds filled. It was his custom to shave himself while seated in the bath and for that purpose he would require a flat piece of wood to lay across its diameter and on which he could set his mirror and shaving utensils. It was also his habit to read two pages of the Bible before leaving the bath: the jemadar must therefore ensure that the Book was laid, together with clean linen, within reach of the bath. Was all this understood?

Ungan Singh, a powerful man who had slit many throats on the Afghan plateau and was familiar with British idiosyncrasy, shrugged with insolence. Patterson pointed to the gear. A tent would be rigged in a suitable place, water boiled and food prepared. Then he wished to see the Sahib Preston.

The hut was already vacated when Preston arrived, the tent rigged fifty metres down, near to the river-bank in the shade of a borassus. It was a fine tent with emerald-green canvas and a double-fly. It would afford the colonel privacy: and in furtherance of this two servants had begun to plait a fence. The grass in front of the tent was arrayed with bags, valises and cases. A collapsible table had been set up and a shape bent over a litter of books, newspapers and cartridge-boxes. It turned at Preston's approach.

III

Patterson was tall, bony and narrow, tightly buttoned in khaki drill. He wore bright wash-leather gloves and high Norwegian boots. The hands, gloved and dangling, seemed huge. An enormous solar topi sat squarely on the head. Preston could see the bulges of knee and elbow pads against the drill of the suit. Behind, no doubt, would be the pad of a spine-protector. No thorn, rock, sun-ray or serpent's tooth would menace this invulnerable figure. Patterson removed the helmet and the gloves, scratched where the band of the helmet had left a red cicatrice. The face was long, fierce and wolfish, the eyes faintly yellow. The ends of a reddish-brown moustache had been twisted up with pomade. The temples were narrow and sharp-boned, the crown of the head almost bald. The topi had disturbed the remaining hair, brought it down so that it hung in a pomaded lick.

Patterson turned to the table, sorted papers, then bent to the assortment on the grass. Preston waited. The hands were opening rifle-cases. They were beautiful cases, mahogany with filigree patterns and tin linings. Patterson took each of the rifles from its case, weighed it in his hands; saying nothing yet revealing the beauty and the value of the guns to Preston. There were a Holland .450, a Remington repeating-rifle, a 16-bore Paradox gun with a walnut butt inlaid with silver, a small .275 with a delicate mechanism and on which Patterson's fingers rested sensuously for a moment, a 12-bore shot gun, a single-barrelled Holland .303. Patterson exhibited each of the guns, returned them after a pause to their cases. This, Preston knew, was a demonstration of personal power; this silent performance a calculated emphasis of their relationship.

Patterson opened a large mahogany box. Inside were a pistol and a batch of coloured rockets. The face turned. The Kaiser moustache had already fallen. The harsh voice spoke. The rockets, it said, would ensure that he never got lost in the bush.

Preston had stared at the rockets, then at the topi and the gloves and the high boots, at the knee and elbow pads, at the rockets again. Nothing, it seemed, could harm this impregnable man. He began to laugh, openly, in Patterson's face.

'I believe they became enemies from that day,' Robert Turk

wrote. 'I told him you better had spit in a man's face than laugh at him . . .'

There is evidence, apart from Turk's, that Preston resented the news of Patterson's appointment. He had expected, and planned, to build the bridge over the Tsavo: he was certainly capable of it. If this Indian Army professional had been less arrogant, less the martinet, less a product of rigid hierarchies of caste and rank, the embryo of resentment might have died. They would have built their bridge in harmony.

But it had not been like that. At root, they were aware of differences. Preston's India had been one of deprivation, of struggle and insecurity; Patterson's had been the India of privilege, power and regimental tradition. Preston had evolved in the shadow of an orphanage, Patterson in the mystique of mess, shikar, polo and pig-sticking. They had no common ground on which to meet; common danger and endeavour, it seems, were not enough.

It is curious, and revealing, that nowhere in his book (a book which tells the story of the Tsavo affair in considerable detail) does Patterson refer to Preston. And Preston, in his own account, appears to have forgotten that his superior ever existed. Perhaps the memory of rivalry, conflict and mutual dislike was too strong. Each thrust out the image of the other.

Preston had once shot blackbuck on a visit to the northern grass-plains of India; and, later, there had been treks into the hills for sambur. But the experiences had not been meaningful. At that time purities of design and abstracts of engineering had engrossed him. If there was a consummation it was in symmetries of stone and steel and not in some bloodied thing of death.

But here in East Africa he became aware of different rhythms. The river, fed from the caps of Kilimanjaro, sustained life; a life of so varied and vivid a pattern, so unexpected a complexity that he felt he had been seized, lifted abruptly to new planes of feeling. He could not define or even communicate this excitement. It came from the land. It lay in the spoors and the game-trails, in flights of coloured plumage, in friezes of form and colour and lyrate heads. This was a red and savage land. It was old. It was nourished on death. But it was also innocent. He walked it and there was a sense of return.

At first there had been elation in this watching of game. It replenished the spirit, it satisfied the eye. It was sufficient in itself. There were great concentrations of animals. They left their dung on the track, their pugs in the embankments. He heard them by night and he saw the marks of their passing in the morning. It was good that they were there, good to be at the centre of these wild harmonies, good to know that men of different form had crouched and listened under the skies of pre-history and that the harmonies had been the same.

But then the eye became sated. It was never enough to watch, to capture living things in a succession of transient images. The beauty was too intense and the senses were now inadequate. They left a gap. A desire lay there; something unrequited which swelled and made demand, wanted from the wild life, wanted physically, wanted a final, positive act.

There was never sufficient fresh meat for the construction camps and Robert Turk and the Suk tracker now made regular forays into bush for game-meat, hunting from Tsavo down to the falls on the Sabaki, and north from Tsavo along the course of the Athi. These were small parties, moving rapidly, killing and caching the meat, moving again, retracing at sundown and bringing the meat into camp for the skinners. Preston had joined one of these expeditions a few weeks after the line reached Tsavo River. He owned no weapons and Turk lent him a .275.

Turk marched north-west toward the Kyulu Hills. It was right to alternate, he explained. The game was thick at all points from Tsavo and you could not shoot it out but it was better to take from an area and then leave it quiet. This was bush-country but, toward the hills, the bush ran into open grassland. There they would find plains-game; great herds of horse-ears (Turk referred to certain ruminants as 'horse-ears'—probably zebra and wilde-beeste in this case: and gazelles, to him, were always 'bright-eyes').

They had moved from the scrub and red stone outcrops of Tsavo into plains which ran smooth into the folds of hills. They took wildebeest, eland and topi. For Preston the killing was without emotion. He shot well, learning the gun. The game was food: its predestiny the belly of beast or man. It died from invincible necessity, falling from the corners of herds like fragments from a whole. The herd bolted and closed and nothing had gone and there was not even the awareness of death.

But it was different with the kudu. Circling back to the camp from the fringe of the savanna Turk pointed to a grove of fig-trees. He saw it: a male kudu luminous with sunlight, the head slow to rise and the horns hung in twin spirals on bars of sun. This was not meat. This was beauty, come again to tantalise; this was the intangible which he could not get at, which hovered beyond reach. He had to have it. He raised the gun and killed it and some ecstasy of pain which he did not recognise released him and this destruction of beauty was the only, the true satisfaction.

Patterson's battery was the symbol of everything Preston detested. The guns were expensive, beautiful, accessories peculiar to Patterson's class. They evoked pictures of the British Raj, princes and caparisoned elephants, chukkers played at hill-stations in evening sun. Preston coveted the guns, envied Patterson their ownership. The antipathy found its focus in the killing of game.

Preston's tent was rigged no more than two hundred metres from that of the colonel. He went to the tent, brought out the kudu horns and fixed them prominently to the tent-pole. They were a declaration. 'The horns were of exceptional spread,' Turk records. 'Our Colonel was impressed. For later that day when P was at dinner I saw him lope across the clearing like a blessed Wolf and measure the horns from tip to boss . . .'

In the same entry Turk also notes without comment: 'Mombasa train brought news from Chandra Baksh of twin boys for my Sumitra . . .'

There are regions of Africa which lie in the native mind like pockets of darkness. Origins have disappeared. Nothing was ever written. Only corporate tribal memory preserves an ancient fear. The fear never dies and the intruder can sometimes sense it. The forest at Rabai is one of the bad places. Another is the Lake of Chala on Kilimanjaro. Another is Tsavo.

Tsavo disturbs the mind rather than elates. The river is good; but away from the river there is an air of oppressiveness. Burned by sun and scoured by crystalline blue light these great areas have their own wild beauty. But the beauty afflicts. The trees and the grass and the lava rock look stricken. There is an acrid smell. It is as if something hot and sulphurous had passed like a sudden wind; to burn and mortify the tips and skin of things and leave them yellow. The place is forlorn. It flowers in the rains and there is a true resurgence: but this is disguise.

Preston, in his book, introduces the Tsavo story: 'All the old caravan leaders had disliked this camp for some reason or other, and it was a noted place for desertions, very few caravans passing through Tsavo without a couple of their porters being missed. . . . A strange feature of these desertions was, that even on the return journey from up-country, the porters would seemingly desert, leaving their loads in the camp; but stranger still, some of the men who had no loads to carry would make themselves scarce.

'Another story told us was that the place was haunted, and that a certain evil spirit had a habit of enticing the men away at night and, after leading them down to the river, made away with them. At the river, indeed, all trace of missing natives was lost, or sometimes an odd sandal or fez cap would be picked up. . . .

'The river being bridged we moved camp over to the west bank and had hardly got settled down when there came the curious visitation to our camp, which I had thought to be free from the ordinary sort of desertions of which we had heard tales from the caravans.'

It began with the incident of the flag. The incident itself is unimportant, except to illuminate an aspect of the colonel's character; but it was on this day of the flag that the first of the coolies disappeared. His name was Narain. He was a worker in stone and, with others, he had come to set and dress the piers of the Tsavo bridge. He had seen sepoy service in India; and perhaps for this reason he had been assigned to Patterson's personal staff.

Patterson was a man who, to use his own constantly reiterated phrase, liked to 'observe slowly and act fast.' He spent two days around the camp: observing. He was followed dutifully by Narain and by a man named Charles Rawson.

Rawson, plump, young and permanently beaming, was not an employee of the railroad. Patterson merely describes him as 'a friend.' Little is known of him. He was in awe of Patterson: that indelible smile was the mark of servility. (But there is no common identity between him and the Frank Rawson who, at this time, acted in Mombasa as Assistant Chief Engineer to Whitehouse.) Charles Rawson was probably one of those who were quick to recognise the value of the railroad as a means to sport. Gone were the days of the up-country caravan. Now, a ticket from Kilindini to Tsavo was as good as a safari.

Patterson and his attendants walked the east and west banks, and it was on this tour of inspection that he began the use of his 'little book.' The book was to become famous—and hated. The colonel moved through the huts, coolie-lines, tents and stores of the camp with that peculiar stalking gait. He watched, made his observations. Rawson listened to the harsh voice and wrote them down.

On the evening of the second day Patterson went to the administration hut. He did not go inside. Spooner, one of three Anglo-Indians upon whom Whitehouse had now begun to lean (the others were Sandiford and Gallagher), had been left in charge. Patterson summoned him, produced his note-book. Narain and Rawson stood respectfully behind him.

He had seen evidence of serious defects, the colonel told Spooner bleakly. The coolies were insubordinate and their quarters squalid, the east camp badly sited, the explosives unguarded, the drinking-water exposed to disease-carriers and the material stores negligently controlled. These and many technical matters he would prefer to discuss later with Whitehouse. But there was one omission—the pages of the note-book turned—of such gravity that its rectification could not be delayed. Is not this land a Crown possession? And are not these men subjects of the Queen? And is not the railroad an undertaking of the British Crown? Spooner nodded. All this was indisputable. Patterson gestured at the camp. Then where, he asked, is the British Flag?

Spooner had looked in desperation at the huddle of tents and huts. He shook his head miserably. Patterson turned to the stonemason. 'Have you understood?'

Narain nodded.

'Are you familiar with the Union Jack?'

'Yes, sahib.'

'And could you make one?'

'Yes, sahib.'

Narain had gone to the stores with a chit. There he obtained strips of Manchester cloth in red and blue, and some lengths of white cotton. He stitched together a flag in the light of a hurricane and, later that night, laid it reverently on the colonel's bed. Ungan Singh admitted him to the tent. The jemadar was the last to see him.

The colonel examined the flag at first light of the following day. Narain's handiwork pleased him. It was not entirely accurate— but it was recognisable. It would be fixed, he decided, to the cap of his tent-pole; and it would be the responsibility of Ungan Singh to remove it at sunset and replace it at dawn. 'Is that understood?' he asked the Sikh.

'Yes, sahib.'

'Now find me Narain that I may reward him.'

Narain could not be found. Patterson waited twelve hours. Then he reported it to Spooner.

Spooner listened without concern. He had been publicly berated by Patterson: he had no interest in Patterson's servant. He merely noted the name. It was a plain case of desertion. That was the end of it.

Turk had come to the admin. hut at that moment. He had spent the night in bush. He was unshaven. His hair and flesh were tinted with the red dust of Tsavo. He had skinned-out an animal and its blood congealed on the sleeve of his shirt. The sight offended Patterson. This, it seems, was the first occasion on which they came face to face.

Patterson stared at Turk's uncut hair. Then he turned to Spooner. No, he said, that was not the end of it. Narain was his man. He was responsible for him. Why should he desert? There were accumulations of undrawn pay. Would a man desert in such circumstances?

Spooner had checked. It was true: two-thirds' pay remained to his credit. Perhaps it was the spirits of Tsavo? he offered laconically. Or savages. There were savages in Tsavo.

Patterson nodded. Yes, there were savages (he had stared at Robert Turk): but it was more likely that Ibrahim and his gang of cut-throats had killed and robbed him. He demanded a search and an investigation. He was familiar with thuggee. He would get to the truth.

The investigation revealed nothing. Narain was gone. Later that day a coolie working ten miles downtrack failed to board the trucks returning to camp. A party of some thirty men waited in dying sunlight but the scrub turned pale and there was no sign of the coolie.

Patterson was a man imbued with almost patriarchal loyalty to loyal servants. Narain's disappearance was a centre of unease. The scraps of Manchester cloth fluttered on the tent-pole, drew the eye, became a symbol of unexpiated crime. If Ibrahim had taken the knife or the strangler's cloth to this his servant then punishment would surely follow. But there were things to do; a bridge to build, thirty miles of track east and west of the river to reinforce, permanent works.

And, of course, trophies.

The collection of trophies now began to dominate Patterson. He built his bridge, his tracks and his railroad structures. But deeper, where pride, envy and the sense of injury lay, he was engaged with Preston. He could not defeat him on the professional level: ascendancy would be measured by an inch of horn, a pound of ivory, a tape laid against a skin. He saw Preston's kudu-horns when he rose in the morning. He saw them at night, reddened in the glow of fires. And sometimes when the sun was slant with evening and behind the horns he saw their shadow elongated on the grass like an immense lyre. The horns were a challenge—and a goad.

Patterson spent four days on the banks of the Tsavo. In that time he determined the siting of the bridge, the volume of river-water at mean and low levels, the rate of current. The river was not yet in spate and he could not gauge its strength at flood-level. On the fifth day a working-party in the charge of his overseer, Purshotam Purmar, began the laying of the foundations to the abutments; and an hour after dawn of that day Patterson left the camp. This was the first of his East African shikars. He took with him Rawson, Ungan Singh and ten Swahilis.

He returned at sundown. The Swahilis were laden. Patterson marched them to his tent and Rawson, servile as ever under the eye of his master, arranged the bag carefully on the grass in front of the plaited fence where all men could see it. It was impressive. Horns and skins lay in profusion. Patterson had discarded the meat, bringing only that which was ornamental. He stood silently by the trophies, rifle aligned against his leg like that of a sentinel, and men came to inspect and touch the sabres of the oryx and the black-white cloak of the colobus-monkey and the bosses of buffalo, to murmur praise.

When Preston came the light had gone. Mists hung like caught fleeces along the river-bank. He came from these mists with Robert Turk and they crossed the clearing into firelight. But Preston had not come to admire. He proffered a length of crumpled blue Manchester cloth and Patterson took it, smelled the stale blood on it, and understood. The cloth and the blood were Narain's.

It had been found by the river, Turk explained. Narain, it seemed, had taken the material for use as a garment, probably a loincloth. The cloth was all that remained.

Patterson was puzzled. All? he asked. But if Ibrahim . . . ? Turk shook his head. Ibrahim was not responsible. The sand around the loincloth was easy to read, the pugs clear and well-defined. Narain had been taken by a lion.

'He seemed put out,' Turk noted in his entry for that day.

'He stared down at his Poppyshow of bits of dead animals and the swank went right out of him. I touched one of the spreads and I said We need meat—not hat-pegs, but he seemed not to hear and he went pretty quick into his tent . . .'

At dawn Turk left camp with the Suk tracker. And it was at this hour that Ungan Singh began to brew tea for his master. He was confused. There had been variations from the carefully-learned ritual. The Bible (which Patterson read for the splendour of its prose rather than the value of its spiritual message) had been supplanted by a Swahili grammar, the fruit salts by a potion of quinine. He was now responsible for the cleaning of the battery; and, after the purification ceremony of the indiarubber bath, there was a weapon parade of considerable tension in which Patterson stared, one-eyed, up the barrels of rifles. Even the mahogany cases were examined. A speck of dirt, a patina of verdigris, was punishable by fine.

Patterson was served by four Punjabis and a cook (inferiors to Singh). Normally the Punjabis lighted fires, swept tents, drew water from the river and heated quantities of it for the bath. But on this morning of calamity Patterson had assigned to them a prior duty. It was the custom in those days to erect a backcloth or vertical staging on which skins and other trophies were arranged in display. Fellow shikaris came to admire, to murmur felicitations. Later, the hunter would sit, fiercely, at the centre of the exhibits and a photograph or two would be taken. The four Punjabis arose at dawn to build a suitable wooden fencing; and Ungan Singh was left with the menial but inescapable task of preparing the bath.

Doubtless the Sikh was agitated at the prospect of the early rifle-inspection; alarmed, too, at the fate of Narain. This was dawn—a time when the predators moved freely through the half-light (he had seen them: bran-coloured forms shifting in the miasmas of the river). Nervously he splashed water into the bath and, forgetful of the inflammable qualities of indiarubber, placed it on the burning faggots of the fire. He mixed a draught of quinine, set out the colonel's shaving-utensils, reverently raised the British Flag on the tent-pole. Then he went down to the river to replenish the ewers. When he returned the fire was out; and a moment's horrified examination revealed that the bath, now black, pungent and bottomless, had dropped its contents into the flames.

Patterson, emerging from his tent in pleasant expectation of soap, hot water and the daily advance in Swahili, had stared with incredulity. Was this scorched and reeking thing the friend which had relaxed and cleansed his body in a dozen different climes? Ungan Singh spread his hands in abject guilt. The Punjabis came to stare. Across the clearing Preston, whitened for the razor, watched with unconcealed delight.

In the days that followed Patterson had little opportunity for hunting. '. . . the first important piece of work which I had commenced on arrival (he wrote) . . . was the widening of a rock cutting through which the railway ran just before it reached the river . . .' The trophies, now splendidly exhibited on the wooden staging, were evidence of unmatched prowess. He was content to ponder the problems of bridge-engineering, to walk the camp and its environs with Rawson at his side, to pounce on error or neglect and to record the names of defaulters in the little red book.

Preston, too, was occupied; thirty-one miles downtrack at Voi. Here, at Mile 100, he had built a triangle, observing at the time: 'At Voi we laid one of our first triangles so that the engines might be turned, for up to this all engines returning from railhead had to go back tender foremost all the way to the coast.'

He spent a week at Voi enlarging the triangle, inspected the girder bridge which spanned the Voi River; on the evening of the eighth day he returned to Tsavo. There he delivered his reports to Patterson and, no doubt, eyed the trophies with a renewal of envy.

In the morning Patterson sent Preston in search of stone and to reconnoitre the ravines and dried nullahs of Tsavo. 'Another great difficulty (Patterson recorded) with which we had to contend was the absence of suitable stone in the neighbourhood. It was not that there was none to be found, for the whole district abounds in rock, but that it was so intensely hard as to be almost impossible to work, and a bridge built of it would have been very costly.'

Unwittingly, Patterson had given Preston an opportunity for retaliation. The camp, spread on both banks of the river, now sustained three thousand men. It was strident with the noise of men and engines and, at night, ablaze with fires. Already the wild life had retreated: it could be found in profusion only after several hours' trek. Preston asked Turk for the loan of the .275; and Turk, seeing the animation in that youthful face, understood. He gave it to him.

Preston, Turk, the Suk tracker and a dozen Swahilis marched into the bush. For Preston these treks through mellow curtains of sunlight into silence, into infinities of scrub and rock and wind-bending grass where time itself seemed to part like something diaphanous to reveal tones of immeasurable age, were now the pinnacles of living.

He shot well that day. He had learned the gun. It fitted his hands and shoulder. It balanced easily in the crook of his arm. His fingers knew the scars in its butt, his nostrils the scent of its metal. It was a good gun because, not heavy or violently de-structive, it needed the cunning of man. He shot sable and roan and lesser kudu, selectively but still without pity.

At noon they ate and drank. The Suk fried cobs in the lid of a tin, picked them from a swirl of yellow fat and filled his leather cheeks. Around, the grass grew high, wavered in the heat-waves of the fire. Many of the trees were ripped at the branch-joints into jags of bleaching wood. Turk pointed to the large khaki balls of droppings and the Suk nodded, took his spear and went like a shifting of shadow into the grass.

Turk, seated on a low stone outcrop, opened his knees, began to draw with the point of his knife. Sand lay in red drifts like detritus washed down from the rock and the knife patterned it into the broadside head of an elephant. Preston watched the point describe the big hanging leaf which was the ear, dig in where the eye socket would be. Turk cut a careful line from the eye to the orifice of the ear, bisected it. This was the site of the brain. He began to talk, the voice hardly louder than the rasp of insects, and Preston listened, wanting desperately to learn this craft of killing.

Preston learned the angles; and, moving through grass behind the Suk's hungry neck, through those tunnels of sun-sweet wands, the burrs hooking in the yarn and the herd near, he felt an exultation he had never known. The Suk stopped in the fringe of thinning grass and he saw them, ear-waving and red with dust, moving, feeding through distance in their immutable way, moving, and his mouth dried with desire for them and he raised his rifle and he saw the bull, *his* bull, long and thick in the tooth, turning now into the angle he had learned and he killed it expertly so that it sank to its knees with grace and the herd, not even discomposed by the shot, moved with mild curiosity around the kneeling bull, then on, ponderously, into new avenues of feed.

Now, standing by the immensity of the bull, Turk looked up and across the ridge of the back to where the sun hung and then at the teeth. It would take hours to chop them out, he told Preston. It would be better to leave them. In three days the flesh would putrefy and the teeth could be drawn with ease. He had laughed, then, at the dismay in Preston's face; and he had turned to the Swahilis, saying something and pointing to the bull.

In that clearing of crushed grass and red rock-sand, the sun lower and vivid in the sand and the smell of fat and blood sweeter now than the grass, Preston watched them dissect the bull. The deep hide, thick with sand in its fissures, defied the knife. An hour passed before the first of the sockets was exposed: another hour before the vertebrae were cut so that the head could be turned. Preston had stared at this ruin, at the trees which palpitated with scavengers. The dignity of the bull had dissolved into intricacies of joint and sinew, blankets of fat, a monstrous cage, into leaf-wrapped hummocks of meat. He turned away. Pride and triumph would return. Now he wanted the clean air off the river.

At sundown, following the river through the blue grass of evening, crossing the trolley-bridge Indian file, Preston ahead and the Swahilis singing and the ivory orange in the half-light, they saw the fires of the camp. The hides, horns and teeth were laid like tribute in front of Preston's tent. Soon men came: to measure the spreads against an arm, to stroke the texture of skins and the pitted surface of the tusks.

The praise was sweet.

That night Ungan Singh was taken.

'I was aroused about daybreak (says the colonel) and told that one of my jemadars, a fine powerful Sikh named Ungan Singh, had been seized in his tent during the night, and dragged off and eaten . . . I at once set out to try to track the animal, and was accompanied by Captain Haslam . . . On reaching the spot where the body had been devoured, a dreadful spectacle presented itself. The ground all round was covered with blood and morsels of flesh and bones, but the unfortunate jemadar's head had been left intact, save for the holes made by the lion's tusks on seizing him, and lay a short distance away from the other remains, the eyes staring wide open with a startled, horrified look in them. The place was considerably cut up, and on closer examination we found that two lions had been there and had probably struggled for possession of the body . . .'

Robert Turk and the Suk were at hand: it was Patterson's obvious duty to call them. The Sikh had been taken at midnight, his tent-mates had waited in a rigor of fear for sunrise; perhaps, by then, the lions had gone. But, equally, they may have lain on the kill through the hours of darkness; and the absence of scavengers suggests that the lions moved into bush only on the arrival of Patterson and Haslam.

Turk and the Suk would certainly have followed. Inexplicably, the colonel did not. He gathered Singh's remains (with one important exception) and interred them under a sepulchre of stones. The exception was the jemadar's head. This he seized by the hair and bore through the camp to the admin. office. 'I was astounded,' Haslam later told Turk.

The effect of that apparition emerging from the river-mists can be imagined. The colonel's path was lined with staring men. He reached his tent, held up the head so that his servants might see it. Perhaps, for one incredulous moment, it seemed to those simple men that terrible vengeance had been exacted on Singh for the loss of the indiarubber bath; that here, for display on the staging, was the ultimate in trophies (even the Sahib Preston would be unable to match it). But the colonel passed. '. . . it we did not bury,' he wrote casually, 'but took back to camp for identification before the Medical Officer.'

Further identification was surely unnecessary. The head was intact. Patterson knew his servant. And the coolies in the tent would testify to the jemadar's fate. The colonel, it seems, had an eye for the dramatic. He could not resist the theatricality of that cortège through the camp. He did not consider the inevitable effect of so macabre and startling a method of proclaiming yet another kill.

At this, the death of Singh, Whitehouse called a full inquiry, held in the mess-hut on the eastern bank. It was now apparent, he told that audience of sun-dark men, that the camp was under siege. Two men were known to have died in the jaws of lion. How many more had perished? How many of the listed desertions were, in fact, attributable to lion? Now one could only recall the evil reputation of Tsavo. 'I thought he exaggerated,' Turk noted. 'I got up and told him it might be just one mangy old lion but he brushed me off.'

One animal, Whitehouse insisted, had not earned Tsavo its history. He had pointed to the window-aperture and its square of white light. Out there, for all they knew, was an army of marauding beasts; whole families nurtured from cubhood on human flesh. Alarm was spreading like a bush-fire. Men were nervous, looking behind them when they should be working; and *that* (he had beaten his fist against his palm) was something that very much concerned him. The line would suffer.

He had stared at them resentfully, swinging the gold hunter on its chain. These were his instructions. One: under no circumstances would the news of further deaths due to lion be telegraphed without his permission. Two: no responsible officer or headman would discuss, or carry the news of, such deaths. Three: rifles and ammunition would be issued by the Armourer

—and guards in a ratio of one askari to every hundred men would be posted throughout the working day. Four: a system of night-pickets would be introduced. Five: Mr Turk would be relieved of all scouting and other advance duties and would devote himself to the tracking and extermination of the lions. Six: he, personally, would present a prize of five gold sovereigns for the skin of every lion known beyond reasonable doubt to be a man-eater. Seven: (he had looked directly at Patterson) the heads or other remains of victims would not be publicly exhibited—they would be buried immediately and without ceremony.

Patterson did not react. Whitehouse's speech had pointed the urgency in the situation, its possibilities: the phrase 'the camp is under siege' sounded the authentic ring of danger. He had turned his head, perhaps without conscious motive, to look at Preston; and Preston, too, had turned. 'I saw them look at each other,' Turk wrote. 'I knew what they were thinking.'

Turk does not elaborate; but it seems that in that crowded hut the rivalry between Patterson and Preston crystallised, moved suddenly to a plane of excitement that neither had expected. The trophies, now, became formless and pallid, the wooden stagings incomplete. Each saw the nailed skins of man-eaters. Each knew that there, lurking in the scrub and rock of Tsavo, lay a prize to be coveted above all else.

At the end of the meeting Patterson stood, waited for the silence of unease which invariably attended him. The measures to meet the crisis were sound enough, he said; but he had one objection. The reward of five sovereigns for a man-eater's hide would turn every man on the railroad with a gun, a streak of avarice and an ounce of pluck into a hunter. How could this be good for the line? The work must surely suffer. Moreover (this sardonically), if the lions were as numerous as Mr Whitehouse feared, the offer might be expensive.

Whitehouse considered. The colonel was right, he agreed. Nothing must be permitted to divert from the work of laying track. He smiled faintly. Perhaps the offer *had* been unduly rash. He withdrew it.

The meeting closed. Patterson stared again at Preston, then

at Robert Turk. They had understood his motives. The field was uncluttered. The hunt was on.

Patterson went immediately to his tent. He was now convinced that the forces of destiny had brought him from the Indian plains to this place of peril on the Tsavo River so that he, the shikari, might rid it of its scourge. Memory revived the hill-stations of the north, the forests of oak and bamboo and the hill-villages quiet with fear under the walk of the tiger. There had been expeditions of honoured ritual: the long colonnaded walks through silent woods to where lay the half-eaten corpse of the victim. And then the karphal-tree, near to the remains or reaching above a tethered goat, and the machan built in the branches, crushing the red sweet berries, the vigil in the night and the dish of tea taken in shivering dawns. Perhaps, with luck, there had been a shot at this splendid beast (which, by now, was referred to as Old Stripes): the carcase would be carried in triumph on poles so that all might see the death of their ancient enemy. And, later, the letter of gratitude penned by the scribe in absurdly meretricious phrases and signed by the thumb impressions of the Headman and the elders.

The wheel had turned: all this was again deliciously near. Patterson examined his guns, selected the .303 and a 12-bore shot gun and some packets of ball and slug, gave the weapons to his new jemadar (a man named Shere Shah) with instructions for cleaning, and made his way to the tent from which Ungan Singh had been dragged.

He was, of course, looking for a tree.

The tent lay within an inadequate hedge of cut thorn. Patterson studied the ground, noted the juxtaposition of the tent to a thick belt of scrubland and, with approval, the nearness of a baobab tree. The baobab was large, strongly-branched and, in common with its genus, thornless. He left instructions for the building of a machan and a ladder to reach it, returned to his tent by the river bank.

The day was given to the bridge over the Tsavo. It was a day of heat. No wind came off the river. The gangs laboured. An askari stood statuesque in brittle light, watched the fringe of bush and the depths of shadow. Nothing went well. Worms of heat moved in the brain. The land was iron (it had waited for the grass-rains of February and they had not come) and these early days of April were not yet relieved by the coming of the long rains. Rawson brought lime-juice and the colonel drank it under the palms, watched, with anger, the fumblings, the errors and the apathy of those torpid men. They were vulnerable. They were afraid. They worked slowly.

Many entries were made in the little book. He recorded the names of seventeen men and against each name a fine by way of punishment. The fines were savage. Coolies, at that time, were paid a monthly wage of twelve rupees; stonemasons, as reward for skill, forty-five rupees. Patterson fined offenders the equivalent of five or six days' work; and there, within the covers of the red pocket-book, wrote a preface to mutiny.

Patterson had planned to spend that night in the baobab. But sun and lack of sleep defeated him. He ate his dinner, went to his tent with the intention of resting for an hour and slept until Shere Shah brought him tea at sunrise.

The day, another of intense heat, was used at the Tsavo bridge. Rain was near and the bellies of clouds were lurid as the green of bottle-glass. Men panted, saturated their clothes with the water of the river, collapsed from heat-exhaustion. More names were taken. By evening there were forty names in the book, and corresponding fines. Even Spooner, whose wage-accounts must profit by the colonel's zeal, felt alarm.

That night a strange procession was seen to pass through the camp. Patterson's own account testifies to his nervousness. 'I did not at all like the idea of walking the half-mile to the place after dark, but all the same I felt fairly safe, as one of my men carried a bright lamp close behind me. He in his turn was followed by another leading a goat, which I tied under my tree in the hope that the lion might be tempted to seize it instead of a coolie . . .'

The illusion was now complete; the good feel of the machan under the buttocks, the sense of enclosure in the limbs of the tree and above them the monsoon sky, below the goat and the rasp of the tether, the sounds and smells of India from the coolies' tents. Surely the earth had turned beneath him and, soon, the sky would part to reveal the cap of Nanda Devi and the sambur would bell in the path of the tiger . . .

But nothing came except rain. '. . . about midnight I heard screams and cries and a heartrending shriek, which told me that the man-eaters had again eluded me and had claimed another victim elsewhere.'

The shriek, near enough to be heard, was not, it seems, sufficiently heartrending to lure Patterson from his perch in the tree. But Turk and Preston, on the second of the night's four-hour pickets, had run through rain in the direction of the cries. The cries came, behind the rain, in pulsations of fear, the rain like drums in the leaves and the cries encompassing the night and the rain, then lost, suddenly, so that there was only the noise of rain. They had stopped, stared at each other, and the rain beat into their oilskins, glistened on the shoulder-bones of the Suk, and they were aware of a fear, shared, which had no shame in it. Something had come; as old as the forest, as old as the black places in it. Then the spear of the Suk dipped and the blade turned in a sliver of faint light and they were released, running, then, to the tent.

The canvas hung, ripped. Outside, the marks of the drag filled with rain. The hedge of thorn was broken and, bending, they saw the rags of cotton from the coolie's dress, a turban, all heavy with rain, and the flesh trembling in small brown morsels on the spines of thorn. The Suk led, bent in rain, and they followed, hearing the noise of the river, the throat of it swelling with rain and, soon, they were enclosed in a darkness vibrant with water, the deeper darkness in which grew rock and tree. The Suk stopped. Something had moved and a smell, faintly putrescent, came to the nostrils and they could not go toward it, or move, or meet it in that jaw of darkness. They heard it retreat, taking its odour of death, and the night was clean again and when they turned the hurricanes of the camp advanced, swung behind rain in bulbs of orange fire.

At daybreak Turk, Preston and the Suk found the body of the coolie. It had been dragged a hundred metres from the tent into a nullah of sand and rock. It was three-quarters eaten. The sand was damp with rain and the pugs were recognisable; deep-splayed, scarred. Standing there in that cleft of rock, the rock acrid with the decay of antiquity and the bed sibilant where water channelled lower in the nullah, Turk felt, again, the presence of the lion. It was old and decayed like the rocks which hid it. It had moved beyond nature and, because of that, was unclean. It had left its taint of senescence.

They left the nullah, the Suk leading and the flesh of the shoulders dappling lemon when sun struck, the back bent so that the corrugations of the spine showed, moving, reading with absolute concentration the faintness of spoor and bent grass blades which led to the river. There, on the bank in remnants of early mist, they saw where the lion had drunk, the deep indentations where the weight of it had shifted across the forelegs.

They lost the trail where the lion had walked, without impression, through rock outcrops. Turk followed the curve of the river to camp, ate and bathed. Preston trolleyed uptrack to railhead. Turk reported to Whitehouse. There had been a second death in the night, Whitehouse told him; a jemadar, taken where the coolie lines met the river east of the camp. The body was there, he had left a man to guard it.

Turk went with the Suk. The body lay under a palm. The guard, recoiling from that place of shadow and dripping fronds, had gone. A marabou-stork stood on the belly, picked at the face. It turned, bleak-eyed, picked again at the face, flew to cover.

Nothing of the jemadar had been eaten except where the marabou had picked. The jugular was torn, had bled down the chest and forearms. The chest, belly and limbs were deeply clawed. The Suk circled the corpse, touched the ground, shook his head. The finger pointed and Turk saw the imprints of sandals. 'Something was wrong,' Turk wrote that night. 'The claw-marks was wrong, as if some crazed thing had gone mad at him, it might have been Leopard but there were no pugs and not a meal taken from him . . . I said nothing to W. He is worried enough . . .'

Patterson, too, had his worries. Many of his Pathans, rated

and paid as stone-masons, had proven useless. Much stone had been spoiled: time had been wasted. 'I soon found that many of them had not the faintest notion of stone-cutting, and were simply ordinary coolies who had posed as masons . . . I immediately instituted a system of piecework . . .'

Patterson is deserving of blame for the bitterness that followed. The new rates rewarded the fast and unfairly penalised the slow. They allowed nothing for those masons who liked to work with care and deliberation. Jealousy grew, flared into quarrels, eventually into violence. Patterson, goaded by heat, sleeplessness and a frustrated passion for the skins of lions, became the task-master. The pocket-book filled. The infliction of punishment, he decreed, must now be seen by all. To this end an ugly ceremony took place each day at noon. Defaulters were publicly paraded at a phase of the day when they needed refreshment and respite from sun, charged in regimental style, subjected to a homily in that bitter voice and sentenced. These men were Pathans, members of a proud Afghan tribe. Patterson must have known their humiliation.

One of these was Karim Bux, an elderly man whose hands, no longer deft, fashioned stone well but slowly. He was a master-mason and his wages, now, were sometimes those of a coolie. He became resentful, a complainant, and, in time, uncaring of the quality of his work. Patterson, as you would expect, stigmatized him as '. . . a prime mischief-maker among the men'; and, indeed, sitting there at the table in the clearing under the brim of the huge topi he had come to recognise the small brown pomegranate of a face, the nod and glower of it in the defaulters' line. This time of trial for Karim Bux was the prelude to the extraordinary incident of the burning bed.

That evening Patterson sat at the door of his hut. The night's vigil in one of the many machans he had built around the camp was about to begin. Rain poised: the camp waited in stillness under congested skies. But the quiet was broken by the sounds of fighting. Patterson ran with a jemadar to the masons' camp. The wave of sudden violence had already passed: it had left a wreckage of seven bloodied men. One of them was Bux.

That night Bux complained of pain and vomiting. He asked

132

for *dawa* (medicine); and Patterson, whose plans for lion-hunting were now disturbed, went to Bux's tent at eleven o'clock. He took with him a flask of brandy—and a good deal of resentment and suspicion. 'It was perfectly evident to me that he was only "foxing," ' he diagnosed. Bux, it seems, got neither brandy nor sympathy.

It was Patterson's custom at daybreak (when not marooned in trees above the tide of the camp's sunrise life) to sip tea and prepare his orders-of-the-day. These were delivered, as if to an adjutant, to Shere Shah; and it was the jemadar's duty to implement them. This morning, the day after the riot, he wrote down the name of Karim Bux. Bux would present himself at noon. The charges: malingering, insolence, inciting to riot.

At noon of that airless day Patterson seated himself at the table. Bux's wrinkled head, which usually bobbed like an old gourd in the line of sullen faces, was absent. 'He is ill,' Shah told him. 'Too ill to walk.' Patterson stared in disbelief. 'Then bring him on his bed,' he said.

Bux's charpoy was brought on the shoulders of four coolies, placed on the ground in front of the table. Many men had gathered. Patterson walked around the table, bent over Bux, lifted the blanket. Some instinct of prudence caused him to feel the old man's temples. There was no fever. He unbent. He had made his decision. He did an incredible thing.

'I then got a big armful of shavings from a carpenter's bench which was close by, put them under the bed and set fire to them. As soon as the sham invalid felt the heat, he peeped over the edge of the blanket; and when he saw the smoke and flame leaping up round him he threw the blanket from him, sprang from the bed . . . and fled like a deer . . . His amused comrades greeted me with shouts of "Shabash, Sahib!" ("Well done, sir!") . . .'

The applause for this piece of boisterous comedy was gratifying; and Bux's reluctance to be cooked on the charpoy like a cake on a griddle indisputable evidence of vigorous health. But the incident implanted considerable disquiet in the minds of Patterson's men. Watching the charpoy, the mattress and the blanket (railroad property) disintegrate in flame, they must have wondered whether claims to sickness would now be tested by a medieval ordeal-by-fire; and, doubtless, the more intelligent of them reflected uneasily that even the moribund might be expected to leap from a burning bed.

At sunrise of the following day the body of another jemadar was found by the river, apparently killed by lion. Dr Brock, accompanied by Turk and the Suk, examined it. The jemadar was torn, bloody and clawed. The throat was open, an arm missing. Brock was hesitant. He had no experience of wounds caused by the big cats, he confessed. But the claw injuries had not bled; and this might indicate they had been inflicted after death. Also (he touched the stump) it seemed that the arm had not been bitten off cleanly: rather, it had been hacked. The Suk found the forearm in underbrush. And that night Turk went to Whitehouse.

Whitehouse was agitated. The watch swung in angry arcs. There were formidable engineering problems, he told Turk. Ahead were the swamps of the Athi, miles of black-cotton soil, the great canyon of the Rift: to say nothing of the tribes—the Masai, the Kamba, the Nandi. Engineering problems, he insisted: *they* were his province. But this . . . He dropped the watch into the fob of his breeches, went to the carriage-window, peered at squalling rain. 'Rain always made him nervous,' Turk comments. 'Maybe it brought back the Taru and the rain we had before the crossing . . .'

Whitehouse turned from the window. What of these dead jemadars? he asked. Brock could be wrong. Perhaps the arm *had* been bitten off by a lion and left uneaten. He was a man of essential goodness and it was his nature to turn from the face of ugliness. But Turk had shaken his head in denial. The jemadars were murdered; the throats torn, the flesh clawed and the arm hacked to simulate attack by lion. No money had been found on the bodies. The motive was robbery. Headmen always carried more money than coolies and it was for that reason they had been marked for death. How many others had been killed and buried—to appear in the lists as deserters?

They had talked far into the night. When Turk left water flowed from the roof of the carriage and he had stared up through rain at the square of yellow light in which Whitehouse's face was framed. The face was tremulous behind the rainwater on the pane, laned with wetness in an illusion of weeping. The face nodded, broke into pearls of water, turned away. The four o'clock picket passed and he heard their capes flap in darkness. Within this darkness were the things of the night; the lions—and Ibrahim.

Turk went to his tent. There he slept until the camp awakened and tea was brought. The rain had stopped and much water ran in the drainage-channels to the river. At seven he left the tent, followed the river in the direction of the railhead. Game always moved freely in the half-lights of dawn and evening: and, this morning, the land slaked and the river filling, he walked in tranquillity and saw the life of forest, bush and river, and was a part of it.

But the serenity of the day passed into night. Two coolies were taken; one from the river-bank and the other from a tent at railhead. Each was unquestionably the victim of lion. White-house decided to shift camp. Railhead was now seven miles beyond the Tsavo. The line, leaving the Tsavo River and following the Uganda slave-road, pointed at Mtito Andei. Ahead and to the west was the rise of the Kyulu Hills. To the east and flowing parallel to the line would lie the Athi River.

By noon almost three thousand men had entrained for rail-head. The camp was denuded of tents, stores and equipment. Preston comments significantly: 'We were generally fairly quick at shifting camp, but this move from Tsavo was certainly a record one so far as time was concerned . . .' And Patterson remarks, with a soldier's philosophy: 'So long as Railhead Camp remained at Tsavo the coolies appeared not to take much notice of the dreadful deaths of their comrades. Each man felt, I sup-pose, that as the man-eaters had such a large number of victims to choose from, the chances of their selecting him in particular were very small . . .'

But now the odds had fallen. Three hundred men were left to complete the bridge and the permanent works. Patterson remained as engineer, Robert Turk as defender, and Ibrahim as headman. The fear moved inward, like the tightening of a ring. Men stood in silent groups, stared into distance along the perspective of the track, watched the curl of smoke from the last of the locomotives dissipate in wind. They felt abandoned.

Patterson suspended work for that afternoon. The tents, widely scattered, were struck, re-erected within a hedge of thorn. Kindling and wood were piled, the lamps trimmed and replenished. The sun went into its slow arc. They waited for darkness.

5. *Headmen and Colonels*

With darkness the fires grew high, bright with the wind in them. Above the darkness hung a weight of rain. Men crouched by the fires, whispered, stared behind them through ambiences of light to where the hurricanes were ringed like red candle-flames, to where the thorn-hedge was black on the blacker night and the shadow of the thorn crept, spiked, on the pale earth.

Beyond the hedge was a single fire, distant. When the flame leapt in wind the shape of a tent came in momentary outline, an apex of a triangle greenly-luminous then gone. This was the hospital-tent. It lay one thousand metres from the camp and, because infectious disease lay therein, Brock had directed that it remain isolate. There were eight men inside. Around this tent were the smaller tents of three Indian hospital-assistants, and around the whole a hedge of acacia-thorn.

Patterson had gone to his hut, taking with him his can of tea. Excitement lay beneath the careful impassivity. The lions were near. Preston, his rival, was encamped seven miles uptrack. Three hundred men, here in Tsavo, begged his protection. Truly, this was an heroic role: the air itself breathed of exploit. When he emerged from the hut he was dressed for the night's vigil in the full regalia of the shikari. The .303 sporting-rifle hung on his shoulder. He beckoned Shere Shah; and the jemadar, gathering chop-box, blankets and cartridges, followed his master.

The line lay a quarter-mile down-river; that is, near to the outer circle of tents but beyond the thorn-hedge. Patterson marched to the hedge, waited for Shah to breach an opening, led him through the darkness to where the rails shone. It was here that he had discovered the perfect machan. It stood thirty feet above ground. It grew no thorn. It was never the abode of tree-snakes. It was equipped with platforms: and a vertical ladder up which no predator could reasonably be expected to climb. It commanded a fine view of the river, the bush and the camp. It was, in fact, a water-tank elevated on stilts; and its less dramatic daytime function was to slake the boilers of the locomotives.

Patterson climbed to the planking which, earlier that day, had been laid across the tank. Below he could see the gleam of Shah's turban and the upturned face comic with fear. He dismissed him; and the jemadar, now unprotected, fled for the hedge. He checked his rifle, put a blanket around his back, composed himself for the watch.

At ten of that night Turk and the Suk escorted Brock to the hospital-tent. There was no moon, only the glow of fires. Brock went into the tent and, through the fly, Turk saw him bend lamp in hand over the pallets. The tent smelled corrupt and, when the lamp swung down, shadow rushed from the face of disease, exposed it. A man had died and Turk watched them drag him on the straw palliasse into darkness. Brock stood and shadow rushed again, darted spiderish to the walls of the tent.

He came out. The stem of the pipe pointed to where the palliasse had gone: it was burning with the pale yellow flame of straw. That one had died of a liver abscess. These others: dysentery, African tick fever, veld sores, a case of suspected smallpox, a few nameless fevers whose origin he did not know . . . The shoulders shrugged. Lions or disease—what did it matter? Death had many names.

Turk took him to his hut. Then, the Suk following, he walked through the coolie-lines. The camp was silent. Nothing moved. The fires burned low. Rain spattered, then withheld, and there was only heat and the sweat-wet skin and humidity pressing on the lungs.

Ibrahim's tent lay near to the river and the enclosing hedge; and, according with privilege, it was large. He shared it with no more than two jemadars. Darkness obscured it. No lamp burned within. Even the wood-fire, near to the entrance, had reduced to a single garnet pricked into sullen glow by the play of wind.

There was no sound, a feeling of absence. The fly was unbuckled and Turk lifted it and saw that the tent was empty. Cupidity, it seemed, had overcome fear of the lions. Ibrahim was abroad again. There, by the quickening river, he felt the evil of the man and the evil of Tsavo: the two commingled, moved somewhere in the night of the camp.

Ground-mist spread from the river, thick and acrid. He walked through this mist, away from the tent and the river, the Suk near and the feet still bandaged in mist and the hurricanes advancing in eyes of ominous red light, then pale, then gone, the river-mist thinning and, now, the first needles of true rain.

With the rain came danger, the sounds of stealth submerged in its unrelenting fall. They stopped, listened; but there was nothing but rain and the noise of canvas and thorn and shuddering river-palms and the filling river. Turk lifted his face to the rain. It was good on the flesh. Then, beckoning, he led the Suk through the tents and across the guys to where the lamps defined the distant hedge. Dull red light ran from the lamps like oil on the puddling ground.

Nothing moved. Behind the rain he could hear the mutter of men in the nearest tent. The smell of chupattis came. He listened; to the faint rustle of garments, the strange plocking sounds of the Pathan tongue. Here, in the rain by the thorn and outside the tent and beyond communication with the men, he felt suddenly vulnerable. There was an impulse to tap on the tent, to seek entry, to put those thin walls of canvas between himself and the night. He turned, deliberately, from this sanctuary of the tent, stared along the line of the thorn and its long ornament of lamplight. In that moment he saw one of the points of light extinguish, then enliven. Something had passed across it. The Suk, too, had seen. They went forward. He thought he saw a change in the texture of darkness; but he could not be sure.

Following the hedge, the cape rattling with rain and the boots sucking in mud, he found where the thorn was broken into a tunnel. Bending, they saw the pugs, deep and filling with rain. He took one of the lamps, held it to the thorn. Minute fleeces of hair, as from a mane, hung on the spines. It had come. It was near. They felt its presence.

He had begun to sweat under the cape; from heat and from tension and from fear of a thing he could not see. This was Tsavo. The name beat like a pulse. Tsavo: the place of rocks which were the colour of blood. Tsavo: where evil images came unbeckoned and scattered in the mind like portents. Tsavo: where shadow was never shadow but the flapping of a dark wing. He was afraid of it now. He thumbed the safety of the Winchester, brought the barrel through the parting of the cape. But the gun seemed futile; he could not shoot or defeat a spirit. Then the moment passed. He nodded to the Suk. They went from the pink aureoles of the lamps into darkness, into rain.

In this darkness of rain, the body bent against it and the rods of it in the face, he patrolled the tents and the huts and the bank of the river, leaving and re-entering the thorn, passing from lampglow to blackness, from the faint bloom of lighted tents to blackness again, to the fringe of riverine trees where the movement of the unseen river came through the feet in throbs of power and water tipped from the bowls of leaves to shock and dry the throat with its sudden deluge, from the river to the silent tents and areas of blackness as deep and bottomless as pits where the wings still flapped and the feet would not go and where, now, eyes which were neither red nor of glass shone, once, like reflecting chips of yellow quartz; and went.

It was the eyes which told him. The Suk gripped his arm and the head, wet and fibred in the darkness like a coconut, turned, shook with urgency: but he did not need the warning. He had seen the eyes. He had seen, or felt, their malevolence. He knew with certainty they were being stalked. His finger contracted under the trigger-guard and the spear lifted until it aligned with the barrel and they waited for the two luminous stones to come, as if catapulted, from darkness, and the downpour slewed in wind and they waited, and the rifle and the spear grew heavy and nothing came, not even a displacement of shadow, and, now, the night was empty of the lion and they knew it had gone.

This perception of danger gone was like a lightening of the mind, no more than that; a sense developed with the bushcraft. Turk obeyed it, led the Suk through the pool of dark where the lion had been. It had left its smell of senility, a faint miasma lost in the earth-smell even in the moment of detecting. He led through the tents and to the hedge and around the periphery of the hedge until the palms came rooted in mist and the river throbbed. All the fires were dead. Above, unseen but felt like a cautery in the brain, were the thunderheads. The night was turning wild.

There, in the rain by the palms, he drank whisky, the cheap trade spirit hot in the throat and the scarves of mist tearing in rain. He would strike once more through the tents, he decided. Something unfurled in the sky and the first charge of lightning came and the camp, its tents and huts and ropes and rutted channels, leapt in a pale green cameo, pinned itself on the vision, vanished. He followed the hippo-path (now cut by the thorn hedge), left it for the outer circle of tents, stepped over the guys and into a swath of impenetrable shadow. The Suk touched him and the sense of menace came and he stopped, desperate for light in that chasm of darkness, and in that moment the second of the charges, riding on its detonation, stood in the sky like a stitching of white light and in this light, ahead and near, he saw four men in the rain, the one imprisoned at the arms, and the shape of Ibrahim above the man, terrible in the act of execution, and the hand, grotesquely clawed, coming down and across the throat and the throat open and black with fluid.

In the blackness left by the charge, the absolute blackness in which the eye saw nothing, in which he, the Suk, Ibrahim and the two men stood transfixed, he heard the torn throat retch and the sound released him and he opened his cape and, in the brilliance of the next bolt, he sighted on Ibrahim, seeing in that fractional second the wan and hating face and the arm uplifted as if to hurl the metal claw and, firing, he heard the detonation of the gun merge in the detonation of the thunderclap and Ibrahim's scream, felt the flung claw strike his side to hook in the flesh of the ribs, hang like an immense spider.

Running through rain, the claw jerking on his body like a live thing, he saw below him Ibrahim's dead wet face and the rain in the beard. He tore the claw from his flesh with loathing. Ahead the two men stumbled on the guys. Blood ran from the wound and into his groin. The camp blinked under the storm in a succession of green-white flashes. He ran through this unstill light, through sheeting rain as far as the thorn. The men had gone. The blood, now, was on his thigh. There was no pain, only anger. He stood, trembling, by the thorn; and in that anger of impotence he heard the screams from the hospital-tent and, turning, he saw the tent distant and green in lightning and the shapes of men in frantic silhouette on the green.

When he reached the tent he saw that the wall was ripped. The pallets lay in disorder. Two coolies were clawed. The man with the sores of smallpox had gone and the hospital-assistants were stupid with terror. He left the tent and its smells of fear and sickness, stood in the abating rain. The storm was passing and the night breathed again. He could hear the noise of the swollen river. He was still holding the claw, this glove of hide with the five metal talons secured in it. He cast it from him. The night was unclean and not even the rain would cleanse. Somewhere in darkness the lion ate disease.

In the weeks that followed, from April into the middle of May, Robert Turk lay near to death. Nothing appears in the journal except the one word 'sick': and this for a period of eighteen days. After that the entries are more explicit. He refers to 'poison from the claws'; to 'Dr O fluttering around like a hen'; and to the hole in his side from which 'O scooped a ball of matter as big as a fist.'

Clearly, the gloved claw, dirty with the old blood of Ibrahim's victims, caused a septicaemia. Orman came from railhead to tend him. During that time of danger Turk stared, half-coma-tose, from the vales of fever. There were nodding masks of infinite sadness (the faces of Preston, Whitehouse, Haslam and Orman), green cliffs of delirium leaning inward like overhangs (the walls of the tent).

At the end of May Whitehouse sent him to Mombasa to recuperate. The island had awakened from the somnolence of centuries. There were new berths at Kilindini. The harbour rocked with shipping; and, behind the coconut palms, it had the colour and vibrancy of a painted scene. Vasco da Gama

Street turned its face to the sun in lineaments of new white stucco. Even the Grand Hotel, that place of grease and gloom and shivering bead curtains, had been refurbished.

Turk spent two weeks with his Goanese wife. He does not describe them. Doubtless he sat in sun, drank thick Arab coffee and beakers of hot tea-and-whisky, lifted the twin boys to a great height above his head, strolled in the Old Harbour on the eastern shore of the island and watched the dhows come in from Lamu. But two weeks of inactivity were enough, it seems. In June he crossed the border of the East Africa Protectorate, went down to Tanga in German territory. There he talked with a German political-officer named Ohnesorge. Turk makes scant reference to the talks. 'He wanted routes prospected to Kilima N'jaro and Tabora, perhaps to Lake of Tanganyika and up to Victoria. He talked of trade and caravans but it is the Rail that interests them. W won't like this. I declined . . .'

Turk gives no reason for declining Ohnesorge's offer or, indeed, a personal motive for the trip to Tanga. He was a caravan-master of extraordinary repute: the Germans wanted his services, approached him in Mombasa. Either restlessness or the need for change or money took him to Tanga. The port lay nearly eighty sea-miles down the coast; and Turk was not the man to make a frivolous journey. Whatever the offer it must surely have attracted him. He was no servant of the Crown. He was a professional and his services were there for hire. But he was also loyal. And the clue to his refusal lies in the comment: 'W won't like this.' Perhaps, listening to Ohnesorge and divining the German plan for a competing line to the Lake, he saw again the sick-bed and the commiserative faces of his friends and the four hundred and fifty miles that lay between Tsavo and Victoria Nyanza; knew that this was a path from which he could not turn.

Turk returned to Mombasa. Toward the end of June he took train from Kilindini to Tsavo. It was a day of heavy rain. The Taru flowered, wearing beauty like deceit. He reached the camp at sunset, rain crystal in the red air and the mud red and the camp seeming to retreat as the wing of red light drew across it and the red recognisably the colour of violence. Shutt climbed

143

from the footplate, broke a cheroot and shared it with Turk. The Uganda Queen was there.

Turk stared at it. Gone were the liveries and the bright paints and the voluted scrolls. Even the flag had gone. The locomotive was sanded down to the metal. It gleamed darkly in rain; a thing of power from which a frill of effeminacy had been deliberately stripped. Turk understood. In this place of death the festive simper of that painted engine had been an insult.

Shutt began to talk, looking intently around him. This wariness, this scrutiny of every patch of tree-shadow, was a characteristic now common to all the men of Tsavo. The lions were still active, he told Turk. A water-carrier had been taken from the hospital-tent. Two coolies working on the line had been killed within a mile of each other. And an African messenger had been eaten by the river. There was trouble in the camp. The men were quiet, too quiet. They were afraid of the lions, afraid of Patterson. Something was in the wind.

Turk ate his dinner with Whitehouse in the small mess-hut which lay next the thorn-hedge. Later, Whitehouse said, consulting the gold hunter, he had arranged a meeting. Now he wanted a pipe and a talk, a glass of whisky with a friend.

Turk, naturally silent, was by the fact of it a good listener. He was not averse to sharing a bottle of his chief's Scotch whisky (a dozen came infrequently on the Mombasa boat) or an ounce of the good mellow tobacco which sometimes came with the Scotch. He was prepared to fulfil a function; to listen while Whitehouse unburdened, to murmur sympathies from his own depth of isolation.

He was under pressure from London, Whitehouse told him. Labouchère had only to open his mouth in the House and blow and the paper (he tapped his pocket where lay the latest of the Railway Committee's tart memoranda) drifted clear across to Africa.[1] What could this Westminster fop know of conditions in

[1] Whitehouse, through the medium of newspapers and Parliamentary reports, had become ultra-sensitive to the name of the Member for Northampton. From the beginning Labouchère was opposed to the retention of Uganda and, therefore, to the building of the railway. Labouchère saw the railway as a jingoist adventure; contending that it was, in any event, illegal, and that the

the African bush? Had he ever seen scurvy and bush-ulcers on a man? Or a man's bowels burst from dysentery? Or what was left when a lion had fed off him? Could he conceive fear in terms of output? Did he realise that here, in East Africa, there were seven thousand exiled coolies—afraid of disease, afraid of lions, afraid of each other, afraid of the tribes? Already three hundred men had sickened and died. Already seven hundred had been invalided home. Already a million pounds had been spent.

Turk smoked, drank, and listened. The questions were rhetorical, demanding no answer. Whitehouse produced a copy of *The Times*, flung it on the table. The newspaper was nearly four weeks old and he had marked a passage in the Commons Debates. *That*, he said, was an example of the flagrant lies to which Government was resorting. On June the seventh the House was told that one hundred and seventy miles of track had been laid. But at that date the plates were down to Kenani— a distance of one hundred and fifty miles from the coast. Government had laid twenty miles of permanent way with a few scratches of the pen. The finger stabbed again. *There* was another distortion: a Government prediction that the line would not exceed five hundred miles in length, a Treasury estimate that the national coffers need be depleted by no more than a further two million pounds. Everyone knew that you could not lay a railroad as straight as the flight of a bullet—when the last key was driven home on the shore of the Lake there would be nearer six hundred miles of track.

Whitehouse sat. Tsavo was his problem, he confessed. There was something here, like a fragment of perpetual darkness. Even in the blaze of sun the place seemed dark. Now the camp lived under a pall. You could smell the menace in the air. The men were slow, silent and fearful. There was a bridge to build, a station, cuttings and sidings, workshops and river-sites. Perhaps when traffic moved and commerce spread the old gods would retreat and leave the place in light. But months of work lay

---

Government had no right to drive a railway through country belonging to the Masai.

ahead. And still the lions came, like visitations from the night.

After Tsavo, Whitehouse said, he had hoped for a mile a day. With the river bridged and ample water and the two new traction-engines and materials flowing from Mombasa this was surely reasonable. But it had not been like that. At first the line had moved rapidly from the area of Tsavo but this (the voice became sardonic) testified to fear of the lions rather than enthusiasm for the work. Then had come the rainstorms. Earthworks had been washed away. He had had to restore a whole series of embankments and cuttings, reballast miles of track. And the lions, it seemed, had followed the track halfway from Tsavo to railhead: occasionally a man was taken and the fear revived and the work slowed and Preston and Patterson went into fevers of excitement.

Later Whitehouse addressed his aides and seniors in the larger of the mess-huts. He spoke, standing, in the light of lamps, against the noise of rain on the corrugated-iron roof. Spooner, Sandiford and Gallagher sat behind him, hierarchically apart. Brock and Orman were there. Preston had trolleyed from railhead; lean, burned and predacious like the country he had learned to stalk. There were many men Turk did not know; engineers, surveyors, quartermasters, policemen. Staring at those rows of red or hickory faces he saw Patterson. He was appalled at the change.

The khaki jacket was unbuttoned, stained with rifle-oil and cartridge-burns. The lick of reddish hair hung unheeded on the temple. The Kaiser moustache, once moulded proudly in pomade, fell forlorn on either side of a mouth pursed with tension. It was an unquiet face, imperfectly shaven. The eyes had sunk: they were febrile, seeming yellow and intense in that sullen lamplight.

It was his custom, Whitehouse began, to speak at all major camps and to acquaint senior officials of the progress and problems of the railroad. The rate of progress (he had lingered on the word to give it the flavour of scorn) was deplorable. The railroad was now the butt of every House of Commons mountebank in search of an easy target. Government was sensitive; and governments, he reminded them, were notoriously fickle, aban-doning that which embarrassed them. He would ask each man for maximum effort . . .

The voice came to those restless men lost in the drum of rain and, sensing this, he had pointed to the roof. The storms were heavy—but only local. The long rains had failed and, ahead of them, the country cracked in drought. Soon the need for conservation would arise . . . He began to talk of water and contamination dangers, of the drying rivers and of the bridges they must build over the Simba and the Kiboko, of the hauling of girders and trestles, of the telegraph-line which now approached Kikuyu. If only the steel of the track had kept pace with the copper of the telegraph, he said with an attempt at humour, railhead would now be three hundred and fifty miles inland.

No-one smiled. Whitehouse peered through brown lamplight and a frenzy of moths to ranks of glistening faces. The voice stopped, as if too dry for further speech. Men sat stuck in the sweat of their loins, waited for dismissal.

Six years ago, Whitehouse said, Major Macdonald marched across country and drew a very beautiful map. As a record of a pleasant safari from the coast to Victoria Nyanza it was undeniably accurate: as a prospective route for the laying of a heavy-traffic, metre-gauge railroad it was two-thirds useless. All men knew this. And because the map must be redrawn there were now three survey parties working beyond railhead. From one of these parties, that led by Mr Blackett in the lands between the Rift and the Lake, he had received an exciting report. Blackett claimed to have found a new and shorter route. This (he brandished a roll of paper) will, if true, save more than a hundred miles of track, a great deal of time and money—and the Government's face. Blackett's claim, he emphasised, was of such importance that it demanded personal investigation. He had decided to lead a reconnaissance party from railhead to the Lake. He would choose his men, march in September.

There had been a stirring of interest. Feet shifted. The three Anglo-Indian lieutenants gave little claps of servility. Whitehouse, now irrevocably cast in the Livingstone mould, inclined his head. Then, after a pause, he pointed to the window of the hut and the enveloping night. Out there, he said sourly, lay a threat more immediate, more destructive to the fortunes of the railroad than the carping of politicians. The progress of the bridge could be measured in inches. And until a permanent stone-and-girder bridge spanned the Tsavo the railroad would be denied those revenues for freight, parcels and mails which, the Committee hoped, might relieve the enormous capital costs. How, he asked, could he report to London that lions were delaying the completion of the bridge? that the labour was in a palsy of fear? that the gallant officer-in-charge was constrained to spend most of his time in hides and tree-platforms?

They had laughed at this. Whitehouse flushed with satisfaction. But the matter was serious, he told them. A dozen Indians and uncounted Africans had died a terrible death. The lions *must* be destroyed. Until now he had been content to leave the killing to the amateur shikaris (a glance at Patterson and Preston): plainly, enthusiasm was not enough. Mr Turk was still very weak and could not be expected to hunt the bush for such formidable opponents. He had decided to invite professional aid; and, to this end, a bounty of two hundred rupees would be paid for the skin of every full-grown lion killed in the Tsavo district within an area of one mile on either side of the track. The offer would be circulated in Mombasa and other East African centres.

The effect on Patterson and Preston was immediate—and predictable. Both men rose. Both protested, joined in brief alliance. The harsh voice rode on the blander tones of the younger man. This offer would draw human scavengers from every cesspool on the Coast. They would shoot out the country for a hundred miles until not a lion was left alive. This was a railroad crisis. Why not leave it to railroad men?

Whitehouse listened. Preston sat. Patterson remained standing. The voice, charged with an emotion the fount of which few in that crowded mess-hut could have understood, lifted above the rattle of rain. Men turned to stare. There was something unquiet in this gaunt colonel of engineers, in the nervousness of the fingers which looped and unlooped the buttons of the jacket, in the intensity of speech which caused the moustache to jerk against the lips. The rainstorm stopped and the iron of the roof discarded water and was silent and in that sudden hiatus of sound Patterson beat his fist into his palm and shouted passionately: 'I will not have it. The lions are mine!'

Whitehouse stared. The audience, suddenly aware of the undercurrent of personal conflict, waited. Whitehouse must have known that authority, if lost now, was irrecoverable. His concern, he said quietly, was solely with what was good or bad for the railroad: not with sport or trophies or the pride of individuals. And the skin of one live coolie was worth more than the hides of a thousand record lions. This was his decision. The offer stood.[1]

The colonel, now, was alone; to brood, to listen again to the derisive laughter of the men in the hut. He was deeply involved with the lions. They had killed two of his servants, eluded him with disturbing prescience, reduced him to a figure of ridicule, taken a part of his pride, robbed him of sleep. He was wounded. He turned.

Like all martinets Patterson was unaware of the hatred he inspired. There were prescribed rituals of discipline and punishment; these had worked well enough in the Indian Army, with the coolie gangs in the Indian States. Was the African bush so different? But he was unperceptive. From within the shell of his own isolation he could not see that these men, too, were isolated; or remember that they were without roots or family, that many of them had never before left the precincts of town or village, that they were aliens in a strange and terrifying land; or that they were volunteers and came freely and with the dignity of contract.

Now, the bridge unbuilt and the lions indestructible, Patterson worked those frightened men from the first pallor of day until the onset of darkness. Gone was that contemplative hour of dawn; the bath, the scrupulous shave, the page of Swahili tinted with early sun, the invigorating tumbler of medicine. He came from the night of the bush and the river-bank. He came defeated. The red pocket-book filled. He held court in the noon-

[1] This was the first of two separate bounties. A second offer was made in June of 1900 when man-eating lions ravaged the district around Kima.

day sun: the line of defaulters grew. He harangued them and fined them. He made them desperate.

In the darkness of the tents the headmen of Tsavo held their own private court. They sentenced Patterson to death. They were used to severity; and the severities of a master would never have driven them to murder. But they were disoriented with fear of the lions and resentment. This Englishman had given them money incentives with one hand and taken them away with the other. He had insulted them. And he had failed to protect them. It seemed logical, in that torrid night, that he should die.

Strangely, Patterson never recognised when the first two attempts were made on his life. They were both covert, in the guise of accident. Even in retrospect, when men were tried for attempted murder later in the year at Mombasa, he could not or would not see the nature of the accidents.

6. Printers and Pig-Eaters

Whitehouse prepared a handbill with a curiously archaic flavour. It was printed in Mombasa by one V. G. Luthje, an engraver and parchment-dealer who thereafter styled himself 'Printer for the Colonial and Indian Services.' The bill drew the eye in a conflict of type and primary colour. It was widely circulated.

REWARD

The Managers of the Uganda Railway, having been incommoded by the Depredations of Man-Eating Lions, will pay or otherwise discharge the sum of TWO HUNDRED RUPEES for the skin of any Lion shown to the satisfaction of the Managers to have been destroyed within one mile on either side of the Railway line and to a distance of five miles East and West of the River Tsavo. Such skin and entirely reasonable proof of Vicinity to be delivered at Tsavo Station within 12 Hours of the demise of the animal.

Kilindini   *G. Whitehouse*
July 1898   *Chief Engineer*

Whitehouse owned a sardonic sense of humour; perhaps it reflected itself in the use of understatement, in the word 'incommoded.' But he could not have intended that the word 'Lion' should appear without the important qualification of 'full-grown.' Either he or Luthje was at fault. The omission proved costly.

The offer caused great interest in Mombasa. Two hundred rupees, the equivalent of a coolie's wages for sixteen months, was no light sum. The handbill passed freely. It went up-country with the caravans, on the dhows to Lamu, on the ships to Zanzibar and Aden and the Seychelles. It went in the pockets of slavers, in the cleft-sticks of Teita messengers. It was read, discussed, and translated for the illiterate. Many a face glowed with the light of rapacity. A man could take risks for such a sum.

Soon men came to the Tsavo. They did not enter the camp. Tents glimmered distantly like green and brown flowers sprung from the parching land. None of the professional hunters had come. For them ivory was still the prize, still the root of fortune. And the sportsmen, those who were willing to live in bush, to accept privation and the danger of disease and tribal barbarism for the sake of a trophy, would not shoot for a bounty. These men who had come to Tsavo with the handbills in their pockets were scavengers. They were silent men; unwashed, ageing and defeated. Greed was their only true emotion. Such a one was Paul Verschoren.

Verschoren, at this time, was a man of sixty-five years. Robert Turk knew him by reputation. 'He had killed a woman in German East. But that was nothing to that one, he would make a Hyena sick . . .' And, indeed, in that continent of brilliant suns Verschoren's name sounded from an underlying darkness. It caught on the mind like something fungoid. 'A gigantic man,' Turk recorded, 'with the fat of animals on his hair and beard. He has the stink of death and you can see the lice in his head. His broken shoulder makes him lopsided and his arm hang low like an Ape.' Paul Verschoren was a terrifying sight. He was dirty and gross ('adipose' is the word Turk uses). He had stumps of carious teeth. He was pot-bellied with hookworm, and some disease had left rosettes across his face which anger could turn into small white flowers. He was without hope and, therefore, a man of prey. The men of Tsavo saw him—and turned away in disgust.

Beyond the thorn-hedge other fires leapt in the night. Out there were the Bavarian, Gerhardt, who spent his days cowering in the reed-beds; the Boer, Kroon, who could not hunt elephant on his ulcerated legs and drank whisky in the heat of the sun and shouted from the hummocks and the rocks; a decrepit Sikh named Ajab with cataracted eyes and the face of a decayed hawk and a son whose duty was to kindle and cook and build stone shelters and fire their Rigby-Mauser when the lions appeared; a crippled dhow-master with an eaten nose and the name of Ahmed and a system of game-pits which would bring him riches; a Portuguese called Marquès with a white head and a yellow skin and a breast-bone which stuck from his fragile body like a peg; and Swahilis from the Coast and Zanzibaris and deserters from the caravans; and others, still nameless, who had come to Tsavo and would spend a night or two in bush and learn this ultimate of fear, and go.

Turk speaks also of a young man who came one evening on the Mombasa material-train '. . . with nothing but a pack & a rifle & 2 coast porters . . . black hair and the eyes of an eagle and the tongue of a Scot . . . He had been one year in B.E.A. But he did not want these lions, he told me very contemptuous. These were not real lions, they were pig-eaters. He was going north as far as Elgon where the elephant were thick. And he went after 3 days . . .'

Probably the young man was Karamojo Bell (although he had not at that time earned that name, or fame as a great butcher of elephants). But it is known that Bell came to Africa when he was seventeen, and likely that he was at Tsavo one year later. The term 'pig-eaters' was not common currency; in fact it was peculiar to Bell.

Bell left for Mount Elgon. Now, in July and the rains failed and the land browning with drought and the water at Maji Chumvi lower than any man had known it, the skies over Tsavo cleared and, for a week, they saw, hazeless, the snow-cupola of Kilimanjaro. Then the cloud came and the mountain was no longer there. Preston drove track more than sixty miles beyond the Tsavo River, toward Kibwezi.

Whitehouse joined him at railhead. There he saw the quality of Preston; the man grown into the true dimension of authority, the track good and making one mile in every day. He was content to leave it thus: he returned to Tsavo. He did not leave the carriage. His face, lemon again with malaria, leaned from the window. He would continue to Mombasa, he told Turk. He was overdue at Kilindini. And things were well at railhead. But here . . . The eyes stared at that silent camp, at the guards and the hedges and the firewood piled for the night and the palliasses which men had tied in trees so that they should sleep above the ground. But here . . . He had signalled and the Uganda Queen went with its smell of hot metal, its flower of steam on the face of the sun.

Turk watched the flower grow small. Whitehouse was on his way. In Kilindini he would read, preside, nurse his fever and dream, perhaps, of Brunel and Stephenson and coffee-pot engines and explorations in marigold lands. He had turned his back on Tsavo. It was a part of the railroad—and yet not of it; a place of obsessions and mutiny, of pig-eaters, pariahs in the shapes of men. There were primal forces here. They were gathering. They were beyond control.

Florence Preston rejoined her husband at Kibwezi. This was one of the good places; and it came, green and pleasant to the eye, after thirty miles of thornbush, dust and the spikes of sanseviera. Ronald Preston had built three temporary bridges: at the River of Hawks (Mtito Andei), at Darajani and Masongaleni. He had laid track to a self-imposed target (on one splendid day he keyed one and one-half miles of steel). He was at the spearhead. And, separated from Patterson by sixty miles, the embittering rivalry had left him. He reached Kibwezi tired, happy and measurably bigger.

Kibwezi was one of those settlements in the dark and aridity of nineteenth-century Africa where all was light and lushness. It was a missionary post of the Scottish East Africa Mission and it flourished benignly in a land where the meek had no place. It had sprung from a depot of the old Imperial British East Africa Company; and, with its stockades and its store-huts, its smithy and its waggons, it had an air, still, of trade and garrisons.

A quarter-mile beyond the Mission ran flat lava outcrops. This was the site of railhead camp; and it was here that Preston built the tiny station where locomotives could take fuel and water. 'Looking up the narrow streak of metals (he wrote) from Kibwezi Station, Mount Mbinzau makes a background strikingly beautiful . . . Here we met the beautiful Oryx again, and guinea fowl were fairly plentiful.'

But Preston thought constantly of the lions of Tsavo. They

were never far. He had wanted them: and the want was unsatisfied. Blackwater, a disease common to Kibwezi, had immobilised a third of the labour. During this time of sickness Preston left the camp, wandering without real purpose into the heat-mirages, shooting at everything that moved. These shapes which came bright in sun across the leaf-sight were not the shapes of lions. But the hunt was still essential to him. He killed; and in the killing found a kind of peace.

Florence Preston seldom went on these expeditions. There is a photograph, taken at about this time, in which she sits with her husband at the front of a double-fly tent. On the back of the picture Preston has written (much later, in a tremulous old-man's hand) 'Our home for 5 years.' To Preston, now rapt and awakened by the wild country, the tent was indeed a home. That well of luminous emerald light, with its chest and pallet and trestle-table, its skins and its horns, contained all that he needed. But for Florence it was different.

In the picture she is seen to be plump, demure—and uneasy. She sits erect. She wears a hard straw hat, a flounced blouse, a spotted tie and a thick dark skirt which covers her feet. She is aggressively Victorian. The hands, if they were not composed primly in the lap, might well hold a china tea-cup. To the left of her is the evidence of a strange environment; the head and hide of a Burchell's zebra, the horns of impala, hartebeeste and oryx, no less than three rifles—one of them across Preston's knee. She looks across these things. She has contrived to ignore them. A wild grey parrot perches on her shoulder but this, it is evident, is a poor substitute for a songbird in an ornamental cage.

One of the stranger aspects of the railroad story is the presence of women. They appear in many of the old photographs; a glimmer of bodice in the depth of a tent, a back bent over a stream, defiant little groups clutching parasols under palms. They seem incongruous. Most were the wives of road and rail engineers and, like Florence, had followed their husbands from India. They were accustomed to tropical service, to shifts of locale, to separation. But this African venture had posed a problem. A maximum of three years, Government predicted.

But they had learned to doubt the wisdom of governments, knew instinctively it would be longer. So they came. They crossed an ocean. They knew nothing of Africa. They were children entering a dark room.

Nobody knows what they expected of East Africa. If they thought of it at all they assumed it to be another jewel in the Imperial Crown, perhaps as lustrous as India. Here they would surely find law, administration and military security; they would exchange one formal society for another. They were disillusioned. They found the Africa of Livingstone.

It was barbaric. It smelled of violence. It was elemental. It was ungiving: everything had to be won. It was beautiful; but the beauty was cruel and concealed the leper's face. Life had no real tenure. There were patterns of survival. And beyond the railroad camps ferocious dramas were enacted and re-enacted. The jewel, it seemed, was a bloodstone.

There was law: but nothing much between Mombasa and Fort Smith at Kikuyu (350 miles inland) to enforce it. In the old days the Charter Company had ruled. It had given the law to the lands around the trading posts. Now, with the Company dissolved, a few District Officers and a few troops of askari supplied an illusory protection.

These women were vulnerable. They were not pioneers. They had not come to settle (although many did). They had come simply to live with their menfolk. And living was now dangerous, without grace or gentility. Living was a tenth of an inch of canvas between themselves and wild beasts. Living was the scouring of pots and garments on the banks of streams. Living was the hood of the cobra and the spear of the tribesman, the scuttle of the lizard and the virus in the blood. Living was all these things. They embellished it with desperate devices; a square of needlework, a mess-can of exotic flowers, a diary for an unborn grandchild. But it was really useless. They were in transit—like other railroad chattels. They could not put down roots. And because of this they became sullen and disenchanted.

Many went home. These were the defeated; and nothing, not even the proximity of a husband, could make life tolerable. Some stayed: to endure, to plod with the rails like nomads, to wait because everything must have an end. Others met the challenge and, in meeting it, grew to love this new and vibrant land. A few, like Florence Preston, militantly shut the country out.

Later, there were other women to follow the camps.

It was at this time of the Kibwezi railhead that the reawakened life of Veterinary-Captain Haslam entered upon its final term. It had been a true awakening and the significant portion of his life could be written into five short months. It began in Tsavo and it ended in the country of the Kikuyu.

It was at Tsavo that Haslam came alive again. Until then responsibility for the Railway Transport Department, its mules, its carts and its harness, its problems of feed and stabling, disease and mortality, had burdened him. He was a conscientious man. He worked to the limit. He made few friends. He was probably lonely. For a time he had eaten a meal or smoked a pipe with Patterson; but he had found no serenity in the company of that smouldering man.

He was attracted to Robert Turk. Turk, with his long mane of hair, his height and his aura of wildness, always aroused curiosity. Men came near, as to a flame—and then withdrew. But Haslam had drawn closer than that. Turk disturbed him. Turk talked of forests and mountains, of giant trees and marvellous beasts, of bizarre plants and valleys of flowers whose colour was so intense that a man must turn away or weep. Turk had filled himself with a richness of experience. Turk was like the scent of musk suddenly returned. It was in his nostrils, he would never lose it.

Whatever had lain cold in Haslam was now rekindled. He had taken from Turk; and Turk had given without knowing. But Turk noticed the change. 'H is always asking questions, gulping up everything you tell him like a starving lizard. He has not a moment to live . . .'

Haslam, indeed, was now a man with an acute awareness of the passing of time. The search for knowledge was like a fever. He was insatiable. Each day was a small essay in wonderment. He arose at dawn, left the zerebas for the river, the rocks and the thornbush. He watched, sketched and noted. He was not oppressed by Tsavo or afraid of its lions. This terrible hunger left no room for fear. He was impatient of his duties. He gave what was required of him, hastened back to his bright new world of discovery. He could never have enough. He ranged the country; from the toothbrush scrubs to the grasslands of Kyulu, from the Tsavo rapids to where the river joined with the Athi. Here, where water broadened into the Sabaki and the riverine life teemed, there were nests of fish-eagles; and here he loved to write. At night he began again by the light of a tent-lamp.

The note-book reveals a mind in tumult. Words tumble, sentences leap. He could not draw and the diagrams are as thick and clumsy as his own fingers. The flowers have no delicacy, the trees no form, the animals no grace. And none of the birds could ever have flown. There is no coherent pattern of study. The text is unrelated. Riffle the leaves of that feverish book and it is life itself in myriad form that scurries from cover to cover. The book, in fact, is one large interrogation-mark. The questions are endless. He wanted to know. But there was no time to answer, only to propound. The later pages of the note-book are incomprehensible. The trumpets of flowers decorate the corners. Vines climb the margins. And captions intertwine with the branches of those improbable trees.

Haslam did not live permanently in this world of natural marvels. It had claimed him, but not to the exclusion of his legitimate work. The note-book contains twenty pages of lucid exposition on the subject of rinderpest. Pinned to the last of the pages are printed reports from Hutcheon, the Colonial Veterinary Surgeon and from the Bacteriological Institute of Grahamstown. The former is dated February 1897, the latter February 1898.

The last date is significant. The cattle-plague had visited the district of Ulu in the Christmas month of 1897, sweeping through Kikuyuland and down to the eastern boundary of the land of the Masai. Government took fright. It recalled the great epidemic of 1890-91. The Masai, too, remembered. The herds (which were sustenance, currency and prestige) had been decimated. The soldiers had come to slaughter their cattle.

Pastoral, savage and nomadic they could not understand this concept of preventive measure. They had had to watch the shooting of healthy beasts and the hands of the young warriors trembled on their spears.

Now, seven years later, Government and Masai watched each other. The land was dry as tinder with the drought. Famine and pestilence marched across that iron soil. Something must ignite: violence would run like a fire in the brush. Then, one morning, the herds and the spears of the *moran* were gone. Lenana, a chief of wisdom, had taken his people, their sheep, goats and cattle, south of Ngong.

Government acted. The epidemic must be confined.[1] Haslam was known to be an expert on scab, horse-sickness and rinderpest. The Railway Transport Department agreed to second him. Early in the month he left for railhead. From there he would march to Fort Smith at Kikuyu.

Haslam reached the Fort by the old Swahili caravan road. The journey had been a revelation. 'Beauty unravelled at every turn of the path as if from the spool of Creation,' he wrote exuberantly. After the Machakos basin he followed a fertile valley to the Athi Plains.

Fort Smith, once the Company's trading station, was now a garrison; and it was in the dak bungalow that Haslam built his laboratory. Here he would live and work. Within the stockade were many tents, soldiers and armaments. Outside were the Kikuyu, their cattle kraals and the rinderpest. The Kikuyu were cultivators. They also owned a wealth of cattle. But they were not nomads. They were deeply rooted. They were steeped in mystic belief; and tribal legend gave them origin on the slopes of Mount Kenia. This was their land. They would not move.

They knew of Haslam's arrival. Like the Masai they had suffered in the slaughter of seven years back. This man with the thick legs and thick body and the absurd square of black tar painted beneath the nose would surely destroy their stock. They

[1] In fact, the disease had moved many months before across the natural water-barrier of the Zambesi and into South Africa. Cape Colony lost almost 600,000 head of cattle.

feared him. The name of Haslam was murmured in the rituals. They marked him for death.

Clearly, Haslam had some prevision of an ending. He passed the last three weeks of his life in a frenzy of effort. Everything raced: time, the rinderpest, the quill with which he covered the pages of his note-book. He worked until the small hours, arose again at dawn. He prepared serums against the cattle-plague: he dissected the bodies of birds, beasts and reptiles for his own private purpose. He sent his porters out on the rinderpest census: they returned with insects and lizards, with the racemes of flowers and the drupes of fruit, with ticks from the plains and tiger-beetles from the beds of rivers.

In the final week he moved the nineteen miles down-country from Kikuyu to Nyrobi. Here, where the wind off the Athi crossed the plain, were a few huts which had served the caravans, a shed or two left by the telegraph unit, a small Army transport stable. He planned a second inoculation centre.

There are differing accounts of the circumstances of Haslam's death. Patterson writes: '. . . as he was keenly interested in finding out all about the tropical diseases from which the animals suffered, he made it his custom to dissect the bodies of those that died. The superstitious Wa Kikuyu were fully convinced that by this he bewitched their cattle, which at the time were dying in scores from rinderpest. So—instigated no doubt by the all-powerful witch-doctor—they treacherously killed him.'

The Official History states censoriously: 'Instead of con-centrating on this work (inoculation experiments), Haslam unfortunately decided to join a punitive expedition against the Wakikuyu of Muluka who had murdered some natives sent out by the railway to buy food-stuffs. He allowed the expedition to start without him and, whilst trying to catch up with it, he and some of his porters were attacked and killed by a band of Wakikuyu.'

The Sub-Commissioner reported: 'Shortly after the departure of the expedition Captain Haslam, who was somewhere in Kikuyu, heard of it and endeavoured to join up with it. He entered Muluka with a few of his men but he appears to have been attacked and to have attempted to withdraw. Haslam was killed but his men escaped. They informed me that Haslam had a .303 but no ammunition as he had fired all he had at a rhinoceros before entering Muluka. When he was killed Haslam was not carrying his rifle. He had handed it to one of his men who escaped and brought it to Machakos where on examination it was found to be quite clean. On receipt of the news of Haslam's death I sent a wire to the officer in command of the Uganda Rifles, then at Fort Smith, to dispatch a strong detachment to get in touch with Cooper and try to locate Haslam's body. The body, frightfully mutilated, was later found by Capt. Cooper, who interred it with military honours . . .'

In those five months Haslam had developed a deep reverence for living things, and in that rarefied state was hardly the man to be attracted by the infliction of punishment or to empty his rifle into a rhinoceros. The rifle, by the Sub-Commissioner's testimony, was clean and had not been fired. But Haslam was not averse to protection. He and a party of six porters left Nyrobi in the wake of the cavalcade of troops. Their paths would diverge. On the morning of the second day he watched the glint of accoutrements and the steel of the Maxims disappear into a fold of the valley. He set his face to the rise of Donyo Sabuk where he would gather fern and lichen and the red-and-white begonias of those golden slopes. There he kept his appointment with the band of warriors which had followed him from Fort Smith; and there ended the brief and marvellous life of Veterinary-Captain Haslam.

Ronald Preston received two telegraph messages. The first, from Nyrobi, brought the news of Haslam's death. The second, from Whitehouse in Mombasa, announced a railhead visit by the Governor of German East Africa. The Mombasa telegraph was terse: a letter would follow. It came, a day later, on the material-train, and it was written in Whitehouse's hand:

> . . . *His Excellency's visit is a ceremonial. But I cannot dispel heavy suspicion of political purpose. Curzon's warning*[1] *is as pertinent*

[1] Apparently: '. . . Nothing is more certain than that if we do not construct a railway to the lake the Germans will . . .'

now as it was three years ago. The German line from Tanga already points to the foothills of the Usambara Range and to the plateau of Kilimanjaro. They greatly covet the trade of Uganda and the countries of the Nile and the Congo. Give them the sight of half a chance and they will take it . . . I enjoin you to extend to His Excellency and his entourage every warmth and courtesy—and to provide such testimony of speedy endeavour as you can humanly manage. . . .

The charge was plain. Preston gathered his foremen and addressed them. It was evening and, behind him, the shadow of the mountain of Mbinzau crept. Within two days, he told them, the Germans were expected. But they would not come to praise —only to observe the performance of a competitor. This must be a day of exceptional effort. He would pay double rates to the labour, a bonus to the foremen. In return he wanted a mile of track laid and linked before the eyes of the Germans like the pieces of a clockwork train-set. To this end material would now be conserved: there must be no shortage on the day. All fish-bolts would be oiled and run down to obviate delay due to rust. And the gangs would work at maximum pace in two-hour shifts.

Ohnesorge, the political-officer, was among the Governor's party. The train steamed through Tsavo without halt, very slowly so that those aboard could stare in curiosity at this place of bloody reputation. Then it passed. A German flag had been fixed on the brake-van.

The train reappeared an hour before sundown. Now, on the downtrack journey and running before its engine, it must stop and turn at Tsavo. This, His Excellency announced, was an opportunity he could not miss. He would inspect the camp. He was a sardonic man with a silver moustache and a smooth silver head that shone like a coin when he removed his hat. The party descended. Lurid sunlight heightened the colours of those exquisite tunics. They began to walk; past the triangle, into the protection of the bomas. They approached the admin. hut. There they came upon a remarkable scene.

Many men were grouped in front of the hut. They formed a crescent, and within that crescent stood Paul Verschoren and

Patterson. Behind them Legge, the pay-officer, fidgeted on the duckboards. Distant and riverward, Kroon lifted his face to the sun and bayed like a wolf. Verschoren's thick voice rode above the baying. The face was suffused: with anger, with the red light of the sun. The hand brandished one of Whitehouse's handbills. At his feet were spread the carcases of three lion-cubs and a lioness. The cubs were very small, like toys. The lioness lay paws upward, displaying milk-swollen paps. There were no wounds on the carcases: death, it seemed, had come on the wave of some awful paroxysm. (They had been killed with strychnine.) Verschoren's gross body trembled with passion. Spittle ran from the mouth to hang like crystal on the beard. The shirt and trousers were ragged, stained with fat and the red soil of Tsavo. Insects circled the larded head. He had begun to stump around the carcases, kicking the cubs into a small, pitiable pile. The men were silent. Patterson stared. Kroon fell from the hummock. Legge shifted uneasily on the wooden slats. The group opened to reveal the Governor's party.

Verschoren picked up one of the cubs by the tail, swung it so that it draped across Whitehouse's boots. They heard the whirr of insects, the escape of steam from the piston-boxes. The light deepened and a flight of birds crossed the clearing. Whitehouse withdrew his boot. The cub's mouth was stretched on the teeth in a rictus of agony. His Excellency bent, lifted the small, tawny cat, dropped it with distaste.

'Eight hundred rupees,' Legge said. 'That's what he wants for this lot.'

Verschoren nodded. Temper took him again and the face inflamed and the disfiguring flowers of disease turned white. He moved nearer, smoothed the handbill, began to quote. Familiar phrases broke in Whitehouse's face in odorous gusts: '. . . will pay the sum of two hundred rupees . . . two hundred rupees . . . the skin of any lion . . . *any* lion . . .' Verschoren thrust the bill into Whitehouse's hand. 'Don't it say that? *Don't* it?' The handbill fell and Ohnesorge retrieved it, gave it to the Governor. The German read it, smiled, folded it and put it into his pocket. He was watching Whitehouse for reaction.

In that silence Verschoren's heavy breathing commingled

with the hiss of steam. Kroon climbed the hummock, cast his empty whisky-bottle into the shale. They heard it clatter. The Boer slapped his pot-belly in sudden rage. Whitehouse stared at the cubs. Flies clustered on the faces. Anger suffused him. But there was no alternative: the offer must be honoured. 'Pay him,' he said to Legge. 'Pay him in full.'

Patterson gasped, turned abruptly, strode through the ranks of men. Legge went into the hut and Verschoren followed, leaving his odour of dirt and sickness. The Governor smiled, led his party to the waiting train. Whitehouse followed with Ohnesorge. 'His Excellency,' Ohnesorge said pleasantly, 'would have had that animal whipped.'

The payment enraged Patterson. He believed that Whitehouse had inflicted a deliberate wound. The scene was the climax to a period of great personal stress. He had hated Verschoren and the other scavengers. They were unclean. They preyed without hunger, passion or pity: and they did it for money. Lions, large and small, had been brought into the camp to be flung to the ground in front of the admin. hut. Most were killed in areas distant from the line. But there was no way of proving this. Legge paid. The total grew. The funds diminished. And still men perished.

He had watched the delivery of the carcases in a conflict of emotions. He felt compassion for these men who were dying a gruesome death. They were in his charge. They were entitled to protection. But, equally, he was tormented by an ineradicable fear that the man-eaters would be destroyed before he could claim them. He, too, was entitled to something; by the right of ceaseless vigil and sleepless nights, by self-respect lost and ridicule suffered. Morally they belonged to him. And as trophies they were matchless. These were not creatures to die squalidly like vermin.

Then had come the poisoning of the cubs. It had sickened him. It was clearly the moment to challenge this coven of human hyenas; and, on the clearing before the admin. hut, he had defied Paul Verschoren. Obviously, he told him, bounty was payable only on the skins of full-grown lions; or at least on those capable of killing men. He had refused payment and the blood had pounded in Verschoren's degenerating body. Violence was near; but, then, Whitehouse and the German Governor and his aides had unexpectedly appeared. Whitehouse had countermanded his order. This was public humiliation.

Whitehouse returned to Mombasa. He must, by now, have realised that the handbill was a mistake, that the offer was too generous and a drain on railroad funds, that it had drawn the flotsam of the coast and the interior to the camp at Tsavo, that the men of the railroad worked in danger and torrid heat for a small fraction of the sums paid to the hunters; and that, simply, it was better that the railroad should do its own scavenging. But he did not withdraw the bill. He chose, instead, to modify it. Henceforth a sum of seventy-five rupees only would be paid for the carcase of a lion. The offer was 'in lieu of any previous offer of reward and is positively dependent on each animal attaining a length of eight feet six inches from tip of nose to tip of tail.'

Tsavo was now a backwater. It felt the ebb and flow of the railroad. But that was all. The freight-trains came, discharged a cargo, went. The steam dissolved, and with it the sense of contact. Events were moving to a climax.

Like all predators Verschoren was jealous of territory. Now the killing must be selective. The rewards were lower. There was competition. The inefficient and the cowardly had already gone. The professionals and those inert from sun, drink and hopelessness remained. He was determined to destroy them. He himself was consumed by hookworm, aware of the fingers of death within his vitals. Life was an affront, whether animal or man: he had nothing to lose.

Reports reached the camp: of a Zanzibari floating in the Tsavo with a broken neck, of a dead Goan in the reed-beds whose skull was crushed. Ahmed, the dhow-master, had lain impaled in one of his own game-pits and had cried piteously for a day and a night and no man had gone to him, believing the voice to be that of the lunatic Kroon. These had surely died at the hands of Paul Verschoren. But the Sikhs, Ajab and his son, survived. They were cunning and alert. They were successful.

Karamojo Bell wrote later: 'The young fellow shot straight and true, and lion after lion succumbed. In nine months these two men claimed the reward on some ninety skins. On about forty-five the reward was actually paid, there being some doubt as to whether the remainder were killed within the mile limit.'

On Patterson fell the task of adjudication. It was a humiliating and terrible experience. He had to bend in the sun, measure and examine, question the killers. There were exhausting arguments. Noses were pulled and tails stretched. Many of the lions were young and vigorous and he had known instinctively that these were not man-eaters. But there were times when a carcase, dark and scarred with age and feral even in death, had been laid at his feet and he had bent to it fearfully, touched it, lifted the weight of the tufted tail—and wondered. Whitehouse could not have devised a more subtle discipline.

August was a month of menace. The skies were congested, the river black. Tsavo seemed thick with heat. For a week there had been no death or attack by lion. Patterson had realised this quite suddenly. He had scrutinised the kills and paid the bounty; and this surfeit of lions had somehow obscured the fact that the terror had lifted. But then had come the realisation. Days passed. He waited. Dawns came and the bomas were unbroken and the tents untorn. There were no pugs or scats or signs of lion. Either the man-eaters were inactive or had fled the district or (his bowels went gelid at the thought of it) they had fallen to the scavengers.

August passed into September and the fear grew into conviction. He had been cheated. The man-eaters were dead. It was this sense of irretrievable loss that drove him to further tyrannies. He lengthened the working day. He cut the periods which, by agreement, had been set aside for food and relief from sun. He fixed unreachable targets; and fined those who failed to attain them. He held a noonday and an eventide court. He walked with stealth. He used the cover of rock and bush. He watched. He went from bridge to quarry, from quarry to track; the men of Tsavo waited for that hostile figure to emerge from shadow, for the flicker of the note-book, for the anger in the voice. 'His tongue was a scourge,' a mistari said later in Mombasa.

On the fifth night of September Purshotam called a meeting. The jemadars and many leaders were there. They were sullen and filled with hatred for this man who took the money they earned in sweat and in pain and gave it to Verschoren and the jackal-men. They resolved to kill him. Tomorrow, Purshotam told them, Patterson would visit the quarry. There they would put him to death. Each man made his mark on a ribbon of paper. It was agreed.

That night a man, who is nameless, came to Patterson's tent and, standing outside the canvas where the head of the truckle-bed would be, spoke in a whisper. Patterson listened through the canvas and the man left. This was the first of the warnings.

In the morning Patterson arranged his work-schedule, marched down the trolley-line in the direction of the quarry. This was his custom. It was also his custom to leave the line a hundred metres before the quarry and approach it silently under cover of thorn-bush. Heera Singh intercepted him. Singh, a Punjab Sikh, was a man to whom mob-murder was a debasement. He spoke softly from a bush. This was the second of the warnings.

Patterson was incredulous of the first warning and only half-convinced by the second. Heera Singh left for the camp. Patterson sat in the early sun, swished with his cane the seed-heads from the grass, assessed the situation and decided that the code of the Sahib compelled him to go to the quarry.

Singh went immediately to Robert Turk. Turk listened, slung his Winchester, called the Suk tracker. Together they followed the trolley-line. At this point in time Patterson had already reached the lip of the quarry. Below him in that rust-brown fissure where the mists of night lay like milk one hundred and sixty men hewed and dressed the rock. He watched them. The noise of the sledges came in flat buffets of sound up the wall of the ravine. He moved and shale fell and a jemadar turned and saw him and beat once with his stick against an empty water-tank and the sledges struck again, heavily, and were stilled as if at a signal. Turbaned faces stared upward at him. The ravine was silent and in that silence he heard the gyrating hum of a hornet moving down the rock-face, down across the grain of it, and he listened and the men listened and the hum went in slow and angry phrases down into the ravine. He knew that when it stopped he would have to move. The sound stopped. They were waiting. He left the lip, walked to the path and down it to the ravine.

The rock-walls closed around him. Behind him the strata ran in perfect parallels upward to the lip, out of the trap, up toward safety. Below, the men stood footless in white mist. He hesitated. Then he went down into mist and imprisoned heat.

The jemadar met him. Further up the gully, the jemadar said, there were men who were refusing to work. If the Sahib . . . ? Patterson followed him. Now they were behind. He heard their feet. Fear or the mist tasted acrid. He would not turn. The sledges could pulverise a man. But he would not turn. The jemadar stopped, pointed to two Pathans. They were seated on the lower stair of a rock.

Patterson went to them. They did not move. 'Will you not stand?' he asked them softly. He saw unease in the eyes. The bearded faces turned away. This, then, was the place.

Robert Turk and the Suk had not gone into the ravine. Scrub grew along the lip, affording cover. They watched. Below, Patterson was bending to two seated Pathans: behind him and sealing egress from the ravine a mob of perhaps fifty men had gathered. The harsh voice came in accents of reprimand. The Pathans were unmoving. Patterson spoke again. The men shuffled nearer. The Pathans pulled their beards. Patterson straightened. They saw his hand go to his breast-pocket.

'Then,' Turk records with incredulity, 'he actually pulled out that blessed note-book . . .' The jemadar could hardly have expected so effective a trigger to the passions of that sullen mob. The colonel opened the hated symbol of punishment. 'I noted their names in my pocket-book in my usual manner . . .' he testified (and reiterated in his book) before Crawford, the British Consul in Mombasa. 'Immediately a yell of rage was raised by the whole body of some sixty men, answered by a similar shout from those I had first passed . . . Both groups of men, carrying crowbars and flourishing their heavy hammers, then closed in on me in the narrow part of the ravine . . .'

At that moment Turk and the Suk revealed themselves, leaving the scrub and moving into vision at a point above and behind Patterson's back. Sunlight touched the barrel of the Winchester, the blade of the spear, drew the eyes of the men in the ravine. Turk's prowess with the rifle was legendary. And the tracker, red with ochre and shivering in ecstasy for the kill, looked fearsome. The sledges dropped. The passion died. A man neighed with laughter in the break of tension. Patterson leapt to the crest of the rock. There, pale of face but determined to die in the best tradition of the regimental officer, he delivered an extraordinary oration.

'Before they had time to recover themselves,' he writes, 'I had started haranguing them in Hindustani . . .' As a piece of histrionics it was faultless. The discordant voice threatened: Government, infinite in knowledge, would discover the truth and many would be hanged. It divided them: a few mutinous scoundrels were urging self-respecting Pathans along a path to murder. It mocked: only fools would allow themselves to be so led. It appealed to their sense of justice: had he not been fair to the conscientious worker? And, finally, it revealed an avenue of escape: provided work was resumed and this darkness of murder was banished from their hearts he would forget the affair and the discontented could return to Mombasa.

He paused with deliberate artifice. The ravine was silent. The men stared at this gaunt figure with the impassioned voice, at Turk and the Winchester which could pour death into them, at the Suk and the spear and the thin black arrows which were surely tipped with poison.

Patterson lifted his arms dramatically. The voice soared and metallic echoes flighted along the walls of the ravine. 'Every man who is with me,' he cried, 'raise his hands like this!'

Hands climbed from a sea of white cotton. They were like rows of brown gloves. Patterson trembled with emotion, wiped his glistening eyes. He was filled with a great love. These were recalcitrant children. He was their Sahib. Some gesture was necessary, some act reflecting forgiveness, authority, respect. He came to attention, stared above their turbaned heads to where the mists clung; and saluted.

Throats murmured a deep response. He smiled, dropped his

arm. They were his. The cotton dresses parted into two respectful lanes. He was free to go. He shook his head, summoned the jemadar. This was plainly the moment for a further affirmation. He would continue his rounds, he announced. For the next hour he measured stones, assessed their quality, strolled with calm insouciance among the gangs, bent his head within inches of the sledges and the steel of chisels. This was victory. The taste was good.

Patterson's faith in the power of his own oratory (he had seen nothing of Turk and the Suk in the gully) was quickly shattered. The informer came again to his tent in the hour after sundown. Patterson listened and the beard moved in elongated shadow on the wall of the tent. There had been a meeting in the quarry, the voice said. They would come tonight, to the tent, to kill. The grotesque shadow left the canvas. He sat in the reddening gloom, suddenly afraid.

Later he went to the signaller. He had written two messages. Both were pleas for help. One was to go to the Railway Police Headquarters at Kilindini; the other to Whitehead, the District Officer. Standing there above the shoulders of the signaller and listening to the tap of the telegraph key he knew that this was defeat; the more bitter after the heady but illusory triumph in the ravine. The failure with the men was worse than the failure with the lions. He had earned not allegiance but disloyalty; not respect but hatred. This was the incredible truth. They wanted to kill him: they actually wanted to kill him.

7. *A View of the Lake*

On the fourth day of October 1898, George Whitehouse wrote a report. It was written on the shores of Lake Naivasha. Its destination was London and it was addressed to the Managing Member of the Uganda Railway Committee at the Foreign Office. The lake lay four hundred miles from the Indian Ocean. It was a place of solitude where cormorant beat from papyrus-islands and water-fowl rocked. The camp was pitched in the thorn thickets and from the tent, writing, Whitehouse could see the rim of the submerged crater which had made a crescent in the lake.

'I have the honour to report that I left Kilindini on September 18th in order to inspect the final location of the line down the Kikuyu Escarpment, and then to continue my journey on to Lake Victoria in order to select the route to be adopted and to decide where trial lines shall be surveyed. . . .'

This was the third week of the great adventure. He had seen it like that; a personal enterprise imbued with the true spirit of exploration. Since that night, three months back, when he had announced that he would investigate Blackett's report of a new route from the Rift to the Lake, a self-formed image had grown daily into heroic dimension. There were trails to blaze and maps to draw and lines to stake; a hundred nights of whispering thorn and tribal drums. From this chrysalis of peril and privation an invigorated man would emerge.

But it had begun badly. The caravan, its preparation and its departure, had coincided with the trial of Patterson's mutineers. Kilindini and the island had throbbed with curiosity. Something was happening at Tsavo: this band of sullen Asians and the gaunt colonel with the nervous tic were the outward signs of it. There had been an embarrassing interview with Crawford. The Consul, a man not renowned for a mellifluous tongue, had spoken at length to him and Patterson. Attempted murder was an ugly charge: some of the odium must cling to those concerned. These men were not criminals. They had come to East Africa to work. They were expatriates in a wild land. They were entitled to leadership; wise and benevolent, not harsh and tyrannical. Of course, they would be punished. The law prescribed that. They would go to the chain-gangs. The sanctity of the Bwana or, in this case, the Sahib (the voice had thinned with sarcasm), must be preserved. But the Government of India would be gravely displeased.

The caravan had entrained from Kilindini. Patterson had joined the train, sitting silently in his private cast of mortification for the whole journey. He had watched him. The man generated unease. The fingers worked on a brass cartridge-case, turning, tapping. In the middle of the Taru he had opened the window and flung the case violently into the wash of crystalline dust as if some spring of tension had suddenly snapped.

At Tsavo the colonel left the train, taking his silence, his dejection and his Gladstone bag toward the hut by the river-palms. Nothing had been arranged; no polite little ceremony of leavetaking, not a Godspeed or an ounce of tobacco or a book. The police and Whitehead's askari were still there. They stood in groups, the red fezzes vivid above their harness-leather faces. The train moved and they stared without interest or bent to spit carefully above the pipeclayed belts.

'. . . On my arrival at Nyrobi I received a report from Mr Blackett who had just completed a reconnaissance from Lake Nakuru to Ugowe Bay, and I at once telegraphed informing you that a possible route had been found, a copy of my telegram is now enclosed.

'A copy of Mr Blackett's report is also enclosed together with a tracing I have made from Lieut. Vandelmo's Map showing Mr Blackett's proposed route. I intend returning by this route and will then send you a further report on the general route to be adopted to the Lake. . . .'

He had reached Nyrobi on 26 September. There he found that Blackett, accompanied by Lieutenant Vandelmo, had already verified the route. The original claim was not only substantiated but supported by a wealth of data. Vandelmo's map was a cartographer's model, exquisitely detailed, as finely-drawn as a square of Mechlin lace. There were subtle gradations of colour, a geological key, heights and levels and a table of abbreviations in the lieutenant's careful script, even the location of tribes. To Whitehouse, bent over that incomparable map, it seemed that every tree and hummock, every pool and rock and volcanic cone between Nakuru and Ugowe Bay had been espied by Vandelmo—and faithfully recorded. He had seen the pride in the youthful face and, rolling the map, muttered a few words of praise.

But Blackett and Vandelmo had faced him with a dilemma. In Kilindini the expedition had begun as a duty. An alternative route to the Lake and a saving of one hundred and fourteen miles[1] was a matter of the highest political importance. The Government, under continuous pressure from the Opposition in respect of leaping costs and slowness of construction, would have grasped at so considerable a straw. Blackett's discovery merited personal verification. But with the production of the map and the report all justification for the long and expensive safari had suddenly vanished. Blackett was a surveyor of exceptional ability. Clearly the documents were reliable. Clearly he was obliged to turn the caravan for the coast.

But he had led it onward from Nyrobi.

He continued the report:
'. . . On September 29th I left Nyrobi in company with Mr Baas who will go through with me to the Lake and then take over charge as Superintendent of Works for Surveys between Naivasha and Lake Victoria.

'Mr Harrison who has been in charge of the Staking-out of the Line between Kikuyu and Longonot Saddle also accompanied me as far as Jabe Hill.[2] . . .'

[1] In practice a saving of seventy-five miles was achieved.
[2] Now Kijabe.

173

He finished it, signed it, attached it to the other documents and sealed them in an envelope. The envelope would go by runner from Naivasha to Nyrobi and then to railhead: by train to Kilindini: by ship to England.

He watched the lake from within the tent. It had moments of torpor in which nothing seemed to move and the life of water, fowl and insect was suspended. Baas crossed his line of vision. The intemperate face glared at him, then turned to the sun so that it gleamed like a red-veined leaf. Baas passed from sight. Ibis stood like stone water-ornaments.

He went from the tent into sun. The lake was a frieze from which ran the pale green plain; deep on the escarpment of the Mau the breast of Donyo Buru rose. Only the light moved, seeming to die in the black obsidian bosses of the mountain. This was solitude. Nothing had ever changed. In this timelessness self-deception stood apart like a shadow. He saw clearly that the adventure was, in part, an escape.

He began to walk; breaking, deliberately, the pattern of silence. A pair of cormorants came from the papyrus and he watched the thin, aligned prows parting the light. They crossed the western shore where volcanic debris lay dark-red like the lees of wine.

But Whitehouse was now committed. Whatever the motive he could not deny his own need; of solitariness, of time and space in which to think, of the greater personal dimension which the caravan would bring. He despatched the envelope. Then, marshalling the caravan, he led it from Naivasha.

More than forty miles lay between Naivasha and Nakuru; and it was here, at the third of the lakes that glittered on the floor of the Rift Valley, that he would meet the point of divergence. Six years back Macdonald had searched for an ascent from the Rift to the plateau above the Mau Escarpment. He had found it twenty miles beyond Nakuru. He had marked the route for the railroad. The line would climb to a height of 8,900 feet above sea-level, then wind across the plateau, descending, strike the head-waters of the Nzoia River and follow its valley, emerge at Berkeley Bay on the north-east tip of Lake Victoria. This, Macdonald insisted, must be the terminus for the railroad and the harbour for the Lake.

But Blackett's drawing took the line up the escarpment at a point much nearer to Nakuru and at a height six hundred feet lower than the summit level chosen by Macdonald: from there a train might steam by way of the valleys of Kedowa and Nyando, find the Lake at the head of Ugowe Bay.[1] Ugowe lay fifty land-miles below Berkeley Bay.

On the evening of the third day the caravan reached Nakuru. For men like Baas and Whitehouse these were fast marches, not walked but endured. Heat had poured into the trough of the Rift, was held there by low green cloud. At the end of each day it seemed that the heat lapped with the movement of oil, that the walls of the escarpments themselves tilted with fatigue. Baas, red of flesh and dissolving in sun and half-blind with glare, went to his tent at nightfall, ate alone and did not emerge until dawn. But for Whitehouse the ordeal had an obverse quality of pleasure. It was like a penance. Blisters and exhaustion and the spasms of enteric were the price he must pay for the escape. Perhaps the guilt would drain with the sweat.

Already he and Baas had established areas of inviolability. Each was an irritant to the other, like nettle to flesh. They touched—and recoiled. Whitehouse was a quiet man, preferring to walk in silence and to conserve even the energy required by speech. Baas distrusted silence. It made him uneasy. It was something to be broken. Through the long marches, after Nyrobi, Whitehouse listened to the monotonous voice. It began with the dawn, it discursed through the heats of day, it muttered over the fires of evening. Only night brought a respite. Baas, too, was a man who liked to display knowledge. He knew the Rift and its peoples, the country beyond, and the Lake. White-house knew none of it. He wanted to know; but through the medium of his own senses. Each turn of the path should have been a revelation: a new configuration of forest, plain and water, another aspect of beauty, another contour of a changing face. But Baas forestalled him. Baas had been here before. Baas knew. The path turned and the country opened—and it was all second-hand.

[1] Now known as the Kavirondo Gulf.

Baas was an ungainly man, heavy and rotund. He was a man of impulsive movement. And because of this he knocked things over. He collided. He spilled food and liquid. He upset the rickety folding-tables on which they ate their meals. He was a kicker of things and a maker of noise. Every stone or branch had to be kicked violently from his path. Every nullah with rock walls and a satisfying echo had to be disturbed with a clap of the hands or a powerful bellow. He threw stones so that they skated on the water of the lakes and detonated great explosions of birds into the air.

To Whitehouse, a man of gravity and deliberation, all this was intolerable. But between Naivasha and Elmenteita he had made an effort; to like Baas, to find a common ground, to lead him into paths of stillness and blessed silence. It had been unavailing. Baas became noisier and clumsier, more intrusive, more destructive.

They had withdrawn from each other. Contact was too inflammatory. They did not share a fire or a meal or a pipe. Whitehouse marched at the head of the column, Baas at the rear. They spoke rarely, and then only of technical matters. They learned not to trespass, to avoid meetings. Messages were conveyed through the headman and, distorted into bastard English, left small, ludicrous pockets of confusion in the mind.

Now, at Nakuru, another decision must be made. Whitehouse walked toward the water, away from the camp. He needed solitude in which to think. It was evening. The lake had none of the tranquillity of evening. There had been insufficient rain and it had drawn its hem from the banks to leave them grey with debris and bleached thickets of papyrus. From this dryness the wind took soda-dust and scattered it in clouds above the lake. He could taste the soda on his lips. Beyond the thickets a group of tribesmen stood. They had followed the caravan from Naivasha. They were emaciated. He watched them. They did not move. Their bellies had shrunk and they waited; for an end, for a deliverance. He did not know what that deliverance could be. He had offered food but, for some reason, they had refused. For him this was the true Africa; thin men with thin spears and hunger the only real inheritance.

His problem was the caravan route; from here, Nakuru. He was committed to the march to Lake Victoria, but not irrevocably committed to the route. The telegram and the written report had ensured that the railroad would drive along Blackett's new and shorter line of survey: that was unalterable. Therefore nothing could be gained by retracing Macdonald's march to Berkeley Bay. The longer march would merely delay his return to railhead and the twelve thousand men who were now poised behind it. All this he saw with clarity.

He watched the flamingos. The lake was still and each bird stood in the indigo of its own reflection. Bird-cry girdled the shores with its unbearable timbre of desolation. The waters of these silent lakes held a mirror to a man's motivations. The decision, perhaps, had already been made. By following Macdonald's route he could prolong the great adventure. And by emerging at Port Victoria on Berkeley Bay he would be reunited with his brother.[1]

Whitehouse turned for the camp. Wind was gathering and the soda-clouds came low across the lake. The soda on the lips was like the taste of guilt.

At sunrise the caravan marched further into the Rift. There was an hour of freshness in which the cold and the vapours of night clung. Then the trough filled with heat. Twenty miles lay between Nakuru and Macdonald's ascent of the Mau. Whitehouse had charged himself to reach that point before dusk: then, at dawn of the following day, he would lead them up the scarp.

These first hours of a march were good hours. Behind were the greying embers of the fires and the place where the camp had been, in front the new day and a destination and the changing land. Behind, too, was the song of the porters. It came in jubilant phrases, or in deep diapasons which were like fragments of a past flung from a man's throat to void him of its weight of

---

[1] Lieutenant B. Whitehouse, R.N., was attached to the garrison at Port Victoria. In this year of 1898 he was already making marine surveys of the northern shores of Lake Victoria prior to the official surveys (also undertaken by him) of 1899.

suffering. Whitehouse could not understand the songs; only that they were joys or revulsions, sunlit or dark, that they told of abundance and famine, of clear water and red meat, of the whip and the yoke. He marched and listened. Past and present fused. Speke and Livingstone had heard these rhythms, had gone like this into an antique land.

But soon the sky and the sun went white with heat and the singing stopped. Looking back across his shoulder at the column he saw the parted lips and the patina of sweat on the grape-dark flesh, heard their effort. Each of the burdens was sixty-five pounds, perhaps more for the strongest of them.

He could not see the walls of the escarpments. They were obscured by mist and cloud. But they oppressed him. Although the valley here was between thirty and forty miles in width there was a sense of enclosure. The walls were there; barriers to the railroad, to honours and ambition.

He had known from the beginning that the Great Rift Valley was the testing-ground. It was here that the railroad would falter, or die, or drive onward to the Lake. He had known this: but it had seemed remote. The first of the escarpments lay three hundred and fifty miles from the coast. That was a long way. The danger had had no shape or immediacy. He had dismissed it or minimised it. It was there. Every obstacle could be overcome: you could not be a rail engineer unless you believed that.

But with the laying of the track the Rift came nearer. Behind them was the thirst of the Taru, the lions of Tsavo. Ahead were the swamps of the Athi, perhaps the spears of the Masai. Beyond that was the Rift. Men like Preston and Turk began to talk of it, or it intruded in the memoranda of engineers and survey parties. They were walking into the coldness of a shadow.

Geologically he had understood it. East Africa was an immense plain. At one time, men said, it had been a forest from coast to coast. But time and the hand of man had diminished the forest; and with the passing of the forest had gone the rain. The forest-animals became plains-animals and men walked the yellow-grey deserts and the half-deserts and the eroding land and cursed their destiny and reviled their gods because there was not enough water. On this immensity of plain, on the map of it, you could lay the Y-shaped end of a stick so that the arms of the Y pointed north and the stem of the stick pointed south. This stick was the Rift Valley system. The left arm of the stick ran up into Equatoria and the Albert Nile: this was the West Rift. The right arm of the stick ran on the other side of Lake Victoria, between the Lake and Mount Kenia, and up into Ethiopia: this was the East Rift. The arms of the stick joined above Lake Nyasa, becoming a stem, and the stem ended south of the Zambesi. Within the furrow made by the stick, if the stick were sufficiently heavy, would lie many lakes; above them the scarps and the plateaux and the volcanic mass. All this, still on the map, was very clear.

But then he had seen it.

The plateau had risen since the plain of Kapiti. For sixty miles he had felt this ascent in the muscles of his thighs. Distance became bluer and deeper. Woods parted and there were valleys and ravines and horizons below the climbing land. The air seemed thinner. This was height: and all height must end in fall. The caravan reached the summit of Kikuyu. The eye saw sky. There was a feel of precipices. Here, his readings told him, was a level of more than seven thousand feet. He halted the caravan. Then, with Harrison, Baas and the headmen, Saidi and Rashedi, he went to the lip.

Below them, unshrouded, was the valley of the Eastern Rift. The lip was grizzled with scrub and, where the lip became cliff, the bushes had lost anchorage. He stood in the red scars of their rooting. The cliff fell in a series of jags and outcrops to the floor of the valley. He stared at this depth of brownness. A hawk came, turned on the air-current, plunged, accenting height. He looked again at the map. Here the fall to the valley was nearly three thousand feet. It was there on the map. It had always been there. It was marked on the surveys, described in the reports. But nothing had prepared him for this brown cliff which was like the face of a mountain, for birds which stood in space and made the mind reel with vertigo, for this terrible edge. Perhaps the Rift could not be expressed. It had to be felt with the senses. There was something here, a component of immeasurable age, which lived in silence and desolation. It brooded. The valley seemed to stretch into infinity. Some elemental force, perhaps the finger-nail of God, had gouged it out of the soft crust when the earth was formed. The hawk had gone and nothing moved in the valley. He knew that the Masai grazed their beasts here: but nothing moved. He searched, taking his eye across the valley floor where mist and silver leleshwa gleamed, across the Kedong to the wall of the Mau and the crater of Suswa; but there was nothing, not even the smoke-spiral of a herdsman's fire. He shivered. He was frightened. This was no place for trains.

Baas, of course, had broken the silence, kicking suddenly so that stones leapt into depth. He had turned at that, leading them from the crest of the scarp and along its lip. There was no end to the scarp. It went in tiers of forest and rock into a vagueness of brown and purple. He felt puny. He pointed to the escarpment. 'Down that,' he told Baas with incredulity, 'we have to send a train.'

The caravan had pitched camp on the plateau. Night came and the immense trough filled with darkness. It was there, tangibly like a mountain would be. It oppressed them. Wind soughed in it. None of the porters sang or quarrelled or told stories. Silence joined to silence. They ate without speaking, Baas apart from him. After they had eaten he opened his pack and spread his maps and documents in the light of the fire, trying to equate the data with the appalling hazard which lay out there in the blackness. Baas said nothing. Baas had known.

'From close to Fort Smith in Kikuyu (the relevant report said) the more difficult portion of the line commences. The route proposed emerges from the Kikuyu Forest, on the crest of the Kikuyu Escarpment, height 7,200 feet, at a point over-looking the upper part of the Kedong Valley, and due east of the noticeable extinct volcanic peak of Suswa. At this point the conformation of the escarpment lends itself most favourably to the descent of 1,400 feet into the meridional rift. The route proposed is roughly that of an old Swahili caravan road. The descent is composed of two main steps of 700 and 500 feet connected by a more uniformly sloping ledge, and the distance by rail will be about 13 miles . . .' This was an extract from Macdonald's findings and had been written into the Parliamentary Report of 1893. Even then it was known that Macdonald had been content to follow the old caravan routes, assuming (with some justification) that time and experience had beaten out direct paths to the Lake. And that had been true for most of the route. But they had also been paths of expedience. There were considerations other than the shortest possible distance between two points; of sweet water, of hostile tribes, of proximity to villages and plantations where slaves and food might be bought. All these had helped to draw the caravan roads. But foot caravans were not locomotives and rolling-stock. A railroad could not always follow in the track of man. A tender carried at least fifteen hundred gallons of water and that meant abundant reservoirs and well-sited tanks. A caravan, beyond the kindling for its fires, needed no fuel. But an engine had an inexhaustible hunger. Here, an engine of the ' F ' Class might use thirty-five pounds of English coal for every train-mile. Coal was scarce and expensive. Wood was cheap and plentiful. So wood must be the fuel. Wood had an evaporating power of only one-third that of coal, but its bulk was six times greater. In fact, an engine would eat one hundred pounds of wood in every train-mile. That meant frequent fuel dumps. Indeed, where wood was used, there was a maxim: every watering-station must be a fuel-station. Macdonald had not always recognised this need of wood and water. And here again were points of divergence.

In March of 1898, six years after Macdonald's march, there had been another survey. Macdonald's line down the Swahili path into the Rift had revealed alarming defects. Some of the sections of the track must inevitably run into gradients of extreme difficulty; and, moreover, the thirteen-mile descent would require two reversing-stations. The survey party had been charged to reconnoitre the Kikuyu escarpment, to find an alternative to Macdonald's route. At the end of the month the party reported. Eight miles north of the point where the captain's maligned caravan path dropped to the valley, was an easier descent.

Whitehouse had pinned the report to the survey of 1892. But he had treated it with reserve. Survey parties, he had learned to his cost, usually found that which was expected of them: they were determined to return with something positive and it was left to others, later, to find the failings. But, unquestionably, the descent must be examined. Macdonald's airy precipice had scared him. He had to decide. In the morning they would march the eight miles north along the escarpment; and hope.

The caravan arose at five o'clock, before dawn. Wind ran on the plateau and was white in the hearts of fires. He had gone to the edge of the escarpment. The darkness was absolute. He could not see the mountains or the valley, not even a summit ridge to define the sky. It was very cold. He waited until the first flux of light came with the greyness of pearl into the canyon, watched the land awaken.

At six the caravan began its march. Ahead at Eldama was an advance caravan and its two hundred loads of provisions, mainly wheat flour. Whitehouse led the column from the crest, following the escarpment ridge. He had checked his Dixie pedometer. Behind, lower on the plateau, were the juniper forests and the lightening sky.

After three hours of this northern march the pedometer told him that they had covered seven and one-half miles. The path had fallen perceptibly. Trees and rock formations parted and the floor of the Rift revealed itself, nearer. He judged that they had descended perhaps one thousand feet. At two hundred paces beyond the eighth mile he found the marker left by the survey party. He halted the caravan.

The valley lay two thousand feet below. Its mood had changed. It was softer. Colour had painted out the tones of desolation. A herd of antelope moved along the floor. He could see the apple-green growth along the course of the Kedong Stream[1] and, further north, the rock-blue slopes of Kijabe Hill. The air was clear and the lava terraces ran like cicatrices under the saddle of Longonot. There, in the Mountain of the Big Pit, the Masai claimed that giant serpents lived. The slope to the valley was thickly wooded. It was steep. A cattle track began near to the marker, descended and lost itself in the trees. He would have

[1] The Kedong Stream was at that time the eastern boundary of the Uganda Protectorate.

to clear those trees, he knew, before he could determine the gradient. The fear had not returned. The escarpment and the trough beneath it seemed less hostile. But this could be illusion; a product of warmth and the new tranquillity of the valley.

The caravan rested. Then he led it down the cattle track. Baas took frequent levels. The track ran obliquely, following the configurations of the slope. Sometimes he saw the valley and the distant Mau; sometimes, on the scarp, the lighter patches of bamboo forest with sunlight in the stems. No line could follow this cattle track, no train could descend these great declivities. It was absurd. The railroad would die, truncated, on the crest of the escarpment and the steels would overgrow with weed and men would stumble over them in the years to come and say: See, this is where the folly ended. The fear took possession again, entrenched now with the rising anger for the survey party. He reached the base of the wall trembling with fatigue and disappointment.

But at the bottom his engineering instinct returned. He studied the escarpment. There were cliffs—but there were also spurs. There were soft earthfalls—but there were also outcrops. And going north the scarp was gentler: still louring and fraught with danger, but noticeably gentler. Above, where the cattle track began, you could cut a marker for the line (if it ever reached there) at around Mile 360. The survey party had marked the base of the Kikuyu incline at Mile 373.[1] That was a measure of the hazard: thirteen miles to achieve a descent of under two thousand feet. But it might be done. It would still be a mountain railway. The train would have to claw its way by slant and re-entrant angle, tack like a ship and crawl like a snail. But it might just be done.

This shuttlecock of alarms and optimisms had left him empty of energy. The noonday heat was building. Already somnolence touched the mind. He ordered them to pitch camp. It was a good place. There was water, shelter and game-meat. In the morning they would march through the Rift and into the blue hazes of the Lakes, march where the train would gather speed to recoup the time lost on the scarp, watch the broad white stalk

[1] The base of Kijabe Hill.

183

of steam and hear the rails sing . . . But this was the stuff of dreams. The Rift was silent under the pall of prehistory. Preston's railhead lay one hundred and seventy miles behind them, somewhere near Makindu.

That was at Kijabe, where they had left Harrison and his staking-out party. Here, marching between Nakuru and the opposite wall of the Rift, the next great obstacle was the escarpment of the Mau. It grew with the march, emerged from its nebulous mass into tiers of forest and lava-rock. It frowned. It dominated. Whitehouse's new confidence began to evaporate. As a barrier it looked insuperable. The Mau rose to over ten thousand feet; and Blackett's route climbed to within two thousand feet of the summit. Macdonald's went even higher. From here in the valley the forest seemed unbroken.

Captain Pringle, one of Macdonald's henchmen, had written of it:

'No living thing is to be seen; there is darkness and a great silence, decay and death, everywhere. The actual summit of Mau here is 10,100 feet. It is cold and damp in proportion to the height, a dense grey mist hangs over the forest, morning and evening, and it is not until late in the day that the sun succeeds in struggling through. . . .'

But the sun left the crowns of those ancient trees before Whitehouse had reached the point of ascent. No caravan marched twenty miles in a day, Saidi told him patiently. The Rift had been there for a million years: it would still be there in the morning. Whitehouse made camp. They had walked twelve miles from Lake Nakuru.

On the fourth day the caravan reached Eldama Ravine and joined with the advance party. The ravine lay one thousand feet above the level of Nakuru. Of this Macdonald and the subsequent Report had said:

'This ravine is 200 feet deep and 600 feet across; the sides are very steep and clad with a network of small trees, creepers and undergrowth; at the bottom flows a small but rapid stream. . . .

'. . . the line, passing through generally thick forest country, reaches the Eldama Ravine at the foot of the Mau Escarpment. The bridge over this Eldama Ravine is a noticeable feature of the line, and the largest bridge. It cannot, however, be economically avoided, and by boldly bridging it a comparatively easy descent of the formidable Mau Escarpment is obtained. . . .'

Whitehouse examined the ravine and the site of Macdonald's proposed bridge. He was appalled. This would have been no ordinary bridge. The cost would have been enormous, the time for its construction an impediment to the progress of the railroad. Alarm became relief. There need be no bridge across the Eldama: Blackett's discovery had seen to that.

At sunrise began the long climb up the scarp. From Nakuru to Eldama the slope from the level of the lakes had been gentle. But now, following the great rampart which determined the southern drainage of the Neriote River, the path made height in a series of sharp gradients. The caravan rounded the Elerobi spur, reached the head of the ravine at midday. This was the highest point of Macdonald's abortive route; and it was here, at an elevation of 8,700 feet, that the tents were pitched. The wing of the forest grew thickly. But, Rashedi told them, there was a point a few hundred feet above where, if the day was clear, they could see the Great Lake.

At dawn Whitehouse went with Rashedi. On the crest of the hill they waited for the light to strengthen, for the sun to suck mist from the plateau and the plains of the west. It was very cold. Below, the forest ended abruptly and the grass, greening now in sunlight, ran in immense meadows, into purple, into distance. There, behind the mist and perhaps one hundred miles distant, Rashedi said, lay the north-east tip of the Lake. The mist dissolved. Something bright at the limit of vision, like a platter of translucent white glass, spread undefined between land and sky. It was a radiance; no more than that. But this was the Nyanza. 'I could have wept,' Whitehouse wrote later. 'It was as if it had never really existed until then, as if I had never before believed it to be there. But there it was, or a bit of a gleam from it, I was glad I had come.'

After this sight of the Lake's reflected light, this suggestion of water which was as ephemeral as a mirage, the caravan made good time. Perhaps it drew and accelerated them. Or, simply, the land declined and eased the marches. The Mau broke into the ranges of Kamasia and Elgeyo, forming a valley. White-house led through the valley: and from Elgeyo began the true descent to the Lake. The caravan reached the head-waters of the Nolosegelli in two marches; and, four days later, the river. Westward was the Guaso Ngishu (the country of rivers and cattle): from these red and treeless plains grew the Three Hills of Nandi. Near to the camp the Nolosegelli, as is the way with African rivers, changed its name to the Guaso Masa, and twenty miles further west (that is two marches) the Masa joined with the Nzoia River. This was the river which ran from its valley, through the country of Kavirondo and the Samia Hills, into the Lake at Berkeley Bay.

Port Victoria, the railroad terminus chosen by Macdonald, lay in the north-east corner of the Lake at a point in the bay between the mouths of the Sio and Nzoia Rivers. The caravan reached Port Victoria on 23 October 1898; and it was there that Whitehouse found his brother.

For Whitehouse this was a day of great emotion. Here at last was Victoria Nyanza. Five years had passed since he had learned that his was to be the task of bringing rail to the greatest of the African lakes. During those years his mind had encompassed nothing else. The Lake was too large, too steeped in history and the myth of exploration to admit of other things. The Lake occupied him, overflowed, it seemed, from the spring of his own ambition. He was of course in bondage to it. Failure of the railroad meant failure as a man: for him nothing would lie beyond. He, and others, would drown in the enormity of the failure. Conversely, success meant professional and public honour.

The Lake was much more than a terminus for a railroad. It had long had a mystical place in the imagination, exciting many of the Great Explorers and those that sent them on their strange and wonderful journeys. An aura of cruelty lay on its southern shores: to these beaches the early Arab slavers had come from

186

Kazeh. It was romantic: only forty years had passed since Speke came to Mwanza and saw for the first time this vastness of water. It was beautiful: behind the tawny beaches the land was exuberant with palms, mangoes and flamboyants. It was malignant: the northern shore was infested by the mosquito, the spirillum tick and the tsetse, and in the groves and islands lived death and desolation. It was unpredictable: it oppressed with its gloom and sullenness and turbidity, it enticed with its colour, it disturbed with its scent of barbarism, it beguiled with its serenity, it frightened with its sudden moods of violence and the electric storms that charged the water with power and turned it black as pitchblende. And, of course, it was the fountain of the Nile. Across the isles and promontories of sedge, papyrus and euphorbia, perhaps fifty miles from Port Victoria, were the cataracts of the Ripon Falls. From there the Nile leapt, and broadened, and became a perfect river. The Lake was no docile basin of water. It was a force: a secret and a mystery: the source of life and fertility.

Whitehouse was deeply affected by the sight of it. From here in Berkeley Bay he could not see, or gauge, its size. The bay was enclosed; by the promontory of Usoga to the west, and by the Samia Hills to the east. South was the island of Masinga. But this lapping of blue water was a hem of the Lake. Out there the Lake would be a sea, and there would be nothing but horizons between sea and sky. He walked through the sedge, bent and allowed the water to touch his hands. The gesture was slightly absurd. No steam had yet been brought to the Lake and railhead was nearly four hundred miles behind him. He had merely trekked here at the head of a caravan. This was not the time for a symbolic act.

The garrison had once been a trading outpost. Near to it, at the head of a creek, Whitehouse was reunited with his brother. This was the second emotional luxury of the day. Lieutenant Whitehouse was his junior by several years, thin, fair and as straight as a cadet, already yellowed with the malaria which was to plague him in the future and cause such grave delay to his survey of the Lake. They embraced, exchanged tobacco and family news, sat in the sun to enjoy their reunion. He had been in Port Victoria for five days, the lieutenant explained. There was no confirmation of his appointment[1] as Lake Surveyor; but already he had made small, unofficial surveys in native craft. And he was building, or rather assembling, a boat.

Whitehouse went with him to where the creek ended in a curdle of mud. There were tents, fires, a lashed scaffold of iron poles and, beneath the scaffold, the hull of a steel boat. Three Kavirondo were working on it. They were splendid blacksmiths, the lieutenant said. They were black, naked and primitive: yet they mined ore in the hills, smelted it in charcoal furnaces, produced first-rate tools and weapons. Their wire was as good as the coast *senengè*. They were intrigued by the steel boat. Its plates and parts had been brought (like those of all the early Lake vessels) six hundred miles overland from the coast on the heads of porters. Without doubt the boat, which he had grandiosely christened *Vice-Admiral* and which would weigh a mere ten tons, would sail tomorrow.

And so it had been. In the morning the *Vice-Admiral* plied in the reaches and around the islands of Berkeley Bay. It was a day of stillness and luminous hazes. Nothing moved except the hippo-schools. Static lightning built in the west in washes of evil blue pigment and heavy scents came on the hot airs from the shore. They felt the power and primitiveness of the Lake. They took their soundings and made their notes and spoke little.

There was no especial significance in these soundings. They were part of a general plan of survey, would eventually be incorporated in the lieutenant's report on the British lake-and-lakeside geography. Whitehouse noted that the bay was deep and sheltered, trailed his hand idly in the water and reflected that, were it not for Blackett's new and shorter route to Ugowe, this indeed would be a perfect harbour for the Uganda steamers.

He had planned to lead the caravan across country from Port Victoria to Ugowe Bay; and there to begin the march back to railhead, reconnoitring Blackett's route. But now a delicious

[1] It was not until June of the following year that the Treasury sanctioned the cost of a survey of the British area of the Lake and appointed Lieutenant Whitehouse (with rank of Commander) its Surveyor.

prospect beckoned. The *Vice-Admiral* was trim and watertight. He had joined his brother and, in the joining, found a harmony and an inner peace. And the balms of this tropical sea were in his nostrils: he was reluctant to leave it. He decided to follow the north-east shore in the steel boat, down from Berkeley Bay to Ugowe Bay. By so doing he would stay with his brother, stay with the Lake—and rid himself of Baas.

At sunrise of 25 October he watched Baas and the caravan begin the march across country to Ugowe. The march, he estimated, would occupy at least five days. He need not rendezvous before then. That gave him five days of release. The railroad had never seemed so distant. At noon the *Vice-Admiral* headed for the mouth of the bay, for the open water of the Lake. He sat in the bows. Behind him in the boat were the lieutenant, two Kavirondo, four armed Swahilis, their packs, food and equipment.

Those five days were among the happiest in his life. Time lost significance: it was measured in climbing and vertical and dying suns, in the need for food or sleep. He learned the moods of the Lake, and reflected them. Mostly the Lake was languid and he saw it through the half-closed eyes of inertia. Sometimes, when the storms came, the dusk went black with menace and there was always a drum and the throb of it entered the blood and enfevered it and drove him on restless walks through the rain and darkness of the shore. The nights were good, he smoking and the fire bright with wind and the lieutenant drawing his careful charts in lamplight. In the mornings the boat wandered further down the coast and they mapped its curves and inlets and its beaches of yellow sand and sedge.

The existing maps were wrong. That became quickly obvious. Nobody had bothered much with these north-eastern shores, the lieutenant said. Marine survey was not a function of the old Charter Company, the present garrison was land-bound, and the explorers had been too excited with the sources of the Nile to concern themselves with unimportant gulfs. They redrew the maps. There was a pleasure in this, a sense of contribution: and it justified the trip. On the sixth day they reached Ugowe Bay. Forty miles in, at its extremity, was the mouth of the Nyando

River: there would be the terminus for the railroad and the port for the steamers.

Macdonald had prepared a map of Ugowe Bay on his survey expedition of 1892. It had been drawn with his customary impatience and, indeed, bore little relation to the shore-line of this broad blue gulf down which the *Vice-Admiral* now made its way. At sundown they reached the Nyando. There was no sign of Baas and the caravan.

In the morning they began a boat reconnaissance of the north-east tip of the gulf. And it was then that the happiness of those last few days was quickly effaced. Whitehouse felt the first light touch of dismay. The inlet was dangerously shallow. That afternoon they took further soundings. By evening their depression was complete. There was no tidal movement to give the water rise, nothing (except a narrow area to the north) to relieve the shallowness.

They ate in silence. Then the old expedition survey reports were produced, spread on the folding-table and examined in the light of the lamp. Of Ugowe Bay Macdonald had written:

'The lake shores are low, fringed with a dense growth of papyrus, and, except on the north side, extremely shallow. A Berthon boat was launched and soundings taken around the coast. At one place a depth of 6 feet of water was found at 20-30 yards from the shore. A suitable landing-place and good anchorage for light-draught steamers exists nearby. A curious fact about the lake is that the water in the evening is usually from 3 to 6 inches higher than in the morning; this gives an appearance of tidal action, but is due to the breeze, which always blows in strongly from the lake towards evening. . . .'

Read in context and submerged in the balance of the report the paragraph seemed not unfavourable to Ugowe Bay. The language was neutral. But dissected and aligned with the afternoon's experience its dispraising note became apparent. Only six feet depth was gained in ninety. The harbourage was suitable —but only for light-draught steamers. This hardly accorded with the purposes of the grand Imperial venture, that is the tapping of the trade and produce of Uganda. But, of course,

Macdonald had thought nothing of Ugowe Bay. He had discarded it. He had chosen Port Victoria on Berkeley Bay.

Obviously, the lieutenant interpreted, Macdonald had been right after all. He had taken a long route but he had emerged, fortuitously, at the right place. The steamers of the future needed the deep waters of Berkeley Bay. The object of the exercise was the link with Uganda; and without heavy cargo-ships the link was weakened. Port Victoria was the proper harbour. The price, in effect, was a hundred miles of extra track.

Whitehouse's state of mind may be imagined. Gone was the tranquillity of the Lakeside expedition. There was only a whirl of regrets and resentments. If he had stayed at Kilindini or with the line, if he had confined himself to a study of the escarpments, if he had kept a cautious silence until all the data was collated, if Blackett and Vandelmo had taken soundings at the end of the route, and, above all, if only he had not sent the despatch from Nyrobi . . . A decision had to be made, but he was too much in conflict to make it that night. He went to his sleeping-bag.

In the morning, before dawn, he walked alone along the shore. The Lake was nearly four thousand feet above sea-level and he shivered in the sunless cold. The sun came and with it the water-carriers across the inlet. He watched them. They had seen him and they stared, unmoving. In that faint, opalescent light, the legs in mist and the gourds touched with sun, they had the faded immobility of an old cave-painting. The scene was beautiful and timeless.

Knowledge brought responsibility. He had been to Port Victoria: he knew now that that was the place for the terminus. He could not escape the fact: he could only disguise or conceal it. But what to do? Nothing political was simple. The Foreign Office had received a telegraph and a report; the jubilant news that the railroad was not going to Port Victoria, that the Treasury was presented with a saving of more than one hundred miles in track.

His duty was to recant. But who would thank him? The Government would be discomfited. Labouchère would use it as another weapon against the railroad. And, for him, it would be

191

a public confession of error. He made his decision. The railroad must drive over Blackett's route to Ugowe Bay. The steamers were not his concern. He was a railroad engineer, not a marine surveyor. The shallowness of the bay would be a problem of the future; a matter of piers and dredging or even a branch-line to Berkeley Bay.

He would say nothing.

8. The Dogs of Kali

After Makindu, Ronald Preston built two bridges; across the Kiboko and the Kifaru Streams. Since Kibwezi, that place of blackwater, ill-health had smouldered in railhead camp. The 'Kibwezi Fever,' as it was known, lay quiescent for a week or two: then, at Makindu, it revived. One half of the labour burned in sickness in the hospital-tents. The line went slowly. '. . . the nights were made hideous by myriads of mosquitos,' Preston recorded, 'and it was by the banks of the Kiboko that the fever laid us all out completely.'

At Kifaru they regained their strength. The sick parades grew shorter. The bridge went well: but there were derailments between Kiboko and Kifaru and, during that respite in which the wooden ties were replaced by steel, Preston roamed the sanseviera country north of the railroad as far as the Salt River. These were expeditions of recovery; trekked through the humidities of November, through the mud of the short rains, until he had sweated out the heats and sediments of the fever, cleansed himself in effort and the strong white air of the scrub. He shot without pity, because this was another kind of fever which would cool only in some distant satiation.

After the bridging of the Kifaru the track ran from bush into the open savannas of Simba. Simba, as the name implies, was the Place of Lions. They had come from the dark of Tsavo through a hundred miles of thick thornbush, of tsetse and mosquito. Here were luminous plains and, when the raincloud parted, a sight, sixty miles south, of the cap of Kilimanjaro. Wind moved on the plains. It was like a lightening of the mind. '. . . we always referred to Simba as the Fresh Air Camp,' Preston wrote. Here, too, he saw the migrations of the game for the first time. The spectacle moved him. '. . . from the crest of the hill I saw game in thousands, and all heading in the same direction, that is towards the Tanganyika border . . . magnificent spectacle . . . the grand animal trek . . .' For a time, it seems, this revelation of an immemorial pattern affected him. It touched the edge of perception, perhaps with guilt. He saw, and was disturbed.

At this time of Simba a thousand men were under canvas at railhead camp. After three days the rain came in deluge. Flood-water moved through the camp. The storm abated. 'Then,' Preston says in language biblical in its tone of catastrophe, 'lo and behold, from every hole and crevice in the ground, came forth in their thousands, scorpions . . .' The scorpions were collected in buckets and destroyed. At noon of the next day, on 23 November, George Whitehouse limped into railhead at the fore of the caravan. This was the end of the foot-safari. He had followed Blackett's route from Ugowe Bay.

That night Whitehouse sat by the camp-fire with Preston, Florence and Dr Orman, his pen poised above Lieutenant Vandelmo's map. The naming of the terminus on Ugowe Bay still exercised him. He was not a conceited man: it did not occur to him that his own name, that of the railroad's Chief Engineer, might fairly be used. Preston was talking; of the wash-away at Kibwezi where the rails had been suspended above a void, of places where ants, crushed to a syrup by the wheels, had brought engines to a standstill, of deaths in derailments and from disease and snakebite, of the scarcity of firewood here on the plains of Simba, of locomotives that went shortwinded on certain woods. Listening, Whitehouse remarked again the change in Preston, the hardening of the man and the growing in stature. He was wilder, darker-skinned, longer in the hair and moustache. In fact, he was becoming like Turk. Perhaps only wild men could bring rail through a wilderness. Preston was the obvious candidate for the honour. There were many men senior to him but none with the strength and the enterprise to thrust the rail to the Lake. Railhead was always a special case. Behind it was the line, a tenuous link with the coast. But in front there was nothing; and it was this area of nothingness where only a caravan or a stake-out party had stumbled that exacted something from a railhead engineer. There were always challenges, always decisions, always despairs. Each day presented its own separate and identifiable task.

But the naming was not that simple. The railroad, like any other organisation, was a hierarchy. You could not shuffle it, or accord privilege or distinction outside its careful grading, without a consequence. That could be resentment or jealousy. He discarded Preston's name with regret; and in doing so saw the movement of Florence Preston's stiff black skirts, the white gleam of the bust. She seemed, now, inseparable from her husband, always there, bringing femininity and the faint smell of lavender to those sweating camps. He smoothed the map. Then, without impulsiveness, he wrote against the inlet the name Port Florence.[1]

Later the fire was rebuilt and more men encircled it. There was desultory talk. Then, in a silence in which they heard the bark break in flame and fall, a man asked wistfully if they could hear about the Lake. There were murmurs of applause. Faces animated, took warmth which was not of the reflection of flame. The Lake was important to them. It was still unreachably distant. They wanted it brought nearer, out of mirage, given tangibility. Whitehouse had known this yearning. He understood it. He had no gift of narrative or the tongue for a vivid phrase. He had felt the essence of the Lake but he could not express it. He began to talk, searching for the words which might evoke its elemental force, the limpid waters which became charged with power and the feel of something living and palpable in the depths, the scents which came sweet as myrrh with the dusk and the air of old sorceries which came with the fall of night. He told of the peoples that lived or wandered on the road to its shores; of the Masai shepherds who spat in their hands as a greeting and of the Nandi who killed their sheep by compressing the noses until they died by suffocation, of the Manyemi whom men said were cannibal and prized above all the buttocks of a young girl. He talked until the words dried. They listened and were grateful.

Rashedi brought him tea. He drank. They did not speak,

[1] Now Kisumu.

holding to that imperfect image of the Lake and the lands about it. Their silence gave him pleasure. Then, in that silence and behind the tap of Florence's knitting-needles and the lisp of crickets, they heard the call of a lion. It was distant, hollow like a sound from a cavern. Preston turned to Whitehouse. He was reminded of something. The man-eaters of Tsavo, he said casually, had returned.

At Tsavo the dark and elemental forces, passive for some months, suddenly gathered themselves and descended on the camp with theatrical effect. Since the punishment of the mutineers there had been no further trouble. Patterson, mortified by Crawford's reprimand, had made an attempt to relax. The little red book was no longer produced. The daily courts were suspended. The lions had gone. The bridge grew and the workings along the permanent way made progress. All this contributed to a period of calm. Patterson's hunger for man-eaters' hides was of course unappeased. He was still dejected, still turned against himself by that curious dichotomy of mind the effect of which was to yearn for their return—and to fear for those who must suffer by it.

Of the scavengers only Paul Verschoren, the Sikh and his son remained. They were convinced that the lions were neither dead nor permanently absent. Evidently Patterson was similarly convinced; for during the lull he built a trap. It was a marvellous trap, made with sleepers and steel rail and chains. It was divided into two compartments, one for bait and one for the quarry. It was camouflaged by the pitching of a tent across it, and enclosed by a thorn hedge. A hole was left in the hedge to entice the lion. The entrance to the trap (to which the colonel refers quaintly as 'the lion's doorway') would be closed by the action of a spring within the cage. Robert Turk scoffed at it. 'These were lions—not mice,' he wrote.

There had been attacks by lion or leopard at other sectors of the line. Between May and October of that year two men had been taken at railhead and three at Engomani—a small fuelling station ten miles from the Tsavo River. But these losses were predictable. The line was an invasion, bringing men, machines and explosive into vast areas where only the wild life and the tribes lived. Things were disturbed, old laws and patterns of survival were broken, that which was new was hostile. But there was nothing concerted, nothing so primed with malevolence as the attacks by the Tsavo lions.

On 17 November the killing began again. Many of the coolies had left the airlessness of the tents to sleep on the ground. From one of those groups a man was taken; and, beyond the sounds of hysteria and the shots of the jemadars and the fence of thorn, the man was eaten.

That day Patterson wrote to Whitehead, the District Officer. The letter invited Whitehead to come to Tsavo 'to assist me in my campaign against the lions'; and, significantly, to bring with him as many askari as he could spare. Now, askari were native soldiers: they were not normally employed in the killing of marauding lions. In requesting them Patterson showed an underlying motive. The September troubles and the attacks on his life had left him hyper-sensitive. He knew that the tension had relaxed mainly because the lions withdrew. Now, with the death of the coolie, an undertow of fear had already begun to move through the camps. He was afraid: the temper of these frightened men must surely rise. The askari were a precaution.

During that night a man was killed and eaten at a camp two miles down the line. Moving from the river and following the line under the mists of the early day Turk found the scarred pugs of the old lion and a scrap of loincloth. Groups of silent men watched. Some were peasants from the hill-villages and the valleys of north-west India: they had known the walk of the tiger, the fear of it was inbred. The fear would spread. Turk went with the Suk, leaving the line and going with the drag into the scrub. Further, they found where the lion had eaten a meal; and further still, in a nullah where a stream ran and the rocks were bright with fern, the head and a shin-bone and a knot of purple viscera. The lion had eaten and drunk. Turk climbed to the lip of the nullah, stared across the watercourse to where the scrub grew up in long shelves of leaf and shadow. Nothing moved and the webs of spiders were unbroken, still crystalline with rain. He turned, went down the rock: then, on impulse or from instinct, he turned again and saw its great heraldic head and the dark of its mane and it was behind the webs so that the face seemed to glitter and then, watching it and unmoving, he saw that the face was old, worn and fissured like something of stone that has been beaten by time and weather, but beautiful with its sense of age. This encounter in the quiet of the nullah and only the rill of water to sound and he unmoving and without impulse to kill was something that he could not afterward explain. He watched it go, heavy with age, into the tunnels of vegetation. Later, with the moment of innocence behind them, he would have to kill it.

There were three tented camps to the east of the central Tsavo camp, and two to the west. The camps lay within a radius of fifteen miles of Patterson's headquarters. All these camps, including the one at the pivot, were visited by lion in the following week; and at each of the camps Patterson spent an uncomfortable night up a tree. At no time did the visits of the lions and Colonel Patterson coincide. At the end of the week five coolies had been eaten and the colonel was in a state of nervous exhaustion. The work on that sector of the railroad was slowly paralysed. The bridge hung jagged on the river. The men were sullen. Patterson had become almost completely arboreal and was seldom seen except as a haggard face half-concealed in foliage. On the eighth day he abandoned the tree-hides. He was desperate: he took to the ground. 'I spent many a weary day crawling on my hands and knees through the dense undergrowth of the exasperating wilderness around us . . .' Only the wash-leather gloves, the knee and elbow pads and the Norwegian boots made these ordeals endurable.

In this, the second week of the terror, Patterson received a telegraph from Whitehouse in Mombasa. All offers of bounty for the deaths of lion were withdrawn. Patterson posted news of the withdrawal. The Sikh and his son, deprived of further profit, went. But Paul Verschoren remained. Sickness and degeneration had so disordered him that he had long forgotten the money motive which had brought him to Tsavo. He lived in the bush — this was his home. For some unremembered reason lions were his enemies and he would have to kill them. The lice and the worm would multiply. He would rot and die. That was all he knew. Sometimes the massive body lurched into the camp, stinking of graves and animal blood and powdered with the red dust of Tsavo and the voice would plead or shout for flour or a knife or a jar of tobacco; and men, recoiling in nausea or perhaps turned by pity, would give these things to him.

In that week toward the end of November the short rains ended. The rains had brought refreshment to brains febrile with heat and fear. But now the land dried and became breathless and the river fell so that its banks were black and odorous and the miasmas of it rose and hung on the camp in lustres of evil green light. It had always been like this, at the river and in that month; and there would be no respite until the light grass-rains of February. But to those simple men the land was marked with omens. Something was gathering.

Patterson watched them. He knew the signs. They were meeting at night, talking themselves into desertion and mutiny. He doubled the guards, armed the senior men, dispensed a few extra rations. He listened for the exhaust-beats of the daily train, waited for the great cowcatcher to sweep around the loop in the line. But Whitehead and his askari were never aboard. The letter had not been acknowledged: pride forbade him to repeat it.

Two Swahilis were taken toward the end of that month; one near Engomani and the other from the small stone-masons' camp to the west of the bridge. Then, on 28 November, a Punjabi was dragged from a tent and eaten by the river. These were the recorded deaths. During those four days one Teita and three Kamba tribesmen were killed. 'Natives,' Turk notes, 'were employed by the U.R. on simple jobs like water-carrying and wood-cutting and bush-clearance. But they were never on the Roll & they had no names, they were paid in wire or knives or food, a lot of them died at Tsavo but nobody knew how many or cared for that matter . . .'

The nights were now hideous. They were resonant with the calls of lion, then ominously silent when the stalking began. In these silences men passed into the ultimate areas of fear. They waited. They listened. The walls of the tents glowed from the outside hurricanes and they watched the fragile drapes for the movement of shadow. Sometimes a lizard or a moth passed down the glass of the hurricanes and a shape like a thing from an ancient bestiary spread on the canvas and a man would break from his cast of fear and cry out. Old terrors, entrenched for centuries, were in those cries. Violent end had always come from the night; the dogs of Kali, the lions of Tsavo—evil had a thousand disguises. In the silences a man invariably died and the sound of his dying leapt through the camps like a sudden wind and was gone. At dawn they came from the tents into cold green light. This was another day: but behind it was a wing of darkness and another night.

After the death of the Punjabi, three men went to Patterson. They were Purshotam Purmar, Mohammed Din and Amir Bux. Purshotam was their spokesman. All men agreed that the lions were devils, he said; but even devils could be attacked. Why had nothing been done? Why had the beautiful steel trap not been used? Where were the hunters and the soldiers? Where was the poison-bait? The men could not work under this threat of terrible death. They begged for protection. They *demanded* it. The Sahibs were safe in their fine strong tents and their timber huts. But the men lay on the earth under thin tents which could be ripped with the touch of a claw. The Pathans were murmuring, fingering their knives. Frightened men were desperate men. . . . Patterson listened. He, too, knew desperation. He was thin with strain. The nervous tic had returned and his cheek jerked under Purshotam's stare. He had asked for help, he told them, but none had come. He had built a trap, but where were the volunteers? Purshotam had smiled with insolence. Were there not white men to bait the trap? Was not white flesh of a succulence and of a quality superior to Asian? Bux and Din muttered agreement. They had left, pulling at their beards in unease.

Whitehead's telegraph came at noon of the following day. A Teita messenger had been taken in the night and men stood in frightened groups around the admin. office. He had been up-country, the telegraph said: he had a District Court on 1 December and he would reach Tsavo on the evening of 2 December. Patterson read the message from the steps of the hut.

Then he took it around the gangs. He mounted rocks or trucks or piled sleepers and declaimed in that patriarchal voice so beloved of the Sahib ('I have good news, my children . . . The soldiers are coming, in three more days . . .') He was of course immensely relieved. They would not mutiny or murder in the presence of askari.

That night, the last of November, the lions came with such concentration of purpose, such precision of attack that terror ran through the camps like fire in wind. To those cowering men it seemed that the wilderness had gathered and then deployed its forces wholly along that area of the Tsavo River. A pair of lions broke through the thorn hedge at Tsavo Station, shredded a tent and ate a coolie within twenty yards of the fence. Lower, at the stone-masons' camp, the old lion came, tore the leg from a Kamba in a tree and chewed it under the founting blood of the man's artery. Upstream, where the quarry was, the rock-walls echoed with calls and the ledges moved with descending shapes. Something broke that night and men were released from the paralysis of fear and they screamed and fired their rifles and beat their mess-cans as if noise were a refuge. Six Punjabis walked to the river and stood until sunrise with the stroke of water at their throats, preferring its cold and its blackness and its unseen life to the compounds where the lions stalked. Hysteria flared and was thrown from man to man and tent to tent and Dalgairns, the Permanent Way Inspector, ran from his hut and knelt on the earth and emptied magazine after magazine into the dark and prayed in a high, preacher's voice for deliverance. This was the terror by night and pagan gods wheeled like bats in the night-sky.

When the sun had climbed and they had eaten and the warmth of the sun had restored them they gathered about Purshotam and listened. They were eager for leadership, for any kind of positive act which would relieve them. The Hindus were now convinced that the forces of destruction were loose, that the dogs of Kali were baying in the skins of lions. The Muslims had sufficient fear to align them with the Hindus. Purshotam felt their unity. Tomorrow, he told them, the soldiers were coming. But what did this signify? Soldiers could not kill devils. But soldiers could impose disciplines. Soldiers could be gaolers. Soldiers, as the Sahib well knew, could keep them here at the Tsavo camps. Today, he said with emphasis, was the last opportunity of escape.

Patterson returned in the afternoon. He had found the remains of a kill but no lion. The camp was silent when he entered, the men assembled and the faces still marked with the memory of the wild night. Each man had tied together his tent, his tools, his blanket and his cooking-pots. Purshotam, Bux and Din came forward. Behind them were some two hundred and fifty men from Tsavo Station, and half as many from the five outlying camps. Purshotam gestured at the gathering. All these men, he said, were leaving Tsavo. This was a place of death. There were many such places in the world: the goddess of destruction came down from the sky like a bird and took her fill and there was no defeating her—only escape. Bux and Din muttered assent. Patterson, too, nodded in agreement. These were situations he understood. They involved grave discussion and hyperbole and flights of sonorous language. There was a form, and sometimes the language was a resolution in itself. It was true, he said, that the goddess had called out her dogs. But she would become sated. She would leave. And were not honour and courage important to a man? Flight diminished a man. Would it not be better to finish the bridge and move away from Tsavo to railhead?

Din smiled sourly. They would not wait to see, he said. There had been a vote. It was decided. In ninety minutes the material-train from railhead would stop for refuelling. They would board it. They would go to Voi where they would be safe. The coolies murmured, nodded violently; and at that point Patterson lost control. Turk and Dalgairns were watching from the admin. hut. 'He got in a terrible temper,' Turk records. 'He started to shout and rave at them.'

They listened to that harsh and trembling voice. Safe? it asked them: they would never be safe from the Government's anger. They would be charged with desertion. They would be sent to the chain-gangs . . . Purshotam interrupted him. Desertion? he asked with contempt. They were not in the British Army. They were employees. They had contracts. They were entitled to protection. They had come to work on the railroad— not to fill the bellies of lions.

Patterson knew he had lost. This was another in the series of personal failures: the graves of coolies and the jagged bridge would be his only monument. He would not plead. He stared at them in the deepening afternoon sunlight, wiped his lips, touched his brow with a child's gesture of bewilderment. Then he went to the signal hut. There he sent a telegraph to Mtito Andei, thirty miles uptrack. The material-train, he instructed, must be stopped, fuelled and watered: then it must steam through Tsavo without halt. He also sent Dalgairns to the signal post. No man must be permitted to tamper with the signal.

The train came toward dusk. They heard it on the river-wind, saw its steam break in the distant tree-line. The message of the signal and Dalgairns and his cocked rifle were plain to see. The night was near, falling like a drape. Fear of the night sent them plunging to the rails to crouch or lie, to feel the vibrating steel, cheeks and hands on steel and the engine coming, to wait without power of movement because the night was near and even the wheels were better than the darkness of Tsavo. Shutt saw them, these bundles of white cotton, from the stretch before the bridge. He braked the train, bringing the cowcatcher near to the bundles and the faces which lifted and emerged from the cotton, watched with incredulity the cotton and the thin brown limbs and the tied burdens move from the rails and pour down the flank of the train and clamber, leap and roll into the open trucks. He had, of course, learned at Mtito Andei of the situation, that Patterson planned to contain the coolies at Tsavo until Whitehead's askari arrived. Now, with four hundred men in the trucks, Patterson would expect him to stop, to await an order.

Perhaps Shutt felt pity for those fear-crazed men; or chose, dutifully, to obey the green of the signal; or, simply, was amused by Patterson's predicament. Whatever his motive he opened the regulator and steamed slowly through Tsavo Station and Patterson ran from the admin. hut and down to the line and stared unbelievingly at the passing train: the coolies, assured of deliverance, began to scream with delight. Now they were children. They made grotesque faces. They shouted derision. They waved defiance. A cooking-pan described an arc and fell at Patterson's feet. The last of the trucks passed and Patterson stepped between the rails. Looking back from the footplate Shutt saw the figure become smaller and the fist shake impotently at the dying sun.

In the morning Patterson counted heads. Forty-five men were left in the Tsavo central camp: of these fifteen were sick. Of the thirty able men three were jemadars, two were cooks and two drove traction-engines. After a trying process of elimination Patterson found that he had only twenty-three men who were good at bridges. All of this calculation was futile since none of the twenty-three would go to the bridge.

The situation was now irredeemable. Work on the bridge was suspended. Tsavo's reputation denied him replacements. The coolies would have disembarked either at Voi or at Mombasa and Whitehouse must by now have learned of the exodus. He had lost his labour force and the loyalty of his men. His failure was bitter and complete. Nothing could now erase that; and only the death of the lions could restore order and industry.

During that day he occupied himself in building a hide in the lee of the bridge. It commanded a fine view of the camp. And even the dogs of Kali would find difficulty in breaching it. Whitehead had not come. Dusk and then night fell across the camp.

'Soon after settling down at my post,' Patterson relates, 'I was surprised to hear the man-eaters growling and purring and crunching up bones about seventy yards from the crib.' There had been no shrieks or noise of killing and, because of this absence, he 'could not understand what they had found to eat . . .' In fact, they had found Abdullah, the District Officer's sergeant of askari.

Whitehead's train had reached Tsavo Station after dark. He was escorted by no fewer than thirty askari. The askari were taken to the mess-hut for food and drink. Abdullah obtained a lamp and lighted his master's path through the cutting which led to Patterson's tent. Whitehead had had a heavy tour and he was tired and irritable. He had missed his dinner. He wanted a bath, a meal, a Scotch and a night of dreamless sleep. He got none of these things. In the middle of the cutting a lion leapt from the bank, ripped the shirt from his back and took Abdullah into the darkness. He had run, half-fainting, to the tent. No-one was there. Whitehead sponged the blood from his back, secured the tent-flap and lay for the remainder of that night in pain and in fear of septicaemia from the claw-wounds.

Patterson and Whitehead met at daylight. Whitehead was furious. There had been no-one to meet him at the station, and that in itself was a discourtesy and an insult to his office. He had had no treatment for his wounds. And he had lost Abdullah— a man for whom he had a deep affection. They quarrelled.

Later the District Officer's back was cleansed and dressed. Food and hot water and a profusion of apologies mollified him. Turk went into bush and found the remains of Abdullah—a boot with a foot in it. He brought it back to camp. There was then a solemn and slightly ludicrous debate. Should the foot be sent in a suitable casket to the sergeant's two wives at Kilifi near Mombasa? or should they bury it here at Tsavo? The problem resolved, a grave, as small as a child's, was dug on the river bank and the foot was interred with ceremony. Six askari fired their carbines into the air and, since rifle-fire was normally the herald of marauding lions, panic went through the camp like an electric charge and many men took to the trees and water-tanks. At the height of this confusion the Kilindini train steamed into the station and disgorged twenty sepoys under the command of Farquhar, the Superintendent of Police.

At this point the affair became farcical. Farquhar, a man to whom the scent of riot, death and mutiny was an irresistible perfume, was disconcerted at the sight of the askari. He had hoped for action: but the camp had an air of emptiness, even of order. Apart from the fact that the branches of the trees swarmed with men (perhaps they had been placed there under arrest?) the camp seemed normal. Whitehead, too, was disconcerted. He had already suffered pain and loss. He had earned the task, and the eventual credit, of restoring conditions of calm and safety in which many hundreds of frightened and mutinous men (undoubtedly they were hidden somewhere) might advance the building of the railroad. But here was Farquhar; to assume command, to whip up violence, to report another insurrection broken.

The exchanges were formal. Police were unnecessary, Whitehead said coldly: the situation was in his control. Farquhar nodded in agreement: obviously the situation was under control —he could see that from the fact that the camp's entire complement appeared to be up trees. At that, Whitehead had stared around him. He, too, sensed the emptiness of the camp. Where were the mutineers? he asked Patterson.

It seems that neither Farquhar nor Whitehead knew until then how few men remained at Tsavo. Patterson, of course, saw the drift of the question, his inevitable ridicule. He had stared at the trees as if he hoped that the four hundred coolies might materialise, provide some justification for this invasion of police and soldiers. Whitehead repeated the question. There was a silence. Men were climbing from the trees. Forty-five Indians remained in Tsavo River camp, Patterson confessed: fifteen of them were sick.

Farquhar and Whitehead stared at each other. Visions of glory were fading. He had always hated arithmetic, Whitehead said laconically, but never more so than at this moment. If fifteen out of forty-five Indians were sick this meant that there were thirty men capable of active mutiny. He himself had brought thirty askari, and Mr Farquhar had supported him with twenty sepoys. He was left with a remarkable result: no less than fifty of Her Majesty's armed troops had been called out to deal with thirty miserable coolies.

Two days passed. There were forays into the bush but not a lion was killed. Only scavengers had eaten of the strychnine. Farquhar and Whitehead, the askari and the sepoys, went on the midday material-train. Patterson watched it steam into the heat-waves. 'Once again,' he writes with an almost audible note of relief, 'I was left alone with the man-eaters.'

The relief was tempered by apprehensiveness. If the lions were mortal (and in the peculiar and darkening climate of Tsavo he had begun to wonder) either he or Turk would kill them. But the element of sport had long since gone. The lions must be destroyed, not hunted; there was a subtle difference. East African interest was now focused on Tsavo. At opposite poles the affair was both a joke and a calamity. In the bazaars and the colonials' bungalows the spectacle of the fleeing coolies, the frustrated colonel and the abandoned bridge might be amusing. But to those in high places this cessation of the bridge and of work on the permanent way in the Tsavo districts was a serious impediment.

London had now dropped all pretence that a moral issue, that is the destruction of the slave trade, was the taproot of the railroad. Uganda, its trade and its security, had always been the aim. And, indeed, since the mutiny of the Sudanese troops in Uganda in July of 1897 and the revolt of Mwanga, Her Majesty's Government had used the railroad as an arm with which to reach and reinforce that unquiet land. In the first month of 1898 the 27th Bombay Regiment had been railed to Ndi at Mile 109. Then, in March and April, a new battalion of the Uganda Rifles was raised with Swahili troops and embarked to Mile 142. The year of the Tsavo lions saw a developing flow of troops, transport animals and military stores: by the end of it 29,000 soldiers and porters, 1,200 animals and 2,500 tons of goods and equipment had been carried to railhead. There, where the line ended and the bush began, the columns formed for the long march. This was the value and the supreme function of the railroad.

Patterson knew this. The temporary bridges, especially that at Tsavo, had never been constructed to bear such traffic. There were material, water and construction trains. Working locomotives (and there were many of them) crossed and recrossed the Tsavo River. The temporary bridge shook and settled under the weight of it all. Near to it, massive in steel and stone but incomplete, was the abandoned span. It was a taunt. It was a reminder of the terror of the coolies; and this in itself was a cause for alarm.

The maintaining of an adequate labour force was always of vital importance to the fortunes of the railroad; and never more so than in this month of December 1898. The railroad was almost entirely dependent on Indian labour. Attempts had been made to employ and organise African natives, but seldom with success. Any kind of system was a concept foreign to the tribes-men. Neither would they move from their tribal region. At this time perhaps 2,500 natives worked at bush clearance and earth-works between Voi and railhead; but the work was casual and irregular. But there were 13,000 coolies. They were engaged in India under contract for a minimum wage. They were shipped, fed and equipped, and paid a bonus for exceptional progress. They were easily integrated and they worked well in tropical heat. In fact they were irreplaceable. Without them the railroad perished. The contracts had all been expressed in three-year terms; and the significance of 1898 was that the earlier contracts were due to expire at, or soon after, the end of that year. On expiration the coolies could claim repatriation, or enter into a further work-agreement with the Uganda Railway, or elect to remain in East Africa.

Patterson, like all of the senior officers, was sensitive to this particular contractual element. It gave the Asians power at an exact point in time. With unity of purpose they could wreck the railroad. There was of course a continuous influx from India, partly balanced by the repatriations of those incapacitated by sickness or injury, and by death. But in general the railroad depended on retaining the 4,000 contracted men of 1896. This core of men was now the nucleus; and, in fact, a private directive had already been circulated from Kilindini which said, among other things: '. . . officers should make every effort to encourage a renewal of contract. It will be of no benefit to the railway to lose its initial and greatly experienced labour-force. Neither is it the wish of Her Majesty's Government that time-expired men should be free to wander[1] without means of subsistence in the Protectorate . . .'

The affair at Tsavo was hardly an encouragement. It was the

[1] On a minor scale this is exactly what happened. Mr F. J. Jackson (later Sir Frederick Jackson), Deputy Commissioner of Uganda, wrote: 'They thought that they could continue to do as they pleased, and go where they liked, outside the limits of the Railway Zone. Provincial and District Com-missioners, including myself, at that time resident at Ravine, took a different view, when they began roaming about as petty traders and without permits . . .' From these men, filtering from the coast and establishing shops and trading posts, stems the present Indian population of East Africa.

worst possible advertisement. Disease, exile and unrelenting toil were accepted. But none of the risks implicit in such a contract could include an onslaught by an ancient and bestial terror. And in India only the most adventurous (a quality not associated with the Asian) of recruits could view with equanimity the prospect of death in the jaws of lion. It seemed, now, to Patterson that the dark of Tsavo was illumined, paradoxically, by a bright and searching light.

The news of the arrival of the sepoys and the askari had quickly spread to the outlying camps. It was of course exaggerated. The central camp was now impregnable. It was clearly the safest place in the Tsavo River region. Soon the small camps had emptied and men came on trolleys or on foot to Tsavo. It was then that the last act of the comedy began. 'They were struck dumb (Turk reports) on finding D.O. and others had gone and not a soldier in the place, they could have gone the other way, but P having got them was not going to lose them . . . he puts a guard on the trolleys and tells them here they are and here they going to stay. Perhaps he thought they would get his precious Bridge going again . . .'

With this unexpected supplement the number of men—coolies, tradesmen and Europeans—at Tsavo rose to about one hundred and fifty. But not an inch was added to the bridge, not a foot of the permanent way was reinforced. The Indians refused to work. Patterson accepted the situation. He could not risk a second exodus (and all that that entailed in further damage to an already eroded reputation) or the graver danger of mutiny and violence. He divided them into parties. He gave them tools, timber and corrugated-iron. He left them to strengthen the bomas and to prepare their defences.

Soon the camp at Tsavo River presented an extraordinary sight. On Patterson's orders no up or down train was permitted to stop at Tsavo or, to prevent desertion by boarding, to pass through at less than thirty miles an hour. Those from Kilindini were loaded with engineers, troops, new recruits from the Punjab. Tsavo was now a name to conjure with. Men stared at this beleaguered place; and marvelled. They saw trees linked by intricate systems of ropes, pulleys, hammocks and charpoys; elevated water-tanks festooned with mattresses and beds; huts double-barricaded with thorn and corrugated-iron; girders and sleepers built into fortresses of steel and wood; even graves, dug from the red soil, in which a man might bury himself for the night under a roof of logs. The trains passed, leaving Tsavo to its silence and its waiting.

At night each man protected himself according to his own favoured device. Trees were obvious havens, but were less favourably regarded after a lion was observed to be climbing sedately into a tree to escape a plague of flies. The more intelligent of the coolies began the search for a less hazardous refuge. Such a one was Natha Singh.

Singh, apparently, was the first to realise the natural advantages of the portable, galvanised water-tanks which were used to transport purified drinking-water. These tanks were immensely strong. And the opening had been devised with such cunning that, whereas it would admit any man of average girth, it was yet sufficiently narrow to prevent the entry of all but the most emaciated of lions. It was Singh's habit to enter a tank at dusk, to spend the night in wet and booming darkness, and emerge at dawn. Of course he had his imitators. Soon every available water-tank received its nightly tenancy of coolies; and, soon, its attendance of lions.

This was a new terror. The lions became adept in (as Turk puts it) 'scooping them out like winkles from a shell.' Some men could not withstand the peculiar thrill of eluding that exploratory claw, others could not abide that breathless moment when, extruding their heads from the tank into the light of dawn, it seemed that a paw might come to scalp them with the speed of light. Many returned to the trees and the pits and the cages. Some, of whom Natha Singh was the first, took loaded rifles into the tanks.

This was a mistake. One night Singh, alarmed by an unusually persistent lion and the claw which hooked and swung in the blackness of the tank, pushed the barrel of the rifle through the opening and triggered it. Only those who have fired an early breechloading Snider within the confines of a metal tank can appreciate the appalling nature of the detonation. The lion fled. Singh was later invalided home and, taking his shattered eardrums to Karachi, spent the remainder of his days in blessed silence.

On that same night one Amam Din lowered himself into his chosen tank, composed himself for the night and found that he was closeted with a spitting-cobra. In the morning no amount of effort could extract his corpse; and Patterson was presented (like Abdullah's foot) with another irritating burial problem. The tank could be entrained to Mombasa sealed, thus placing the burden of disposal on the authorities. Or it could be buried, intact, here at Tsavo. The former course seemed macabre and would hardly redound to his credit: the latter would require an enormous excavation. Patterson rejected both, and decided that since Amam Din had been a mistari (stone-mason) it would be appropriate if the tank were carried to the centre of the bridge and thrown reverently into the river. This, he explained to the man's doubting companions, was hardly a Hindu burial rite, but cremation in the tank was a physical impossibility. At noon a small party assembled on the bridge. Patterson muttered a few unsuitable words from the Order of Burial and the tank was levered over the side. Watching it he saw with some consternation that Amam Din had not been entombed, but launched. The tank, buoyant with air, floated sluggishly down the breast of the river. It was then that Patterson displayed that quality of self-command in sudden emergency which had won him rank and decoration. Seizing a carbine he fired four .303 bullets into the metal casing of the tank below the water-line. It sank in midstream.

After that the water-tanks lost popularity as places of refuge. Men secured themselves for the night: but for three days after the death of Din no lions were seen or heard at Tsavo. The ninth day of December was significant. It marked the beginning of the end of Patterson's private ordeal. In the darkness of the late evening he killed a man-eater.

This day of valour began in a small kraal by the river-camp. In the kraal were kept the transport animals, several scores of mules and donkeys. The animals were valuable and even more difficult to replace than the coolies. Because of this the kraal was of exceptional strength. A party of Teita had come to Tsavo the previous evening to purchase copper wire; and, observing with the tribesman's instinct for safety that the animals were better protected than the men, decided to spend the night within the kraal. This they did. At sunrise a man emerged with the intention of fetching water from the river; and, a few yards from the wall of timber and corrugated sheets, he was attacked by a pair of lions. He speared the first of them, and the lion, retaining the spear in the belly, ran into the thickets by the river-palms. The second, unaccountably, left the man and leapt into the open kraal. There, among the plunging hooves, the dung and the panic of the Teita, it killed a young donkey, dragged it from the kraal and into the thickets.

Within the thicket Turk found only the speared lion. It was a female and it was almost dead. The spear had passed through the vitals and had broken the back above the haunches. He raised the Winchester and then lowered it, understanding from the Suk's quivering body that the man needed to kill. The lion had courage and the eyes were yellow and implacable until the spear entered the throat. She was young and the body was much scarred from the thorns of the bomas. Turk left the thicket. The lion might have been carried into camp and exhibited. It would certainly have heartened the coolies. But he would not take it from its place of dying. Something had ended in the thicket. There was nothing beyond that.

Patterson found the carcase of the donkey a quarter-mile from the camp. It had been dragged from the thicket and only a small meal had been taken from it. All the timber near to the carcase was cut and nothing but stumps grew. It was reasonable to expect the lion to return to the kill; and unthinkable to spend a night on the ground. During the day he caused a staging to be built. Four twelve-foot poles were set in the earth at the angles of a square; and across the top was lashed a plank. At the hour before dusk his gun-bearer, Mahina, held a ladder to the staging and he climbed to the plank. Because the lions of Tsavo appeared to be of unusual accomplishment the ladder was prudently removed; and, as a further precaution, the dead donkey was tied by a length of wire to a stump. As you would expect, Mahina looped the wire around the base of one of the poles. Night buried the land. Patterson waited.

Near midnight the dark was still intense; and when the lion came he could not see it. It began to eat and then, because it was aware of him, dragged the donkey until the wire was extended. The staging swayed, the man-eater pulled with powerful jerks of the body, the poles leaned gradually from the perpendicular. 'I was so terrified,' he confesses, 'that I nearly fell off the plank . . .' He emptied the magazine of the rifle into the vagueness below him. The sounds of the shots, the lion's pain and then of its dying carried to the camp. Soon men came from the camp, their fear suspended, and the night went yellow-red with the light from lamps and torches and flares. Patterson climbed from the staging. Somewhere in the undergrowth the lion was dead. It seemed unbelievable.

No man could sleep. They danced and beat drums and sang because there had been a conquest and the evil was, after all, destructible. At sunrise Patterson led them into the scrub, and there they found the lion. It was big, maneless, scarred by thorn and age, so heavy that, bearing it to camp, its weight was apportioned among eight men. At camp began the rituals of measurement and photography. It stood (with assistance) three feet nine inches; and by judicious pulling on the tail its length was stretched to nine feet eight inches. This was a prize.

The group in the photograph is carefully arranged. The lion lies on a sheet of corrugated-iron. A board under the armpits gives height to the shoulders: the head is propped on four sticks. The backdrop is a plaited staging on which is nailed a leopard-skin. Between the backdrop and the lion squats Colonel Patterson. The helmet sits squarely on the head and the Kaiser moustache has a confident twist to it. He looks sideways at the lion with understandable reserve. This was only the beginning. But already, you feel, the nervous tic has left the cheek. And surely the eyes show a faint gleam of returning arrogance.

That was on 9 December. Three weeks later Patterson killed his second man-eater. Also on that day died the old lion; and with these deaths the terror lifted.

In that week the scarred pugs of the old lion were seen in the river sand. In the earth around Dalgairns' hut was the spoor of a younger lion. Goats were kept in a zereba adjoining the hut and, in the days that followed, the younger lion returned, broke the wall of the zereba and took two goats. Patterson selected a thorn tree near to the spoor and, at dusk, he ascended its branches.

The night was moony and calm with a zephyr of wind to bring the scents of the river. The light strengthened and Patterson watched the land define itself. At three o'clock the lion came; belly-low, moving always around the fringes of the moon-pools, a sinew of stealth and a component of shadow. Patterson watched it with admiration. 'His skill showed that he was an old hand at the terrible game of man-hunting,' he wrote. There was no cover between the scrub and the huts. The lion emerged, stood mane-ruffling in the gathering wind. He was beautiful. Patterson shot him in the chest. He did not fall. There was a movement and an integration with shadow. Patterson fired three more shots but the clearing was empty in the white of moon.

At daybreak Patterson found that the soil where the lion had stood was stained with blood. There was a blood-spoor and a place, further, where it had vomited. He did not go immediately into bush. This was an occasion, a day with all the portents of triumph. He went to his hut, washed and shaved scrupulously. A report awaited him. A Teita tribesman had been killed by a lion in the hills to the south-west of Tsavo. Mr Turk, the message said, would go.

At eight o'clock Patterson left the bomas, following the spoor into scrub jungle with Mahina and a native tracker. At the same time Robert Turk and the Suk marched for the hills.

The Teita was not a tribesman, but a small boy. He had been half-eaten. A group of men stood without compassion around the corpse. It lay in the shadow of a bamboo-grove, and the grove ran into terraces of coloured rock and from there into forested hillocks. It was a pretty place, made ugly by the death.

The scarred pugs of the old lion were there. The Suk led through the terraces, heat coming off the rock and beards of moss and lichen hanging above them as bright as verdigris. Turk looked back once and saw that the men had gone: already a jackal with a spine of grey fur stood paw-raised and quivering by the kill. Then the jackal moved from the kill and a man came from the striations of sun and shadow. It was Paul Verschoren. Even at distance he could see the degradation of him. He was hatless and the hair was stuck in matted clots on the face. A shirt-tail hung outside the belt. The face turned upward into sun and the flesh had the look of dead grey tissue. He stumbled, then stopped with legs apart as if he had lost all sense of balance. He had seen them on the terraces and the mouth opened but when the shout came it was thin with weakness.

The lion had bled liberally and Patterson had no need of the tracker. The light in the scrub jungle was soft-yellow and diffused. It blended with the silence so that when they stopped the silence lay in thicknesses of yellow. In this yellow silence was the lion and its pain and its need for a last act of killing. There were pools of vomit on the floor and the spears of grass were black with blood. Some of the grass bent under the weight of ants on the blood. Where the trees thinned the light became white and brittle and sound was re-asserted and this sound of insects was a danger, blurring the edge of alertness so that they would not hear the move or throat of the lion. Then, where the trees grew thick again, the sound (never really absent) was muted and absorbed and, pausing, they heard the lion. They heard its breathing, rapid and faintly liquid on the blood. It waited somewhere behind the cataracting yellow light.

The stream had dried in the nullah and Turk went down into it and stood between the walls of rock and fern. The pugs of the old lion had gone and the Suk stood listening. Nothing moved. The silence was so palpable it seemed they might hear the parting of the filaments of a web, the growth of vegetation. Then the Suk beckoned and they climbed up and through where the fern grew. Above the nullah the rock was hot and heat-waves rose from it: behind the heat-waves the rock ran, shimmering, down into scrub, was covered and re-emerged in slopes of fern, wild roses and begonias. There, where the light ricocheted from rock and the polished surfaces of leaves and hurt the eyes with its intensity, the Suk found the fresh scats of the lion. The trail ran upward across the flowering rock and down again into a hollow scarped out by rain. The hollow swayed with grass-heads. The grass was beaten flat in the centre of the hollow and, behind the fringe of interweaving blades, they saw the tan mound which was the lion's haunches and the khaki fabric of Verschoren's leg.

There was no movement except the faint swaying of the grass-heads and the breeze making bright green ripples and, walking through the grass and to the flattening of it, they found the lion and the Boer and the involvement of their deaths. The lion lay across Verschoren's chest and the belly of the man was open from the chest to the pubic bone. Staring at that putrescent mass Turk saw exhibited the years of pain and decline, the erosion of disease. It was like a new aspect of the face of death. He levered with the stock of the Winchester and the lion rolled from off the man. The dew-claw of the left foreleg took part of the entrails. Verschoren was corrupt; from the lice-infested hair and beard to the ulcerated shins. Then he examined the lion. There was no evident injury. Only time had ravaged it. The skin of the body and face was scarred. The legs were cratered with open suppurations. The teeth were yellow with decay, broken and worn. One of the ears was ripped and the side of the face which he could see was roughened with a colony of engorged ticks. The deaths were a cause of unease. The man had no rifle and even the sheath-knife was undrawn. The lion had no wound and no pair of hands could have throttled that immense throat. The man had lurched through his darkening world toward his appointment with the lion because the killing of lions was his reason for being. The lion, perhaps already moribund, had risen and wheeled on the man with a last reflex of the claw. They were dead; and, touching, they were joined in a common putrefaction.

Turk turned and left them. Looking back he saw that the

joining of the man and the lion in death was beautiful. The head of the lion was set in the dark of the mane with the dignity of an old engraving. The face of the man, seen in profile, was good, gentle and comely above the thrusting beard. Both these creatures had known the raw days of youth. He went back to them, spread the flattened grass above their bodies. Then he jerked dried grass from the soil and covered them. Then he fired the grass. From the rock above the hollow he watched the flame fill it. Smoke came white off the flame and was channelled by the contour of the hollow into a pillar. He could not see the bodies of Paul Verschoren and the lion but the flame above where the bodies lay was clean.

When the lion came from the underbrush Patterson shot it twice in the bloodied area of the chest. It fell with the second shot, raked the soil into red clouds, rolled and was propelled in one fluid movement of the sinews into another charge. Patterson broke its right hindleg with the third shot and the lion rolled again and the blood from the chest was flung with the roll into an arc above it. The lion, slower now, went into its third charge, the blood gouting and the eyes yellow and (Mahina and the tracker now in trees) Patterson dropped the magazine-rifle and leapt for the branch below the tracker's feet. The lion reached, collapsed on the broken leg, rolled under the spray of blood and, losing power, turned for the underbrush. Patterson took Mahina's carbine and shot it through the body and, falling with the shot from the branch and into the haze of dust, he saw that the lion was still. Then, behind the haze, he saw that the eyes were white-yellow with hate and the lion came again, back-broken and leg-trailing and vomiting blood, and he gave it the Martini in the chest and the lion fell, rolled, cascaded blood, bit through a branch with the last of its life-force; and died.

It was very quiet after the lion died. Mahina and the tracker were unmoving. Patterson sat in the dust until the tremor of reaction passed. Then, leaving the lion for Mahina, he went back through the thick yellow silences of the scrub jungle and out into sun. Men were running from the camp and, in the south-west, he could see, distant, a pillar of white smoke standing in the sky.

There were a thousand lions in the lands around Tsavo and there was no reason, of any tangibility, why the terror should lift (immediately and perceptibly) with the deaths that morning of the two lions. But men knew that the danger had gone. They knew this with an instinct older than reason. The sky was clearer, the air sweeter: the oppressiveness had gone like the hem of a cloak drawn suddenly away. Soon the camp was flooded with the return of the deserters from Voi. They came exultant and with a childish sense of shame. They had deserted the Sahib: they would be punished. But Patterson forgave. These were heroic days, and no sourness of recrimination must spoil them. The telegraph was never silent and praise sang continuously in the wires. Men came from the Coast and from the interior to marvel at this the last of the man-eating lions. Patterson displayed it with the pride of a small boy. It was not young. It was disfigured by thorn and torn by bullets. And the mane which had seemed so majestic in moonlight was as sparse and short as the hair on a man's head. But to Patterson it was beautiful. There in that skin, now pegged and sprinkled with arsenical powder, was all of self-respect and valour.

One month after the death of the lion there was a solemn ceremony of presentation. A great audience of Europeans, Asian headmen and colonial officers gathered in Tsavo's central mess-hut. The chairs and benches had been arranged to leave a middle gangway. At the end of the gangway was a dais with a table and three chairs. Men smoked and talked in hushed voices. Precisely at eight o'clock the door opened and Patterson entered. He was followed by Spooner and Sandiford. He paused on the threshold and men rose at the sight of that martial figure. Patterson surveyed them. Then he marched down the gangway. His heels rang. He was erect. He carried a cane which he had tucked between arm and body. He climbed the dais and waited for Spooner and Sandiford. The audience stared. Patterson placed his topi and cane on the table. He shone with pride and authority. His cotton drills were immaculate. The leather of his boots reflected a waxen light. The shoulders were drawn back so rigidly that the jacket strained against the buttons. The moustache was heavily pomaded into an arrogant curl. The face, bloomed from the razor, was calm and patrician and devoid of nervous affliction. Patterson seated himself, gestured to Spooner and Sandiford. They and the audience sat.

The presentation was made by a mistari named Roshan Bakhsh, native of the village of Chajanlat in the district of Jhelum. It took the form of a silver bowl and a poem of extravagant imagery. The bowl was pleasant, the poem poor. But for Patterson it was a paean of the purest and most exquisite language. It was written in Hindustani. Spooner translated it, standing, in a round, oratorical voice. It told the story of the lions—'savage creatures whose very jaws were steeped in blood' and of the workmen who had died and those who 'would sit in their huts, their hearts full of foreboding and terror.' It told of the man who delivered them, of Patterson Sahib . . . 'so brave is he that the greatest warriors stood aghast at his action; tall in stature, young, most brave and of great strength is he . . .' It described the deaths of the lions . . . 'one glance from Patterson Sahib cowed the bravest of them . . .' The phrases swept impressively over the men in that crowded hut. Patterson listened, the cheekbones flushed with pleasure and the eyes averted in a fitting humility. This was triumph. The British Flag could stream again in the equatorial wind. No man could ask for more.

9. The Watering-Place

No research into the early days of East African colonial history can be complete without a study of the old maps. Most of the maps drawn by the Great Explorers were affixed into the backs of the books they wrote. The maps unfold into great linen-backed squares; and there, for the imaginative, is the authentic shape of mystery. The maps arouse a sensuous pleasure. The colours, now pale, give a sense of age: once they were rich and vibrant like the lands they depicted. The mountains are drawn in ascending whorls so that you seem to look down into the craters, the forests are hatched with a fine pen into dark areas of menace and the papyrus swamps stand in tiny, symbolic tufts. The maps are good and stout under the fingers. The linen rustles provokingly and, held to the nostrils, smells of old bibles and missionary-stations, of fevers and ant-dust. Descriptions of terrain are written across some of the maps. A finger, drawn upward from the foothills of Kilimanjaro, passes through a 'Great Waterless Desert' to a 'Warm Spring' and a 'Bamboo Forest'; from thence to the 'Firewood Plain' of the Masai; around 'Steam-Holes' and 'Lavas and Tuffs' and as far as the 'Uninhabited Forest—Elephants numerous.' It is all wonderfully evocative of an Africa which has gone and, despite the barbarities, the disease and the violence, the maps glow with a luminous quality of innocence.

But it is the paucity (and even the inaccuracy) of the information that makes the maps exciting. There are great areas of blankness about which the explorer knew nothing. Rivers wind off course or are omitted altogether. Many of the place-names, corrupted by time and tongue, are unrecognisable. There is an effect of groping; even a faint emanation of the spirit of men who were impelled to walk those dangerous lands so that they might draw a simple chart.

On none of the maps of the exploratory period will you find a reference to Nairobi. Joseph Thomson's route map, prepared after the Royal Geographical Society's East African Expedition of 1883-1884, is a good example. The Kapté (now Kapiti) Plain is marked; and designated as a 'Rich grassy Plain—no Trees.' The branches of the Athi River drop with approximation and between them is the village of Machakos. Machakos was important in those days. It was a halt on the caravan route. It became a depot of the British East Africa Association; and after that the centre of the Provincial Administration. (Had the railroad not paused before its ring of hills, and avoided them, it would, perhaps, have become East Africa's capital city.) But to the north-west of Machakos the map shows nothing but a 'Grassy Plain.' And there is no trace of the slender filament of the Nairobi River.

But the Nairobi River was known, both to the caravans and to the Masai. The caravan-masters had established a camp there. The Masai knew it as a watering-place; and, with that instinct for descriptive names which never fail to be apt and poetic, had named it. It meant 'cold water' or 'cold stream' or even, with the flexibility of African names, 'swamp.' Thomson's map shows another name of common root one hundred and twenty miles south of Machakos. It is a small stream which rises at the base of Kilimanjaro on the western flank. It is called Ngarè N'Erobi —the stream of cold water. George Whitehouse was never troubled by the orthography of African names. He wrote them phonetically; and the name Nyrobi recurs with stubborn persistence in his earlier Reports.

'Nairobi in the month of May 1899 (Ronald Preston wrote), the month and the year in which we moved camp to this place, may be described thus: A bleak, swampy stretch of soppy landscape, wind-swept, devoid of human habitation of any sort, the resort of thousands of wild animals of every species. The only evidence of the occasional presence of human kind was the old caravan track skirting the bog-like plain . . .'

The paragraph, written years later from inadequate diary entries, testifies to the fallibility of memory. The Athi Plains were indeed bleak, featureless and sodden under the swollen clouds of the long rains. And the game was thick. But already the nucleus of a community had begun to form. The old trading-station had not been abandoned with the revocation of the Company's charter. It had been maintained; and it had grown. It was the centre for the continuous barter of trade-goods and produce. It replenished the caravans. It supplied the tribes (currency, the rupee and the pice, was not yet used). Nairobi itself lay within a triangle formed by Fort Smith at Kikuyu, Fort Hall near Nyeri and Machakos in Ukamba. There were Swahili garrisons at the Forts, and a bazaar and a Government Administration at Machakos. From these three points caravan traffic converged on Nairobi; and sustained it. There were a telegraph-office and many huts built by the Army and by the railroad staking-out parties. Indians, scenting trade, had come from the Coast and from Machakos and already a few canvas, bamboo and corrugated-iron shops leaned in the mud. And Sergeant Ellis of the Royal Engineers (the first European to settle in Nairobi) had kept a transport-station with stabling for oxen and mules since 1896.

This scattered settlement lay between the Athi Plains and the Aberdare Mountains. It was a place of gentle valleys, channelled by the Mathari, the Nairobi, the Masongawai and Ngong Streams. The clay-stone banks of the Nairobi Stream (or River) lost themselves in a papyrus swamp; and, at times, the sun sucked miasmas from the swamp and spread them in thick white draperies over the huts of the settlement. But it was not malarial; and whatever diseases were to afflict Nairobi (and they were many) the causes did not lie in the anopheles mosquito. The settlement had grown on the western edge of the Athi Plains: it defined the end of a flat and easy traverse. The plateau on which it lay was really a segment of the eastern ramp of the Rift Valley; and this, the Kikuyu plateau, rose steeply. Ahead were the hills, poised in great wedges of ironstone: the soil changed with the elevation and a spade turned therein at intervals would produce burdens of yellow, then pink, then, finally, the red colour of fertility. North and growing down to the Nairobi River were the junipers and podocarpus of the Kikuyu Forest.

The rails reached Nairobi on 30 May 1899. Whitehouse had known from the beginning that the railroad, stretching almost six hundred miles to Port Florence, could not be administered indefinitely from Kilindini. There was too much wilderness, too many men spread from the Ocean to the Lake, too many places where the seeds of calamity might suddenly sprout. Somewhere between the point of origin and the terminus must be the site for a central administration.

The Report written on 30 November 1898 (at the end of his caravan from Lake Victoria) presented considerable detail; but it made no mention of a new headquarters site. He had reconnoitred the route, he had measured the rises, the falls and the plateaux of the terrain. But at that date he had not chosen. The line advanced. Data from surveyors and engineers filled his file. Sir Guildford Molesworth[1] arrived for a tour of inspection and, evidently, the locality of the Nairobi River was suggested. But it was only tentative. Sir Guildford had come to inspect, not to advise. Whitehouse could not evade his responsibility: the decision was his. Sir Guildford went up-country and, in January, Whitehouse sent him a telegraph. Nairobi was the site. Like most decisions made after an interminable period of meditation it was the wrong one.

Whitehouse's eyes were continually turned toward the Lake. But his was a pure and unalloyed engineering vision. It was canalised into a narrow professionalism. Two steel ribbons must be driven to the distant shore of Port Florence: that was all. He had no political sagacity; and, indeed, the personal dilemma in the choice of the terminus had left him resistant to the tug of political undertow. He had recoiled. From then on decisions would be made on engineering grounds. He chose Nairobi as his central site. He chose it solely because of a change of gradient.

But, of course, the railroad was inextricably linked with the future of a developing Crown colony. And it was for this reason that the Foreign Office had urged Whitehouse to avail himself of the advice of its Consul-General in Zanzibar. There is no

[1] Consulting Engineer for Railways to the Government of India.

evidence that Whitehouse consulted Sir Arthur Hardinge in the particular matter of the Nairobi site; or, more important at that time, that he ever took the counsel of medical and sanitary experts. The truth is that he had become isolate. Sir Arthur was, in any event, a long way away. He had no personal bonds with either the Sub-Commissioner at Mombasa or with John Ainsworth, the head of the Provincial Administration at Machakos. None of his subordinates was a friend or confidant: few of them, in fact, could match his technical ability. And, significantly, years of continual friction between the railroad and the Civil Administration had eroded all prospect of liaison.

This friction (and the inevitable estrangement) was a contributory cause of many of the wrong decisions. The railroad zone, of two miles width, crept through the administered territories creating a curious tear in the fabric of government. Powers and rights were never properly defined. Turk called the zone 'Tom Tiddler's ground.' Sir Charles Eliot[1] wrote in his book *The East Africa Protectorate*: 'By a most unfortunate arrangement, the local administration of the railway was made entirely separate from the administration of the protectorate, although it included a great many things which really had nothing to do with railway construction, such as the policing and sanitation of the whole line and of the most important stations on it . . . (ensuring) a permanent squabble between the two administrations . . .'

Now the siting of a future capital was a question of immense importance. But, in fairness, neither Whitehouse nor any consular official not gifted with powers of prevision had any means of knowing that this scattering of huts in the early months of 1899 was the first animation of an embryonic city. Settlement had hardly begun and there was no flow of produce to suggest to the far-sighted that here was a new centre of commerce. In this raw and awakening land nothing much could happen in the way of development until the railroad track had passed; and, then, a city might arise in any one of a dozen places. Cities were living organisms and grew in a curious and dynamic manner from converging streams of people and trade. In those days they were never planned; and a hamlet must become a village and

[1] Commissioner of the East Africa Protectorate 1900-1904.

224

a village a town before the motive force was recognised. But in moving the headquarters of the Uganda Railway from Kilindini to Nairobi Whitehouse must surely have known that he was the builder of a new community. There would be houses, stores and workshops, roads and station quarters, bazaars and transport depots, concentrations of traders and permanent railroad officials; in fact all the restless and predictable growth of a railroad township. By the end of the year the number of Indian coolies and artisans would reach 18,000, a not insignificant proportion of whom must certainly settle in, or be based upon, Nairobi. To have failed to see, clairvoyantly, the mists of a swamp reform into the pillars of a city was blameless: to fail to anticipate the natural expansion of a township and to ignore all considerations of soil, sub-soil, drainage and water-supply was inexcusable.

Between Mombasa and the Nairobi River the track had climbed 5,400 feet over a distance of almost 330 miles. This was an average gradient of 1 in 323—a progressive but easy rise. But ahead and beyond the settlement the land lifted steeply. The track, Whitehouse calculated, would need to climb 2,200 feet in only 35 miles to the brink of the Kikuyu Escarpment. This produced a disturbing average gradient of 1 in 84; and, moreover, there were sections where the gradient would be as bad as 1 in 50. Surely, he had reasoned, this gently sloping plateau, which was like a natural field of demarcation between the easy and the difficult, was the place where the railroad might pause, recoup its strength and gather impetus; and point again to the valley of the Rift.

At this time of the Nairobi railhead famine lay on the lands of the Kikuyu and the Kamba. The short rains, due in the last quarter-year of 1898, had failed. The light grass-rains which, in a perfect year, would fall and bring refreshment in the February, had withheld. And the long rains, due in the middle days of April, had engorged the sky and greened it; and had not come. Some of it had spilled, as if from a gourd too heavy and swollen to keep intact, and the black-cotton soil of the plains had yielded and become sodden so that mud as black as oil had spewed from under the wheels of the locomotives and men had thanked whatever gods they had for the beginning of the true rains. But, then, the rains had not come. The portent was false. There was no weight of rain or feeling of engorgement in the sky and the light was sharp again. The streams dried and the land hardened into iron and men knew with certainty that there would be no rain.

Soon there was no corn to wave on the hill-tops and the land was shorn of food. The pasture died and the cattle, sheep and goats went gaunt. People came to where the track ran and the face of hunger could be seen from the trains. It was always grey, always accusatory. This was the white man's railroad. There was food at the coast where the line began, food at the depots and the posts and the stations, food on the trains. They came to the line and waited for the trains and for the food which might be flung to them. In the beginning the trains passed and there was nothing. Then the men of the railroad were stirred by guilt or pity and the trains passed very slowly through the famine area (which lay between Sultan Hamud and the Kapiti Plains) and sacks of rice or corn or maize or fruits or vegetables were dropped to the starving. There was never enough; and those who had not eaten waited for another train or followed the line because somewhere along it there would be food. Many died by the line.

The great hunger of 1899 was a facet of a general misery. It was the inevitable product of four disastrous visitations. These were rinderpest, locusts, drought and smallpox. John Ainsworth, the Sub-Commissioner and Vice-Consul for the Province of Ukamba (which contained the Districts of Ukamba, Kikuyu, Teita and Taveta) wrote: 'Rinderpest began to appear in Ukambani in 1897 and continued through 1898, when it spread to Kikuyu. During 1897 and 1898 we were visited by swarms of locusts, which remained in the Kikuyu and Ukamba Districts . . . and caused considerable damage. The natives dealt with them by lighting fires and beating drums and old tins. They also gathered untold thousands which they dried and ground into powder which is mixed with their food . . .'

Whitehouse was a sensitive and compassionate man. He was disturbed by the fact of hunger, by the barren lands and the groups of skeletal bodies which stood or shuffled by the track. These were the shapes of conscience: he could not ignore them.

He had known that railroad provisions had, for many months, gone to the feeding of the hungry. He had not authorised the giving: nor had he forbidden it. In this land of the heathen a little practical Christianity was no bad thing. But, of course, charity, like all pleasures, exacted a price. In the early months of 1899 the groups of starving people swelled into legions. They came to the railroad zone and, in the coming, became a responsibility. The cost mounted. To Whitehouse it seemed that ten thousand shrunken bellies lay between Voi and the Athi River. In March enormous loads of food were sent, continuously, to the Roman Catholic settlement at Bura and to the Church of Scotland Mission at Kibwezi. In April the Audit Department at Kilindini gave him a note of the reckoning.

The expense had been formidable. It was likely to increase. The railroad accounts (which were sent quarterly to the Committee in London) could hardly sustain so gratuitous a burden. Whitehouse knew that he had to make a decision. At the end of April he travelled uptrack as far as Sultan Hamud, Kima and Ulu. The spectacle of suffering caused him both pain and resentment. He wrote to Rawson in Mombasa, with understandable vexation: '. . . Why is it *our* responsibility? We are building a railway. We are not a relief organisation. These poor people must be helped but I have fifteen thousand coolies to feed. The Civil is not doing nearly enough, and perhaps neither are the natives. There is plenty of game for them, why cannot they go and catch it . . . ?' Back in Kilindini he gave the order. The provisioning of the tribes must stop.

Whitehouse had spent more than three years in East Africa. He must have known that the presence of game was too simple an answer to the complex problem of famine. The Kamba were still great hunters; but many of the tribes were agricultural or were raisers of stock. The Teita farmed in their loamy hills and, with the aid of banana-stems, cultivated the old arts of irrigation. Some sections of the Kikuyu were pastoral and would not eat game-meat even to fill the emptiness of hunger. Many refused to eat the flesh of animals which were not cloven-hoofed; and most would turn from the eating of the fishes of the rivers since these, as all men knew, were really snakes. Some were static and would not move, or were lazy or apathetic. Many were too young or too old or too ailing to survive under the heel of calamity. And, in any event, the rinderpest of the two previous years had decimated the buffalo, the wildebeeste, the hartebeeste and the eland. When famine came it found a multitude of victims.

The accusation that the Administration was 'not doing nearly enough' was a half-truth. As with all administrations the purse-strings were loosened reluctantly and only under pressure. But the pressure came from Ainsworth in whose province the suffering was rife. He was a man inspired by a deep and enduring love of Africans. But love could not produce food from a starving land. Like the railroad he had to buy it: and to buy it he needed money. He pleaded and cajoled—and waited. It was in that agonised period of waiting for the release of Government funds that Whitehouse stopped the supply of victuals to the tribes. The order was ill-timed. It turned the Kamba into warriors. It brought them down in murderous hordes against the railroad. Patterson wrote: 'During this period they several times swooped down on isolated railway maintenance gangs and utterly annihilated them, in order to obtain possession of the food which they knew would be stored in the camps. These attacks were always made by night . . .'

The Kamba used poison-arrows. The arrows came flighting from darkness wherever men gathered in silhouette against a camp-fire or emerged from a tent into moonlight; and those who had suffered and escaped the attacks by the Tsavo lions now found themselves exposed to a new and peculiar form of terror. Many died. 'One night,' Turk wrote, 'six Indos got the arrow, they had not a hope. This was at Kima. In the morning we went out & found the Wakamba village. We shot two or three but they was half-dead from starving and the pox . . . a bit of food would be better than bullets . . .'

But Whitehouse was stubborn. Fear was spreading among the coolies. Soon a situation might develop in which they would either strike or demand escorts of police and askari. In that case the giving of food to the tribes would be cheaper than the aban-doning of work or the cost of protection. Whitehouse knew this. He was reminded of the dangers by Preston, by Patterson and

by Spooner. But he would not yield. The root of the stubborn-
ness was a dislike of the Administration grown from a year of
continuous friction, and the conviction that here was an issue of
responsibility.

The friction, as always, stemmed from the two-mile zone. It
was a vacuum in government; and, worse, it was a vacuum in
law. The railroad authority had no power to sit in judgment or
to impose penalties on Indian offenders. It was an employer of
labour and there was a contractual relationship; but that was
all. Almost from the beginning there had been a Travelling
Magistrate, seconded from the Indian Government, whose role
was to dispense justice to the Asiatics, to apply the Indian Penal
Code, to move to any point on the line where offences had been
committed. In theory there were advantages. Court proceedings
were conducted in English or Hindustani or even in dialect
(whereas only English or Swahili could be used in the courts of
the District Commissioners). The magistrate was a man accustomed to the labyrinths of the Asian mind and, further, there was
always a Goan clerk. Trial was prompt; and, in an alien
land, at least the processes of the law were familiar. The Commissioners enjoyed an overriding jurisdiction but, except in cases
of serious crime (for example the conspiracy to murder Patterson),
they were expected not to exercise it. This was the theory; but,
of course, there were weaknesses. Law in the Protectorate at that
time was enforced with scrupulous care. It was the basis of
confidence and the bedrock to government. To the District
Officers the law was indivisible; and a two-mile strip, defined
by the vagaries of a railroad track, with its own resident magistrate,
its own procedures and its own court-on-wheels could never be
anything but an irregularity. Sentences were ludicrously light.
In time it became apparent that the function of the Travelling
Magistrate was to protect the indentured coolie, to stand between
him and the severities of the justices, to keep him at work and,
by so doing, to avoid disruption. Railhead must advance and,
it seemed, all else was subsidiary. There was also a dangerous
form of drumhead 'court.' Headmen sat in conclaves of three
and inflicted penalties and, under cover of darkness, offenders
were flogged or made to suffer pain for an hour or two. The

coolie-camps were centres of depravity and lawlessness. None of this commended itself to the District Officers; and, inevitably, the cleavage between the railroad and the Administration widened.

Whitehouse, as Chief Engineer, had been subjected to continuous complaint, and this at a time when he was under considerable pressure from London. Thus, when the peoples of the Teita, the Kamba and the Kikuyu converged, starving, on the railroad he was in no mood to accept an indefinite burden. He hardened his heart. He closed the doors of the warehouses and locked out the sight of hunger. And when, finally, Ainsworth got his money the damage (avoidable by a simple agreement to recoup Uganda Railway funds) had been done.

'It became necessary (Ainsworth wrote) to bring food to the district and in certain areas (including Ndi, Kibwezi, Machakos, Nairobi and Kikuyu) to open relief camps. The government granted a considerable sum of money for the purpose. In some of the areas the natives killed numbers of their livestock to supplement the food supply; in other cases animals sick of rinderpest were eaten . . . I estimate that in the Ulu and Kitui districts approximately 25 per cent of the people died, while in Kikuyu the average must have been 15 per cent . . . Information was sent all over the country to the people that they would receive food if they came to the relief camps, but thousands died before they either got our messages or could reach the camps . . .'

At sunrise of the day after his arrival at Nairobi Whitehouse began a tour of inspection. He took with him Spooner, his District Engineer: Preston and Turk joined him at the south bank of the river. The purpose of the inspection was to determine the sites of the station, the workshops, headquarters and living quarters and to prospect the railroad zone. The direction of the track had already been staked out. It ran roughly parallel to the old caravan road. It crossed the Ngong River (which was south of the site), looped the Nairobi Swamp, bridged the stream where the Kirichwadogo and Kirichwakuba Rivers joined to run down into the swamp; and drove north-west, bisecting the caravan road below the forest. The zone of one mile on either side of the track could thus be precisely drawn. It was White-house's intention to examine it with the greatest care.

This primitive settlement on the Athi Plains was hardly comparable to Mombasa where veins of commerce had throbbed for more than a thousand years. But, in selecting the site, he had implanted the cells of growth; and, in the knowledge of this, he had obtained from the Foreign Office an authority to appropriate all land required for the legitimate purposes of the railroad. This precaution, he reasoned, would obviate land speculation and a bout of enthusiastic compensation claims. Thus armed, he went with Spooner, Turk and Preston through the reddening mists of the river.

Nairobi was astir. This was railhead and activity was to be expected—already Preston's men were building huts on the flat adjoining the plain. But there was something purposive in the air. It disturbed him. Masai kraals clustered to the north of the river and there were great herds of sheep, goats and cattle. Below the forest edge he could see long lines of tents, soldiers and the colours of a Union Jack. These, Preston told him, were the military lines. They had walked to the lines. There was a group of Sudanese guards and their wives. To the left of the tents a score or so of East African Rifles were digging hut foundations under the eye of a British junior officer. The O.C. Troops, the officer told Whitehouse, was over there—he had gestured to where the ground rose high beyond the swampland—with Dr Hinde. They walked to the rising ground. Whitehouse was silent with perplexity. The mist, sucked upward by the sun, was breaking into tatters and they could see the net of streams, now low and turbid from the drought, and the plains going purple into distance and quivering with game. North were the molars of Mount Kenya; and, turning on the slopes so that they faced southward, they could see a napery of whiteness in the sky which was Kilimanjaro. Much nearer were the mellow rises of the Ngong Hills.

But Whitehouse was unreceptive to the sight of beauty. He was angry. Something was happening here which he did not understand. Dr Hinde was a sharp and volatile man with a ferret nose and ferret eyes. Swahilis, under the direction of a

British Army captain, were hammering pegs over a wide area of ground. A lieutenant of the Engineers was taking levels. Hinde introduced himself. He was not a medico—he was one of Mr Ainsworth's District Officers. He had been here, at Nairobi, since the beginning of April. There was so much to do; sites for offices and bungalows and the Sub-Commissioner's house, a hospital and a court-house and the police-lines . . . Whitehouse listened in amazement. Hinde explained carefully why he had chosen the rising ground as a site suitable to the dignity of the Administration. 'W was all at sea,' Turk recorded, 'the administration he asks, what administration? Hind looks dumbfounded too. Surely you know, he says, that the government is going to move itself down from Machakos to Nairoby . . . ?' Turk, it seems, enjoyed the situation. '. . . It was as good as a cross-talk act with W scratching his nose and swinging his watch and blurting out questions and Hind getting cold and toffee-nosed like the Civil lot always do . . . Finally W turns to Preston and asks him why he never told him. The earthwork gangs must have been in Nairoby long before the railhead got there and he must have known what was going on, why hadnt nobody told him . . . ?'

Whitehouse was entitled to his temper. He had selected Nairobi as the site for the railroad headquarters in January of 1899. Dr Hinde and John Ainsworth inspected it in early April. Somewhere between those two dates Hardinge (or someone like him) had decided that, since the line would not touch Machakos, the centre of Provincial Administration must clearly be shifted to the place where development (and an accompanying importance) was inevitable.[1] But they had not told him. The friction, exacerbated by the famine, had thrust them apart.

There had been a quarrel. The captain and the lieutenant joined them. He would remind the District Officer, Whitehouse said, that the railroad not only had control over a zone of one

[1] Ainsworth's papers reveal that '. . . in April 1899 I visited Nairobi where I had already arranged for Dr Hinde to establish a temporary camp in view of the near approach of railhead and of the intention to make Nairobi the Railway Headquarters . . . Early in August 1899 I received instructions to make arrangements to move the Provincial Headquarters from Machakos to Nairobi . . .'

mile on either side of the line but now enjoyed an express power to appropriate land. That was true, Hinde agreed; but he would remind the Chief Engineer that no line, at the moment, ran through Nairobi—there were only markers. That, of course, Whitehouse replied, was pure pedantry . . . The absurdities continued. The railroad's requirements, Whitehouse said, had first priority. All stakes, markers, levels, flags, profiles and other Government impedimenta must be immediately removed. And, he suggested, an early meeting with Mr Ainsworth was plainly of the first importance.

John Ainsworth, at this time, was a man of thirty-five. Photographs of the period reveal a sturdy, thick-thighed, broad-chested body, a shaven face with heavy jowls, a generous mouth and large, lustrous eyes, strong frontal bones and light, cropped hair. There is a feeling of power about him, something generated even from a picture. This, you sense, is a man of formidable strength of mind, a man who sits scrupulously in the seat of authority: already the stamp of the great administrator is upon him.

But that morning at Nairobi he had nothing but resentment for Whitehouse. It was Whitehouse whose decision to bring track to Nairobi and to by-pass Machakos would leave the little township aborted.[1] It was Whitehouse who would transplant him from the pasture and sweet water of the Iveti Hills to the miasmas and wind of the Athi Plains. It was Whitehouse who had criticised him during the early days of the famine. And it was Whitehouse who claimed the right to appropriate land and, it seemed, to build a city around a swamp.

The meeting took place in front of Sergeant Ellis's transport store. Ainsworth had brought Lane, his A.D.O. at Machakos (who was to become District Officer after Ainsworth's departure); Dr Hinde (who later became District Officer at Fort Hall); and Captain Cooper, who had come from Fort Smith to find a suitable site for the military buildings. Whitehouse had brought Spooner and Preston. Robert Turk had gone to Mombasa in

[1] Ainsworth had believed that Machakos would become East Africa's capital city.

defiance of Whitehouse's decree—which imposed a loose camp-quarantine on any man making a smallpox contact in the stricken Kamba villages; and it was this defiance which took him to the meeting in a far from conciliatory frame of mind.

Both men were aloof and unfriendly. Neither would make concessions; except, as Ainsworth said, to admit that the position was ill-defined. The Uganda Railway, he contended, had no more than a limited power of management over the two-mile zone. These were Crown lands; and all that the Proclamation of 1897 had done was to reserve the zone for a public purpose, that is the building of a railroad. The railroad could not usurp or supersede the functions of the Crown. The conception of a zone had been suspect from the beginning and whereas Her Majesty's Commissioners had accepted the railroad's occupancy of ownerless and unused land from the Coast to the Athi the situation here, in Nairobi, was quite different. . . . Listening to that formal voice Whitehouse saw the calibre of the man, knew that Ainsworth would never be content with sites that were incompatible with the dignity of Government. But he was in no mood for compromise, much less surrender. He enjoyed an express right of appropriation, he told Ainsworth; not only in respect of sites required by the railroad but over all land within the two-mile zone. He intended to exercise those rights.

The others were silent. These were deep waters and, perhaps, none of them, including Ainsworth, saw the situation clearly. If Nairobi were to be no more than a railroad headquarters, Ainsworth said coldly, Government would have no immediate claims. But within a few months Nairobi would be the centre of the Provincial Administration. The Crown, in occupation, must surely have precedence: it would require bungalows, civil offices, police lines, a suitable house for the Sub-Commissioner and, having regard to the bestial and lawless habits of the railroad's Indian workmen, a court-house and a substantial gaol.

The remark, according to Preston, was ill-received by Whitehouse. He took it to be, as indeed it was, a reflection on the quality of his authority. There was now no hope of agreement. Nairobi, he told Ainsworth, had been chosen as railroad head-quarters; and, first, the railroad's needs must be satisfied. These were a station, workshops, access to water, warehouses, bungalows for the Europeans and the railroad police, huts for the coolies and (this with sarcasm) a suitable house for the Chief Engineer. He had a power over unappropriated land and, if it would serve to prevent speculation, he would exercise it.

They had parted at that. Whitehouse went to his coach, Ainsworth to his tent. Then, later in the day, Lane made an approach to Spooner. The Sub-Commissioner, he said, obviously recognised the *essential* needs of the railroad. It was suggested that these be plainly marked: the remaining areas could then be examined and, perhaps, there would be no significant field of disagreement. The message was conveyed. Whitehouse replied. Further messages passed—all phrased in the stilted language of diplomacy. Ainsworth, who had played this game a hundred times with native chiefs, found nothing absurd in the situation. Finally both men emerged. There were stiff handshakes. The parties began the inspection.

By sundown Whitehouse had marked the station and accompanying workshops and warehouses. He had approved the site for the coolies' huts. All of this lay to the south of the Nairobi River. The military lines, he suggested, could remain below the forest-edge. And the north bank could be reserved for the Civil Administration. But, he emphasised, none of the rising ground on either side of the river must be claimed or staked in any way. This land was destined for European housing, railroad or Government; its use must be a matter for future discussion. Ainsworth agreed. But, he qualified, the determination of land policy was the province of the Commissioners; and, despite the power of appropriation, he must expressly forbid the granting of land-leases and settlements.

Whitehouse returned to Mombasa the following day. He spent an unprofitable hour with the Vice-Consul in Leven House (who merely referred him to Hardinge in Zanzibar). Later he confided in Frank Rawson at Kilindini headquarters. Ainsworth, he thought, had agreed a little too quickly to his propositions. There must be a reason for that. Ainsworth, perhaps, would make the move from Machakos sooner than any of them expected. In that case it would be 'very much a matter of squatter's rights.' It was imperative, Whitehouse instructed, that the shift from Kilindini to Nairobi be made at the earliest possible moment. And, since neither Preston or Spooner was a match for a man of Ainsworth's stature, it seemed equally urgent to appoint a Divisional Engineer of sufficient aggressiveness to press the railroad's interests in the Nairobi area. He suggested Colonel Patterson.

Patterson, tented on the bank of the Athi River, struck camp on 5 June: at noonday the railhead train steamed into Nairobi. The train discharged an army of coolies, their stores and equipment; some crates containing Patterson's trophies; Doctors McCulloch, Brock and Waters; and a horse. The horse was Patterson's and was named (appropriately) Blazeaway.

Patterson built a small camp for himself and his servants where the ground rose, south of the river, into Nairobi Hill. From the hill he could see the papyrus of the swamp and, beyond it, the military lines. Captain Cooper, like Patterson, was a zealot: the tents, huts and installations formed a miniature army citadel. There was a flagstaff and the daily rituals of raising and lowering. A company of East African Rifles was paraded, drilled and exercised in the early hours of every day. Bugle-calls crossed the river in melancholy phrases. A Union Jack graced his tent-pole and, when the wind crossed the plain, he could hear the satisfying flap and ripple of it and the sound was as nostalgic as the voice of the bugles.

Ronald Preston and the other railhead engineers were under canvas on the lower ground on the fringe of the swamp. Florence, at that time, was the only woman. The early months of the year 1899 had been fraught with danger. The drought and the famine brought the tribes nearer to the line and, beyond the camps, they were entrenched in desperation. Their nearness was felt like a tangible thing, creating guilt and unease. Then when the need smouldered into hostility and the arrows came many of the women were afraid. Smallpox, too, was running south from the Kikuyu villages like flame in brush and this, for some, was more fearful than the arrows. In March a road engineer, O'Hara, was dragged by a lion from the side of his sleeping wife and eaten; and it was the killing of O'Hara and the widowing of his wife which crystallised the fear of the women and of the men who were concerned for them. Soon the women left; for Mombasa or Fort Smith or even as far as Machakos.

But Florence stayed. She was aloof from all things African—including its dangers. 'She was never the one to look under a cot for a snake,' Turk observes, 'or to stop from taking a hand of water from a stream.' The bodice was always white and starched, the long dark skirts severely pressed: the plump body moved sedately in the grip of whalebone corsets. The men brought her silks and threads from the trading posts and the fingers worked at embroideries which were incorruptibly English. The tent, wherever it was and despite the zebra skins and the rifles, the lizards and the flutter of the grey parrot, invariably produced the atmosphere of a Victorian parlour. But outside there were wilder rhythms. 'It was unsafe to walk out at night (Preston wrote) after dark between the railway line and what is now known as the Railway Hill, the whole valley being one series of game pits. The game used to come down in their thousands to drink at a small spring trickling through the long grass at the spot where the present Military Siding stands. Nearby, the natives had dug a number of game pits and here they used to lie in wait for their prey, firing poisoned arrows at the game as it passed . . .'

From the papyrus Preston could see Patterson's tents and the colours of the British Flag. He had had little contact with Patterson since railhead pressed beyond the Tsavo River. The separating distance grew with the passage of time, Patterson's image blurred and the resentment faded. Then, with the killing of the man-eaters, it re-entered him. He had wanted a man-eater and the want was a lust as fierce as that of Patterson. But his work had taken him from Tsavo and he had been deprived. Patterson had grown into heroic dimension and, for a time, the jealousy and the frustration took him and reduced him like a dormant fever suddenly re-kindled. But even that had passed. He himself had grown; not on the plaudits of others and in the aura of exaggerated stories but from a developing power. Africa was seasoning him and he was less vulnerable to men like Patterson, to disappointment and to unrequited passions. The line reached

Nairobi and ahead was the challenge of the Rift and the run down the plateau to the Lake.

But, now, here was Patterson again; set above him on the hill, set above him in authority as Divisional Engineer. And, in the weeks that followed, it became plain that Patterson came arrogantly and proudly on the crest of a reputation. This was no ordinary builder of bridges. This was a lion-killer, a deliverer. Patterson rode the orange stallion through the valleys and the streams, inspecting and surveying, commanding from the saddle. He watched the gangs from cover or from the brows of hills. He sat the horse as stiff and autocratic as a chieftain. A small-bore rifle was always slung on the shoulder ('. . . riding about like a blessed Hussar . . .' Turk described it). It was easy for the old animosities to revive. Patterson had assumed the role of over-lord. Preston built his timber-and-corrugated-iron huts, his roads and his permanent way—and waited for the horse to ride flamboyantly from out of the sun. The horse, now, was as hated a symbol of authority as the red pocket-book. It was hated by all. Its face was as supercilious as its master's. It was fascinated by dust-devils (like a zebra) and, despite the rein, made its way stubbornly to wherever the wind whipped the red dust of the lower hills into spirals. The orange hide turned red. Men watched this red and monstrous thing gallop through avenues of sunlight; and felt unease.

The women returned. Nairobi grew daily, and in the growing became safer. At the end of June Ronald Preston called a meeting. It was attended by the ten railhead wives and their husbands. Nairobi, Preston reminded them, was to be the centre of railroad and Government administration. As such it would be an important town. There would be a large garrison, a bazaar, a hospital and doctors; in fact all the blessings of a civilization in the midst of a wilderness. Plainly, the time had come for the wives of railhead engineers to put down roots. Three were pregnant and for these the advantages were obvious. But for all those whose futures lay in East Africa, settlement, here in Nairobi, could be prudent and profitable. The Chief Engineer had a power to lease land; and, surely, who had better claim to land than the men who had brought the rail? There would be separation. But railhead and town would be joined by the line; and, perhaps, land and a home were better than the wandering.

They had talked. For most of the women the prospect was inviting. They had spent three years in the bush. They were as hard as teak. Some were like men; strong and leather-faced from sun, shabby and patched. A taproot was essential for a woman. Children, too, were essential. They were tired of dust and heat and the relentless move toward a lake they had never seen. Perhaps a home and a bottle of lavender-water and a new petticoat would restore them. They agreed.

After the meeting Preston laced Florence into her tent, walked down to Sergeant Ellis's store. There, behind the stables, drinks could be bought. The path lay around the papyrus and the feathers moved in wind and were silver in moon. A family of lions crossed the path and he watched them go grey and purposive into the seascape brightness of the plain. They were followed by Robert Turk. He seemed directionless. The face, caught suddenly in moonlight, was intense and distracted. Preston called to him but he did not answer.

There were three men at the store. They were drinking German whisky. The faces were empty and unresponsive in the glow of the hurricanes. There had been a telegraph from Mombasa, one of them told him. Both of Turk's twin boys had died from the smallpox.

From then until the end of the first week of July there is no entry in Turk's journal. Those unmarked spaces are more eloquent of anguish than any written expression of personal grief. Even when the entries resume there is no mention of the boys; and, on 8 July 1899, he merely comments '. . . a derailment at Emali of food-train, we shall all be on short-commons for a bit . . .' It is not until Christmas Day, when railhead was poised above the Rift at Limuru, that the emotion of that day compels him to write '. . . I should never have gone to Mombasa, God Bless Them, if I had not gone they would still be alive . . .' Turk, it seems, suffered the pain of guilt. He was convinced that he had carried the pox direct from the Kamba villages to the house in Vasco da Gama Street. Death had been his gift. There is

239

nothing to indicate how the missing week was spent. Perhaps he went to Mombasa on receipt of the telegraph. Perhaps he went into the bush and stayed until time and solitude eased his grief.

During that time Preston laboured to prepare the yards and the station. Already the line was moving from Nairobi toward Kikuyu. Drought still lay on the land (there would be no relief until the end of the year) but isolated rain-storms came suddenly from a pewter sky—and passed. The swamp filled and the sun drew mists of evaporation across the tents. The black-cotton soil, where the huts and the tents were spreading, would not drain. It took the water and held it and would not relinquish it except to the sun. 'We had carried out a moderately successful irrigation scheme (Preston wrote); with drains and ditches we had succeeded in keeping each tent in our camp just above water-level . . .' But the site was bad. The earth had the smell of sickness. Nothing grew except stunted thorn and papyrus and, when the rain came, an evil efflorescence of weed. It was here, on the crust of a semi-marsh, that the coolies and the low-grade workers would be housed.

But Nairobi was changing. The administrations of both White-house and Ainsworth had converged upon it, bringing some five or six thousand men. Buildings, tents and shanties were rising on the soft lands around the swamp. The Masai kraals had been shifted from north of the river down to the Ngong; and where the kraals and the cattle had been the military lines ran in geometric patterns along the Kiambu track. The station was finished, and a road west of it to the Nairobi River. The road was named (predictably) Victoria Street and was the main Nairobi thoroughfare. Near to the station Wood's Hotel was rising. There were many familiar names. Boustead and Ridley had come from Mombasa to build a European Club (always a priority); George Stewart & Co. had a circle of warehouses; and a German named Huebner was building a trade-post for Lansing & Co. Below the bridge Alidina Visram had formed the nucleus of a bazaar. There was a half-built soda-water factory under the name of Jeevanjee (that acute Indian who had already made a fortune from railroad contracts). The place was unstill. It vibrated with noise and a febrile air of urgency.

Across the river John and Ina Ainsworth had built their house. It was a low white bungalow and the ground around it was fenced and planned for the flowers and vegetables they would grow. It was named Daraja. Below them Nairobi was naked of trees. But they planned to clothe it. This was to be a capital. It needed the dignity of avenues, the shade of leaves. The important roads were already dug for the planting of eucalyptus trees, the holes which would take the roots spaced so that a bullock-team might turn. Even the swamp would be drained, the papyrus cut and the soil turned for the seeds of vegetables.

The town was vividly described by a missionary from the Sagala Mission Station: '. . . The shacks, or landies as they are called, lean into each other to join and shut out the light. It is a labyrinthine place in which people and rats live together in a common squalor. The ground squelches under the feet like the crust over a morass and one treads with care around great piles of garbage and open gutters transporting night-soil to one or other of the big open cesspools. Here, they say, one can cut one's finger and it will fester within an hour.

'The town has already divided into sections. The Indian commercial district and the bazaar sprawls over several acres and adjacent to it is the market for produce, vegetables and meat. The filth is incredible. Garbage rots in uncleared heaps. Rats abound. Meat and other edibles hang within inches of human ordure and all of it stinks in the tropical sun. The market area gives way to the Dhobi Quarter, a gloomy alley of brown men and women all scrubbing feverishly at a variety of clothes and fabrics and where the stenches of pollution are joined by the smells of sour steam and yellow soap. One crosses the stepping-stones of the Nairobi River to official residences and newly-cut roads leading to the Military Barracks. Here, all is good order and cleanliness but, again, it is evidently thought proper that sewage should run along open cement channels and into a river from which most of the population draws its water.

'There is something strangely Oriental about Nairobi. One seldom sees an African. They are not town-dwellers and a natural, well-founded suspicion keeps them from entering therein. Thus one walks through a living microcosm of Asia or the Far

East. Chinese and Indians rub shoulders. Black, brown and yellow faces shine with sweat in the alleys. Dialects smite the ear and naked chests brush against kanzus and silk burnouses. There are conflicting scents of foreign food and the smell of Calcutta seems to mingle with the incense of temples. It is terribly overcrowded and one longs for the quiet benison of the plain. The Indians are industrious, working and scurrying about like ants in a larder. They divide, curiously, into castes of occupation. The Goans, or Portuguese Indians, make excellent clerks, the Hindus are cunning and avaricious traders, the Sikhs are supreme in all manner of crafts, and the Moslems break their backs at manual work.

'But it is at night that Nairobi afflicts the mind as well as the nose. After darkness the lamps burn in Victoria Street and Government Road, casting great orange circles on to the mud, the ruts and the water-filled holes. Horse-carts lurch through the puddles, driven straight through the throngs of promenading people. People jostle each other, shout, scream and jeer. There is much drunkenness, robbery and fighting. It is turbulent and as vivid and colourful as a box of paints. Arabs sweep by in their long robes, turbaned Sikhs stalk imperiously, Zanzibaris and Chinese, Baluchis and half-castes, soldiers and railway gangers, all jostle through lantern-light and shadow in a medley of silks, sashes, brass buttons and bracelets, topis and rags. Beggars extend entreating hands from the shadows. There is a whole parade of disease and deformity. One turns from the leper's face, from blind eyes and the sores of framboesia, from twisted limbs and skin moving with filarial worm.

'The bazaar is the centre of the town's nocturnal life. One cannot move for the intermingling streams of humanity. The noise is as appalling as the smell. Bells ring, men shout and quarrel, women beckon. Merchants cry the merits of their wares. Here one can buy almost anything; a tusk or a box of cartridges, a bag of hippopotamus teeth or a bolt of cloth, a knife or a gun or a leaf-shaped spear, a handful of bhang or a pellet of poison. The stalls are hung with kerosene-cans filled with pombe, a brew distilled from sugar-cane or honey, and into these men dip their mussucks and gulp it until their brains are stupefied. There is much depravity. Men stagger from the hemp and the pombe to the arms of prostitutes. There are alleys where perfume sickens the senses, where eyes glittering with kohl throw an invitation, where men and women lie intertwined in hovels and make their shameful bargain. Procurers thrust a tariff into one's hand. One reads with distaste that a Somali girl costs 5 rupees, a Seychelloise 4, a Masai 3, and a half-caste 1 . . .'

Preston, by now, had prospected the land above the flat. Here, where the foothills of the first Kikuyu escarpment began their rise, the soil was good and fertile. It would drain and decompose night-soil. And as a building foundation it was adequate. One day the land would be valuable. There, and on the other rises, Patterson and Hinde were involved in endless dispute. But it was an immense area; large enough to meet the needs of the railroad, the Administration and the settlers. Preston, his friends and the womenfolk chose their land and staked it. Dreams were woven. Already there were gardens of hibiscus and bougain-villaeas and white houses with vines, the voices of children.

The dreams were as ephemeral as the mist from the swamp. The orange horse came in a cloud of red dust to where the track crossed the old caravan road and a marker, painted with his own initials, was flung at Preston's feet. He had looked up and across the soft grey lips of the horse to the martinet face of Patterson. A riding-crop pointed. The marker, the harsh voice said, was one of a number of illegal boundary demarcations which he had torn out of the ground. The land on the rise was retained for the use of permanent officials; and in any event was at the dis-position of either himself or Mr Ainsworth's deputy. Agreement was difficult enough without the intervention of land-hungry squatters. At this point in time it was not the policy of Her Majesty's Government (the accent, now, was that of a Consular officer) to alienate land to settlers . . . The didactic voice har-angued him and he bent and retrieved the marker, hearing, then, the horse wheel and the receding sound of hooves. The marker, with its pathetic white letters, was as worthless as debris. He cast it from him.

Patterson was angered by the abortive land-claims and, on

243

14 July, he sent a letter to Whitehouse on the Mombasa train. 'Every Indian peddlar, Arab trader and Punjaubi headman (he wrote with exaggeration) is scrabbling for a parcel of land. Even our own engineers are more occupied with the selection of choice sites, with which to endow their futures, than with the advancement of the line . . . Ainsworth has not yet shown up but Hinde and I argue a little for the sake of form but get on well together, and would get on better without the interference of outsiders. Nairobi is at present a railhead camp, and the quicker it loses that doubtful distinction the better . . .'

Patterson's tour of duty in East Africa was due to expire. His work would finish with the building of a small bridge[1] across the Nairobi River at that point where a track led to Ainsworth's bungalow. It had been a good tour. He had fulfilled his contract. He would leave a permanent memorial in the shape of the Tsavo Bridge. And the work had been leavened with the excitement of mutiny, attempted murder and man-eating lions. He had obtained many trophies the best of which were already crated in Mombasa for transport on the British-India ship. The tour was to end in a climax of fire and recrimination.

Patterson was a man of extreme cleanliness. Outwardly he was scrubbed, shaven and laundered with scrupulous care. Inwardly he was flushed, irrigated and generally medicated with a variety of salts, potions and purgatives sufficient to defy all but the most virulent of African bacteria. For this reason he had conceived a gradual disgust for the worsening conditions of Nairobi. He believed (wrongly) that the swamp was malarial and that some component of river or swamp mist produced the disease.

Patterson saw clearly that the Nairobi site was badly chosen. To his credit he had made representations to both Whitehouse and Ainsworth. The Chief Engineer was stubborn. Although he could hardly be blamed for the descent of the Civil Administration upon a station destined to be no more than a railroad headquarters he must, then, have foreseen the growth and eventual importance of Nairobi. But the time for decision was past. He was committed. He could not now survive a change of site and all that that implied in terms of time and cost. Curiously, there

[1] Now known as Ainsworth Bridge.

244

is no record that Ainsworth acted upon, or even agreed with Patterson's complaint. He disliked Nairobi, he hankered for Machakos; but, perhaps, to the man who had known the disease and the primitiveness of the Congo in 1884, Nairobi was not unduly alarming.

But McCulloch, the Chief Medical Officer and the only man whose technical opinion might, at that late date, have moved Nairobi, was on leave. Neither Brock the physician nor Waters the surgeon had the power: both were apprehensive. The train brought daily cargoes of bundle-clutching Indians. Nairobi grew and emptied its bowels and its slop-cans into the gutters and the rats were fattened and, soon, pestilence ran through the alleys.

The town at that time was supplied wholly from the Nairobi River. The river, low from prolonged drought, was barely sufficient for its needs. There was never enough water for the cleansing of roads, houses and latrine-trenches. To the dysenteries, the venereal infections and the filariasis whose worms were now coiled in the bodies of a quarter of the coolie population were added the dirt-fevers of tick, mite and louse. But, worse, the water of the river was contaminated. Held to the light it would always reveal in suspension the red soil of Kikuyuland: clinically examined it sometimes showed the flukes of cattle, the cercariae of bilharzia. Concerned by this, Winston Waters had followed the river upstream, away from the town. There he had found the Kikuyu and Masai herds watering in the river; and, in the water of the river, the snails which were the hosts to the bilharzia.

Patterson, that man of passionate hygiene, was revolted by this. His acquaintance with Brock and Waters, the occasional hour of camp-fire talk, had brought him close to the problem. The talk, casually professional, was, for him, a recital of medical horrors. Everywhere, it seemed, invisible regiments of destruction were proliferating; in the blood, in the tissue, in the sewage in the roads. The anxiety was magnified into fear. It was in this frame of mind that Patterson went one day into the bazaar with Waters; and saw a case of plague.

Patterson had seen the plague, once, in the slums of Calcutta.

He had never forgotten those choking galleries of hut and hovel, the stench and the garbage and the fecal matter and the men and women sweating with the pain of the big tender buboes and the flesh glaucous in the blue-green light of the slum. Now, here in Nairobi, the experience repeated itself. Waters led him into the shop next to Visram's. It was a small general store set on a shallow board-walk. There were sacks of salt and grain, coils of wire and bolts of Manchester cloth and americani, dried meats and looking-glasses and festoons of beads. In the back of the store a Sikh lay on a sleeping-mat: even in the failing light they could see the bed-bugs in the fibres of the mat. The face was suffused and stuporous. Waters turned the man and there, on the hip, was a large plague carbuncle and an ascending rash of purpuric spots. There was movement beneath them and Waters lifted the board and shadow whipped and was still. A dead rat lay on the soil and, holding the lantern to it, they saw plague fleas in the skin.

Outside there were many people. They were silent with fear. This was something from antiquity, from an old area of buried knowledge. The plague had always come. This was the plague. Waters pressed them back from the shop. Then, on impulse, he took a bar and levered up the wood of the board-walk. Momentarily the brown rats plunged in a vortex of pink bellies and threshing tails. Then they were gone.

Waters evacuated the bazaar, removed the Sikh to quarantine. Now it was nightfall. They washed in disinfectant outside Patterson's tent. Below them was the unlighted sprawl of the empty bazaar, a pocket of blackness within the lantern-points of Nairobi. Filth, rats, plague, plague-fleas, man: the cycle seemed unbreakable. But not to Patterson. Only fire could cleanse this festering place. After Waters had gone he called his servants. They were to load a cart with oil and cotton-waste. Then they would follow him to the bazaar.

Patterson began the fires in six different sites. There was a second in which oiled waste flickered like the lighting of new lanterns. Then the flame took life from the wind and gathered and unravelled the darkness and was crimson from the oil and was running down the alleys like gouts of red liquid and the shops were immersed and leaning into the current of it and the wind came again and, suddenly, the fire joined and was one and the bazaar exploded its heart on to the sky in an immense yellow flower and the flower dripped racemes of fire into the surrounding huts and men were running and shouting behind the ferocity of the fire. Patterson went to his tent on the hill. The bazaar burned in a reservoir of clear straw-yellow light. The fire was clean. Nothing could live in it; not the rats or the fleas or the lice, not even bacillus pestis. The corrugated-iron of the roofs was changing colour with the heat and he could see the sheets hanging in the debris like small red wafers.

In the morning smoke was still coiled on the sky: the roads and houses of Nairobi were covered with a cerement of grey ash. 'For this somewhat arbitrary proceeding (Patterson wrote) I was mildly called over the coals . . .' This was a remarkable understatement. Whitehouse was furious. Property and goods had been destroyed. Already the Asians and Arabs were making exaggerated claims for compensation. How could the railroad resist? There was no proof that the stocks did not exist. And what had the fire achieved? Infected rats had merely been driven into the outer areas of the town.

But Patterson was unconvinced. The fire had cleansed. And that dramatic surge of flame into the sky above the bazaar had given him a moment of the most elemental satisfaction. He left Nairobi unrepentant. This was the first stage of his embarkation from East Africa. The train moved across the Athi Plain. The head was high and arrogant. The Kaiser moustache was pomaded into two imperious curls. He had built them bridges. He had delivered them from lions. And he had saved them from the plague. Duty was sublimely and triumphantly done.

Colonel Patterson's letter to Whitehouse produced its effect.

'. . . I received a telegram (Preston wrote) stating that the entire Coast Head Quarter staff had entrained for Nairobi, that our camp must move and be clear of the station before their arrival. A tall order and, we thought, an unkind one . . . The order from Headquarters was imperative. We had to move, and that quickly. The available means of transport consisted of our solitary rail-head locomotive, and a very limited number of trucks. Over 2,000 men, with their tents, baggage and plate-laying tools were to be hauled up the Kikuyu bank . . .'

Track had been laid to a distance of nine miles from Nairobi, near Fort Smith; and it was there that Preston built the new railhead camp. All the women came. Roots were denied them, even the first exploratory filament of a root. But this was the forest. There were many roots.

10. *Into the Rift and over the Mau*

Preston brought the line to the edge of the Kikuyu Escarpment on 2 October 1899. The edge lay 1,500 feet above the Kedong Valley in the meridional rift. This was the point, at Mile 362, where Whitehouse had left his marker, where the railroad must, for a time, end its forward thrust. The line emerged from the forest, from the blackness of tree-shadow to effulgent light and, running toward this emptiness of light which hung as if reflected from a distant floor, stopped. Preston had walked between the rails to where they lay truncated above the Rift. The day was clear and he could see the cones of Longonot and Suswa and the floor of the valley and, toward Kijabe, the green where the Kedong Stream ran. Nothing moved. Nothing had ever changed except the scarp where they had cut down the trees and the scrub. The new scar was red below him. He could hear the locomotive and its faint suspiration of steam and when the sound stopped the silence of the Rift came. This was the silence of antiquity and everything, the scuff of boots and the breath on the lips, was an intrusion.

He had understood the mechanics. From here would begin two separate engineering operations. To his right ran the wall of the valley; and this they had marked on the map as the Kikuyu Incline. The permanent line would descend the wall, laterally and holding to the wall, until it debouched into the valley at the base of Kijabe Hill. There would be many viaducts taking, perhaps, one hundred girder-spans of from twenty to forty feet length. From there the line must run on the flat of the valley, around the lakes and to the escarpment of the Mau. The Mau rose to a height of over 10,000 feet. It was black with forest. It looked impregnable. But, in fact, its scarp was easier than this, the opposite wall of the valley, on which he stood. At Mau Summit the line would reach Mile 488.

But that was the permanent way. And the thirteen miles from the top of the Kikuyu Incline to the base of Kijabe Hill must be frustratingly slow in construction; too slow for the London critics, too great a delay to the announcement that the Lake was gained. So, below him, was the expedient, the second (and correlative) operation. Fifteen hundred feet of rail would be pinioned to the scarp, dropping without deviation or concession to the appalling angle of the slope to the valley. Locos and rolling-stock would be 'lifted' and, the valley thus achieved, would run on temporary track toward the Mau. This was the theory. It was a good theory and he had applauded it when Whitehouse had drawn it for him. But now, standing above the Rift and the slope falling, falling into a perspective of depth and getting dark with distance and the wind bringing the smells of raw earth from the swath they had cut and the sense of height fastening on the mind, it seemed impossible of execution. It could not be done. You could not lift a hundred tons or more of deadweight down such a ramp. Nothing would hold. Like all of the schemes of all of the visionaries it was flawed. Resentment grew from the fear. Whitehouse had presented him with an engineering fallacy. Nothing would hold. Whitehouse, aloof in Mombasa or Nairobi, had left him on this terrible brink to weave a rope of sand. Nothing would hold and the whole precarious parcel of rail, engines, cables and winding-gear would slough off the wall and into the valley.

The resentment, and even the fear, passed. Railhead was his; from the Ocean to the Lake. It had to move—that was the only creed. There was too much weight of hope and effort and sacrifice behind it: it could not falter. And everything was relative. There was a wall and there was a valley. But there were also ratios of power and weight and stresses.

Like most railroad engineers Preston did not mistrust instinct. Instinct operated where the readings and the measures gave neither warning nor confirmation. It was an integral of decision. He clambered over the edge. Below, on the scarp, he would pause, turn and make his assessment. The descent was perilous.

It was ledged in parts. There were craters from which the roots of trees had been torn. Runners from the roots were looped like snares. The swath was spiked with the new white wood of cut scrub. He was followed by Sharaf Din. Sharaf had followed him with devotion since he had joined the railhead gangs at Stony Athi. He was a coolie from Lahore; an ageing Muslim with a tangle of white beard, a fierce and lupine face, immensely dignified. He had a great love of trains and trolleys. Because of this, because he was breaking with the exhaustion of digging in heat, Preston had appointed him one of a pair of trolley-boys. Sharaf was grateful. Sharaf became watchdog, friend and servant. Sharaf seldom left him.

Now, on the scarp, Sharaf followed, close and protective, bringing that rancid smell of India which had never left him. They had stumbled, lurched and fallen. The valley opened and the perspectives altered and, above them, the edge was ragged with the small black figures of the gangs. Five hundred feet down the scarp they found a ledge. The ledge was wide and long and Preston marked it as a feature of exceptional utility. They rested on the ledge. This was morning: he watched the light strengthen and the Rift reveal itself and ripen into a map of subtle colour.

The ledge was a natural division. Sitting there he could see that it demarcated two differing slopes. Above, the slope fell at a grade of perhaps twenty in one hundred feet; and this, he knew, was no obstacle to the lift. But below the ledge the declivity sharpened. He began the descent, holding to Sharaf Din, to his stick, to the spikes which bristled from the red-brown stairs. After seven hundred feet the gradient levelled again. He had fallen once, impaling his calf on a needle of wood. His knees and hands were abraded, his sock and boot wet with blood. The inclination, he estimated, had fallen as much as fifty in one hundred feet. Staring upward the slope looked fearsome. Segments of it hung like a cliff. He marked its grade, knowing then that no loaded waggon could descend at such an angle. The fear returned. He needed reassurance and he went down into the valley, down the remaining three hundred feet of the incline. This was comparatively gentle—no more than a ten per cent gradient. From the floor of the valley he looked back to and up the escarpment. The swath was like a sleeve between the trees. Distance reduced its dangers and he stared at it, unmoving: even an illusion of feasibility was better than the fear.

Preston spent most of the day on the scarp. He measured, drew and calculated. Sharaf Din climbed to the camp on the top of the Kikuyu wall; and returned with food and drink. The valley changed colour with the phases of the day. There was game in the valley, and silence, and innocence. Soon it would know the rush of locomotives and the game would flee and the furnaces would eat its trees. They regained the camp at two hours before sundown. The rails had been stacked and Preston pointed at the stack, at the headman and at a group of coolies. He needed six men, he told the headman, and a ten-yard length of fifty-pound steel rail. He watched them align along the length of the rail. They were creased with puzzlement. 'Now take it down the scarp,' he told them.

For Preston this was always a test of a gradient. Men had to carry, lift and manœuvre heavy plant; and railroad plant was among the heaviest. The rail was a good test. It was rigid. It was slippery. It weighed five hundred pounds. They took the rail, shouldered, down the easy incline to the ledge. They were slow and afraid. They reached the ledge, set the rail at their feet. Already, he knew, the steel had begun to hurt the flesh of their shoulders. They were peering, now, at the steep descent below the ledge. He shouted at them and they lifted the rail and moved from the ledge and on to the slope of the second incline. Now they were braced against the gradient. He could see the white of their turbans and the rail and the six right hands across the rail. He heard their curses. They seemed almost stationary on the narrowing angle of the scarp and he shouted and they cursed him and moved again toward the valley. Now they were small, like white insects under a wand of grass. Behind him men were laughing, the laughter touched with fear or relief that they were not bending on the slope under the weight of the rail. When the rail slewed and disengaged itself he heard only the faint scream of panic and the metallic noise of the rail as it leapt down the scarp. He did not hear it hit them but they were spread on the slope like bundles of white rags and two of the men were crying in reedy voices. He watched the rail run like a ski, leap once in a parabola of reflected light, settle on the lower slope. At that distance it was small, bright and fragile like a dropped pin.

He sent men down the incline. When they returned with the two injured coolies the first flux of evening was in the valley and there were crevices of dark-blue dye where the green of the stream had been.

It was good by the fire that night. Robert Turk had brought eland-meat and the ribs dripped fat into the wood-smoke and the fire sputtered on the fat and went yellow with it. They were downwind of the coolie camp and wind came channelled from the Rift, cold on the flesh that was away from the fire. Florence was there, the hands expert on needles and wool; Gailey, who would build many bridges between Nairobi and Muhoroni; the Church brothers, one very tall and the other short and known, inevitably, as High Church and Low Church; Sergeant Turner, a telegraph-signaller seconded from the Royal Engineers; and Nesbitt, a foreman-carpenter. Sharaf Din waited in the darkness beyond the firelight. Turk sat silent and apart, the shadows of the two dead boys in his face.

Preston had begun to worry at the problem of the scarp, leaning into the radiance of the fire, sketching, lobbing the balls of spoiled paper into the flame, talking along the process of his thought so that they might share. He drew the incline in elevation. Here, he told them, were fifteen hundred feet of scarp. If the angle of inclination was constant there would be no problem. But the scarp was not like that. The first five hundred feet produced a gradient of almost twenty per cent: the central, and dangerous, section of seven hundred feet produced a fifty per cent gradient; and the lower section of three hundred feet ran easily and gently at ten per cent to the base of the wall. There were three good ledges or platforms: at five hundred, eight hundred and twelve hundred feet. In effect the scarp was divided naturally, by ledges, into four separate inclines.

He gave the sketch to High Church. Church was a grave, appositely-named man with calm eyes and a high, ecclesiastic dome of a forehead. The fingers played sensitively on the draw-ing. The first and fourth inclines, he thought, could be worked on an ordinary gravity principle: drums, hauling cables, and a loaded waggon descending in counterweight to an ascending, empty waggon. For that you would need two separate tracks on each of the inclines. That was simple enough; but, plainly, you could not use gravity inclines on the third and fourth sections where the fall was one in two. He marked the sketch, passed it to Gailey.

Gailey studied it. He agreed with Church, he said. You could not send a loaded waggon down at so acute an angle. It would retain neither its contents nor its stability. That meant some kind of a carrier, something on to which the waggon would run and be brought to the horizontal. He returned the sketch to Preston. A carrier could not run on ordinary metre-gauge track, Preston said: it would need a gauge of perhaps five and one half feet to ensure lateral stability. He completed the drawing. Theoretically, he observed, it was now possible to move a waggon from top to bottom of the scarp; but (this with humour) not even a hypothetical waggon would expand itself to run from a metre track on to a five and one half feet gauge. He would leave them with the problem.

Dr Orman came after they had eaten, pouring stewed tea from the big blackened kettle which was licked by the flames of the fire and staring at the lanterns of the coolie-camp. The face, still comical and clown-like under the cloth cap, puckered in distaste. Already, he told them, the camp was a sink of squalor. Already some twenty or thirty coloured prostitutes had come from God knows where to add their own spores of disease to the dysentery and the bush-sores and the fever. As for the two men injured one had a smashed pelvis, the other a shattered knee. Surely, he asked Preston with severity, that was a high price to pay to slide a rail down a hillside?

Whitehouse had charged Preston with the completion of the cable inclines by the middle of November. During that time the earth-work and platelaying gangs would move into the valley, laying the temporary track from the base of the escarpment to Kijabe

Hill. From there, at Mile 373, the terrain of the Rift (flat and without natural impediment) would lend itself to a rapid advance of at least one mile a day. At Mile 466 the ground would begin to rise, up and toward the summit of the Mau.

Preston spent a week on the scarp, in the valley and on the Kikuyu Incline where work on the building of the masonry abutments for the viaducts had begun. The problem of the differing gauges had been solved. Beneath the ledge at the end of Number Three incline he had sunk a pit into which the carrier would descend on the wider-gauge track. The horizontal platform of the carrier would be pinned with ordinary metre-gauge track; and on this platform would be secured the item of rolling-stock. With the slow descent into the pit the metre gauge of the rails on the carrier would meet and join with the metre gauge of the lower (Number Four) incline, the rolling-stock running, then, freely from platform to track. Similarly, an ascending carrier would find a junction for the two metre-gauge tracks at the top of Number Two incline.

But all this would require plant. He prepared an indent and sent it to Nairobi. The reply brought dismay. Nowhere, from the Coast to Kikuyu, was there sufficient plant. There were only two Howard Clip Drums. There were no steam-engines to work the central inclines. There were no carriers. There was very little eighty-pound rail and even less of one-and-one-quarter-inch steel cable. The deficiencies were inexcusable. Whitehouse had reconnoitred the escarpment in October of 1898, Sir Guildford Molesworth in the following January. Even the tools at railhead were desperately inadequate. '. . . the entire stock (Preston wrote) consisted of a couple of screw jacks, a dozen each claw and crow bars, two sets of rail-carrying chains, a dozen spanners and a dozen hammers.'

At railhead he was joined in a common frustration by Gailey and Nesbitt. The steel for the viaducts on the Kikuyu Incline had not arrived. Had Whitehouse mentioned it? Was there a sign of it in Nairobi? Eight of the viaducts would reach structure-heights of seventy or eighty feet. That was a great deal of steel.

They were anxious. They waited. On the night of 11 October 1899 a telegraph came. The second South African War had begun. This was the worst of news. A war was always a calamity. It consumed men. It also developed an insatiable appetite for plant and steel.

In the following weeks Preston ranged the country in search of trophies. The game was thick. He went with Turk and the Suk tracker into the Rift, the Kikuyu Forest and beyond Nairobi to the Athi Plains. The expeditions were essays in pointless killing. He owned many fine trophies; so many, in fact, that they could not be transported and were stored at points along the line. Perhaps the old fever had revived; or he shot to relieve the frustration of the silent inclines. Christmas Eve came, and still the track poised truncated above the Rift.

The camp had been decorated. The mess-tents were festooned with paper-chains. Dark green leaves had been painstakingly scissored into serrated shapes and entwined with red berries to give a semblance of holly. There were cans of flowers; pink Cape chestnut, kaffir and moringa, aloes and blue pentas brought from the plains. Cheap tallow candles, rubbed red and orange with ochres, burned in the halves of coconut shells. Tin foil had been shredded and then twisted on string so that it glittered in light with an effect of tinsel.

That night, by the fires, gifts were exchanged. Most had been bought from Indian and Arab shops in Mombasa or from the trade caravans. Some were small personal possessions taken from the depths of chests and given because there was nothing else to give. And a few were absurd; antimacassars stitched in the glow of hurricanes or squares of linen embroidered with forget-me-nots or straw hats embellished with sewn roses. There was even a damask valance of the kind used for curtaining the frames of beds. These absurdities were fashioned with love and given with love but they had no relevance to the country or to their way of life, no function other than to accent the pain of exile. At midnight Preston led them in the singing of hymns, they standing around and near to the leap of flame and the faces opening and cavernous in the effort of song and beyond the aureoles of firelight abysses of darkness which were boundless and alien and in which their voices died without echo. It was this

The Rift Valley. Above: Whitehouse on left of trolley and Preston on right, descending with the wagons of a goods train. Below: The first and second inclines

The railway today. Above: A viaduct on the Kisumu branch line
Below: A diesel-hauled train in the highlands

dying of the voices which made the hymns meaningless. There was no-one to listen. The sentiments were too fragile to live in that throbbing night. The hymn (which was their third) faltered and they had stared in embarrassment and were silent; and in the silence they heard the cry of a hyena and the cry was suddenly unbearable and there was no Christ in the wilderness, no love or pity or good or bad, only life—expiring or beginning or surviving; nothing but that. The cry came again and it was the sound of mockery and something arose in them like sickness and the day of Christmas had as little meaning as the hymn.

The day passed slowly. The engineers were restless and the festival had no significance for the Asians and the Africans. 'It was a mistake,' one of the bridge-engineers wrote. 'There were no children—perhaps that's what was wrong. Even the Christmas pudding had a cankered heart when we cut it open, we ate the outside and it tasted like curry . . .'

A week later they re-assembled. Now, on the escarpment above the Rift in the last darkness of 1899, the century was changing. Midnight was a minute away and they were standing in quiet groups. The men were clean-shirted and sober of face, the women white-busted and lavender-scented and different from the women who knelt by the banks of streams and pounded clothes and went pallid under the sweat of exhaustion. This was an occasion and, in other places, people would herald the coming of the new century with peals of bells and streamers and submerge their fears in the noise of congregations. A whole world would mark its advent. Here in Africa, the old, the nineteenth century, passed like a canoe into darkness. It went in silence and the darkness of rivers was still there when it had gone.

They had made no preparation for the coming beyond the clothes and the closing of their community. There was no ceremony and none of the missionaries had come to railhead to read a prayer. When the moment came they were undecided. The hand of a watch had moved and this, now, was the twentieth century. There was no sign to dignify it, no solemnity of bells, no opening of the night-sky to reveal the moon, not even a variation in the wind that came soughing from the Rift. They embraced or clasped fingers or murmured little phrases of hope for the future or drank a glass of whisky in the firelight; and were silent. There was nothing more than that. The clean bright clothes and the perfumed throats were absurd: there was nowhere to go except the tents and the whip of lizards.

Preston walked with Turk to the edge of the escarpment. Behind them the groups stood in silhouettes of self-consciousness against the fires. There were fires deep in the valley where the plate-laying gangs were camped. They could not see the scarp and the abandoned inclines, only the points of fire in the fabric of blackness. They did not speak. Time had no significance. Centuries lay on the Rift, so many that they escaped the mind in their infinity. Preston came again at sunrise and this was another day, the mist in the valley as opaque as a pond of milk and the trees on the lower Mau rooted in the mist like mangroves.

Photographs of Whitehouse taken at this time reveal none of his anxieties. The face is serene, the eyes direct, the moustache ragged but combed with a flourish. In one of the pictures he is seen descending the second incline of the escarpment. He stands at the front of a carrier, staring across the Rift at the forests of the Mau. The hand rests nonchalantly on the rail and the chin is uplifted. He is as impressive as a captain on the bridge of a ship. Here, you feel, is a man incontestably in command.

But, in fact, he was at the centre of a most acute personal crisis. Nothing had gone right since the beginning of the year. The drought had broken at the end of December 1899 and from then until late April of 1900 the skies had poured an unceasing deluge. These were no short-rains to refresh the land and fill the wells. This was a torrent. There were flash-floods in the hills. The land opened to receive it and was replenished and then sated, regurgitated it so that the black-cotton of the Kapiti and the Athi became a marsh and the unballasted track sank and skewed and denied passage to the trains. For a month no steam crossed the plains. The labour was returned from the Rift to rebuild the line and the valley was silent again and Preston's men struggled in the mists and rains of the scarp and waited for the steel which the war had taken. In Nairobi the swamp had spread its softness under the huts of the coolies and the soil polluted slowly with the ordure which would not drain through the underlying rock, and the water, coursing through the town, left its detritus of filth. Soon, men began to die. The hospitals filled with the enterics, the pneumonias and the tick-typhuses. Costs mounted without any commensurate advance. On the Kikuyu Incline, between Escarpment Station and Kijabe, the wall bristled with the ribs of abandoned bridges. There was not enough steel, there was too much rain. Whitehouse prayed for it to stop.

But with the stopping of the rain began the criticism. Some of it was insidious. Most of it was open and hostile. The medical statistics[1] provided incontrovertible evidence of the dangerous qualities of the Nairobi site—and ammunition for his opponents. But, for him, this was an old issue. It was already decided; and, for good or ill, Nairobi would rise from the watering-place. The transfer of Government had made that certain. More important, the railroad had overspent its estimate. In London the Uganda Railway Bill entered its Second Reading. The object of the Bill was 'to provide further money for the Uganda Railway.' The line, Parliament was told, would cost not three but five million pounds.

The Bill, its debates and its readings, could hardly have been presented at a less propitious time. The Imperial forces had been embroiled in South Africa for more than six months and, now, Kitchener, Roberts and Buller were locked in combat with the Boers. Names like Spion Kop and Ladysmith and Mafeking engaged the mind. War and all its myriad excitements was in the air and the awareness of a nation and its parliament was pinned, like a flag in a map, on an area two thousand miles south of the railroad. There were no emotions, or even loyalties left for the vagaries of a metre of track in the heart of a wilderness. There was certainly little money.

Whitehouse was inevitably caught in the backwash of the Bill.

[1] By the end of March 1900 deaths totalled 1,164 from the beginning of construction. Nearly 700 of these were concentrated in 1899-1900—the year of the Nairobi railhead. In that year the hospital-tents received 22,532 patients.

It was the custom of the Railway Committee in London to send him copies of Hansard's Parliamentary Debates whenever the railroad was discussed. To these the Committee added critical memoranda of its own. The April package made painful reading. The taunts of Labouchère and the reproofs of Sir Edward Grey and Sir Henry Campbell-Bannerman were accompanied by a letter from the Managing Member of unexpected severity. In it he was urged to make 'economies and austerities as stringent as the U.R. will bear . . .'

Whitehouse set about his task with enthusiasm. He spent several days in the offices at Nairobi. Then he went slowly downtrack toward Mombasa. He stopped at every station, at every halt, at every yard, store or workshop where men were gathered and were paid and victualled from railroad funds. He watched and noted. No handful of men was too small for his inspection, no station too remote. Nothing small escaped that careful inquisition. As with most economy campaigns it was the trivial and the insignificant which was attacked with ruthlessness. The largest single item of expenditure—the wages of the Indian coolies—was ignored. At that time there were more than 18,000 in East Africa (it was to rise to a peak of nearly 20,000 men). Perhaps ten per cent of these were superfluous. But the influx continued. The cost swelled. Most of them would join the sick-lists at one time or the other, the sickness attributable in the majority of cases to conditions of overcrowding, dirt and medieval sanitation. Here, by restricting the engagements and enforcing the elementary rules of tropical hygiene, Whitehouse might have achieved a considerable saving. But nothing, there, was done. Instead, every allowance paid and privilege granted to the European staff was weighed in the balance.

The salaries of the Europeans were contractual and, by the fact of it, unassailable. But there were many perquisites (tobacco, drink and servant allowances, additional leave and subsistence payments, incentive bonuses and hardship money) which White-house could attack. This he did—with a savagery which surprised his friends and dismayed Rawson. At the end of four days most of the inducements which made service on the railroad endurable had been withdrawn or eroded.

Whitehouse's motives are obscure. Undoubtedly he was embittered by the continuous criticism in London, resentful of the implication that he was responsible for waste. Here was a great Imperial enterprise in an alien land now tainted with the muck of politics. He needed support, not a campaign of denigration. He was, by character, a fair and scrupulous man. Perhaps he acted out of pique, or to preserve himself in a seat of authority which had become unstable. Whatever the goad he could never have anticipated the violent consequences.

It was at this point that Whitehouse displayed that trait which, at times, impelled him to retreat from the pressure of events. There had been a time, before, when he had marched beyond railhead, through the Rift and onward to the Great Lake, leaving behind him the complex thing he had helped to create. Now, with the economy measures authorised, he felt the old, periodic need for isolation. Tomorrow, he told an uneasy Rawson, he would return to Nairobi, there to make preparation for a reconnaissance of the Mau. Rawson would be expected to announce, and implement, the measures.

Kima lay on a rising line at Mile 261 between Sultan Hamud and Kiu. It was a small station set in a country of scrub and thorn. There was a siding and a store and a water-tank, a station-master, a signalman and a pointsman. There was also a hut in which slept twenty coolies from an earthwork gang. 'At Kima station (Preston had written) we met large troops of baboons . . . These baboons have often been mistaken for lion, and there are more lion about Kima than is generally supposed. . . .' But there was no mistake about the animal which took the coolie Atma Ram from behind the water-tank, dragged him into the brush and ate him. This, without doubt, was a large and malevolent male lion.

Whitehouse's train stopped at Kima two days after the killing of Atma Ram. There were no Europeans at Kima and he was received by the Asian station-master. He had hoped for a stroll and a pipe while the locomotive was fuelled and watered. But the station-master's news deprived him. It was too dangerous to walk and tobacco, now, could bring no solace. He questioned witnesses and examined the bloodied bones and tattered dress of the coolie. Then he went with the station-master to the station building. Last night, the station-master said, the lion had returned. It was of such appalling savagery, of such formidable appetite that it had leapt on the roof and had torn a sheet of corrugated-iron from the timbers. He had lain on his cot, rigid with terror: above him the lion's paw hooked the air and the great body struggled to compress itself between the rafters. He owned no weapon and, with great presence of mind (which he hoped would not go unobserved) he had blown his whistle. The lion fled. Then he had sent a rather desperate telegraph message to Nairobi.

Whitehouse had not at first believed him. Then he had seen the buckled sheeting and the wrenched nails and the blood on the iron where the lion had torn its flesh. Some of the blood had dripped from the roof to the floor.

Whitehouse left Kima for Nairobi in a state of alarm. There was, of course, something comic in the situation. Station-masters and lions were now joined, in East Africa, in a hundred jokes and anecdotes. But behind the comedy, the man's fear and the whistle and the animal on the roof he had sensed the approach of tragedy, like the coldness of night attendant on the heat of day. The events of Tsavo were still fresh in the minds of men. The lion of Kima could revive the fear, spread the contagion of it up and down the line with unforeseeable results.

Whitehouse spent two days in the town arranging his safari. Then he left for railhead. The train reached the edge of the escarpment at noon. Turk and Preston were there to greet him. Neither was friendly. Turk was gaunt and cold because the pain of his bereavement would not leave him. Preston was almost hostile. The cable inclines to the valley had not begun to operate until the first week of May 1900. There had been six wasted months. For Preston the railroad was an organic thing: it had coiled behind him like a spring. He had felt its power but he could not release it. Now, here before him, was this man whose lack of foresight, he believed, had suspended him on the scarp without the means of descending it.

Whitehouse ordered Turk to Kima. Then he inspected the

first half-mile of the permanent track they were building along the flank of the escarpment to Kijabe. The ledge had been cleared and cut to the base of the hill thirteen miles lower, and most of the stone abutments and piers were built. But there were only three viaducts. There was an air of abandonment. Men stood in forlorn groups. He had planned to take steam down this, the Kikuyu Incline, within nine months of reaching Escarpment Station.[1] But this was the eighth month (the last days of May 1900). Gailey and the Church brothers waited for the girders and the bracings that were needed for the bridges, went daily to the material-train—and found it empty. In England they were turning the steel into guns.

Whitehouse returned to the top of the temporary cable-inclines, took his place in the first of the descending waggons. There was a moment in which the waggon poised on the edge and the Kedong Valley tilted below him in a distant marquetry of luminous green. Then the waggon slid down the first incline and the steel cable was taut behind it and he heard the whir of the drum and the tap of the Howard clips. In the valley he could see the waggon, small as a toy, ascending in counterweight. At the head of the second incline the track levelled on to a ledge and the waggon moved from there to the horizontal platform of a waiting carrier. This was the beginning of the steep declivity where, for seven hundred feet, the scarp would fall in a grade of one-in-two. He had time to light a pipe while they secured the waggon. Then it lurched, stopped, began the descent down the wide, eighty-pound rails. The chuff of the steam winding-engines was raucous in the silence. Now, from the horizontal, he could stare ahead of him through the wreaths of pipe-smoke at Longonot and the lava cicatrices which marked its face in lineaments of infinite age. The valley opened and the stream, as delicate as a rill, gleamed in an apple-green loop. At the end of the third incline the carrier slowed, ran with immeasurable caution into a pit: its platform, now, was level with the continuing metre-gauge track. The floor of the valley was near. The trees had emerged from their blue-green mass of interlocking crowns and he could see the branch patterns, black and ramified

[1] In fact the Kikuyu Incline was not in operation until 4 November 1901.

under the crowns. The waggon moved again, down the gentle slope of the last three hundred feet. The valley encompassed him. The waggon stopped. This was the floor of the valley. Its scent was around him; that scent of water, seed and vegetation which touched the nostrils like ancient pollen and was the effluvium of a million years.

He looked upward from the valley, up the scarp to the crest where Preston stood, knowing that the descent was a feat of engineering and that he could not refuse some form of tribute. He waved, and waved again, but the minute black figure turned away and there was only the brightness of the sky.

Whitehouse's foot-reconnaissance from the railhead in the valley coincided with the first outbreak of violence in Mombasa. Ahead lay the silences and the inaccessibility of the forests of the Mau: behind him, four hundred miles away at the Coast, was a cauldron. There is nothing, at this distance in time, to suggest why Rawson's proclamation of the new measures should have provoked such bitter passions.[1] Resentment and protest were to be expected; but not this wave of rage which leapt from Kilindini to Nairobi. Perhaps there were underlying causes, old dissatisfactions which the economy measures touched and set alight. Perhaps there were men of ill-will eager to incite. But whatever the causes the passion ran from the Coast like a powder-trail, igniting here and there into dangerous explosions. There were meetings from which leaders emerged and, inevitably, a pattern of strikes. The strikes erupted into violence and mobs of coolies (sometimes European-led) ran through the labyrinth streets of Mombasa. Soon the smoke from burning buildings was pillared on the sky. Stores were destroyed and the rails which led from the Macupa Causeway were torn from the earth. The violence, now, was an intoxicant: men carried the taste of it uptrack to the little halts and stations and, soon, the smoke was on the sky again. If there was ever a true and honest cause it was forgotten. Men fought, robbed and burned without a reason. On the third day the trains stopped running.

[1] All mention of the strikes and the riots was, apparently, excised from railroad records: no reference now remains.

At this point in the story appears a man of exceptional strength. C. H. Ryall was, at this time, the Superintendent of Railway Police. The police were a small corps of some two hundred Indians and Europeans whose authority held in the railroad zone. They were armed, uniformed, answerable only to Ryall. Ryall was a very tall man; humourless, melancholic and introspective, burned lean by the tropics. He had black, ragged eyebrows and deep unkind eyes, a cruel mouth and big, aggressive hands. He was ruthless and friendless. He lived for the law and its enforcement; and in the living found a lonely fulfilment. He was a martinet. He ate and drank frugally. Each day was a discipline, discharged like a penance. He was disliked—and obeyed. He had fashioned a nucleus of fierce and intractable Pathans into a police instrument of exact effectiveness. The Pathans were feared by the coolies, the Europeans, the Africans and the Civil police. But they were Ryall's men. They were in a kind of liege to him and they would do nothing without him. At the time of the violence Ryall lay in the Kilindini hospital in the tremors of malaria. For two days the mobs ran, their fever as intermittent as his own. Then, on the day on which the trains stopped, Ryall emerged from hospital.

He came haggard, yellow of face, and possessed of a terrible fury. But it was a controlled fury—he was not emotional. Gods of law and order had been defiled: someone must pay. He appraised the situation, gathered the Pathans and read the Riot Act. He arrested five of the subordinate Europeans (he later described them as 'half-breed scum from the Bombay almshouse'). Then he moved through Kilindini and the Old Port, into the mobs. They had broken the law: he broke their heads with equal enthusiasm. By nightfall the island was quiet. The gaols were full. Mombasa relaxed. But the telegraph spoke of up-country strikes, of places still turbulent with temper and mutiny. These were Voi, Mtito Andei, Makindu and Stony Athi. Nairobi, with its Civil police and its unit of East African Rifles, was peaceful. At dawn Ryall left Kilindini in a small, fast train. He took with him forty Pathans and a sergeant of police, Ajab Khan. His own inspection-carriage had been joined to the train. This was a mobile police-station, equipped with arms, manacles and other restrainers: there was a compartment for a servant. The train steamed into the Rabai Hills, bearing Ryall to his inescapable appointment with death.

Ryall settled the troubles at Voi and at Mtito Andei. On the second day of his punitive journey he reached Makindu. Within the hour he had arrested an Anglo-Indian riveter and three Punjabi coolies. During that period two telegraph messages arrived. The first was from Stony Athi: it informed him that the rioting bridge-gang had moved back to Nairobi and that the station was calm again. The second came from the station-master at Kima. Overlaying the exquisite prose was a note of hysteria. 'Pumping-engine employee wickedly assassinated by fractious carnivore. I unable pacify it. Situation perilous. Implore you alleviate my predicament.'

There were two other Europeans in Makindu at the time of the messages. One was Huebner, the German trader who managed Lansing & Co's store in Nairobi. The other was Parenti, an Italian merchant. Huebner had come to Kima to investigate a loss of grain on consignment from Mombasa. Parenti was prospecting the route from the Coast to Nairobi for avenues of trade. Both were at Ryall's side in the tiny telegraph-office when the Kima message came. The three men were unacquainted.

Ryall had planned to continue to Nairobi, taking with him the arrests (there were now thirty-five men under restraint). There they would remain in gaol until the Travelling Magistrate arrived. But the message could not be ignored. Fear was as potent a destroyer of the peace as discontent. He was a sober and dedicated hunter of men, not a mindless hunter of animals. But, plainly, he must go to Kima. He sent for Ajab Khan. The sergeant, he told Khan, would escort the prisoners to Nairobi. He himself would leave the train at Kima.

Huebner and Parenti rode with him in the inspection-carriage. Kima lay fifty miles uptrack from Makindu. They were a strange trio, thrown together by circumstances and moving toward an isolated African bush-station with that curious air of inevitability that sometimes touches the affairs of men. The German and the Italian were much younger than Ryall. They were opposites; and, oddly, each was a caricature of the other's national image.

It was Huebner who was small, lissom, swarthy, grape-eyed and excitable. It was Parenti who was muscular, slow of movement, fair-haired and Nordic-complexioned, stolid. Ryall sat in a corner of the carriage, the despotic face still yellow with fever and the hands toying, revealingly, with a set of manacles. He was uncommunicative. Huebner and Parenti talked together with the diffidence of trade competitors; of goods and freight-rates and native markets, and, of course, of the Kima lion. At some time during that journey they suggested to Ryall that they remain with him at Kima. Both were good shots and, in any event, three guns were better than one. Ryall agreed. The train reached Kima.

Another victim had been taken since the death of the driver of the pumping-engine. The remains, those of a coolie, lay scattered on the edge of a siding. They examined them. The ground around the bones was well-marked but none of them was skilled enough to read it. The station was silent and there was only the whisper of steam from the locomotive. The station-master stood behind them, comic with terror. Mr Turk, he told them, had killed five lions in the Kima area; and had left. But, obviously, the quadruped assassin had not been among them. The voice quivered with awe. It was a most cantankerous animal. He would show them.

He led them around the station. The doors of huts were gouged with white wounds from the claws. Wooden stanchions were gnawed. Sheets of corrugated-iron hung from the roofs. In one place at the rear of the station-building the timber was scored in a pattern of whorls and lines and the window was broken and, beneath it, the earth was raked and flung upward so that clots of it were spattered on the timber. It was as if some deranged thing had abandoned itself to a paroxysm of fury. They had stared across this evidence to where the scrub wavered in hot yellow light. Distant was the breast of Mendatini. Nothing moved except the heat-waves.

Ryall detached the inspection-carriage into the siding, near to the coolie. The train and its frames of Pathan faces and its stalk of white steam ran into distance and was lost. Now, even the sound of steam had gone. Kima waited in the raw and

267

nervous silence. In the late afternoon Ryall and the two traders scouted the fringes of the station, walking into glare until the bush thickened. There were families of lion under the acacias but these somnolent groups fixed in still ecstasies of sleep had nothing in common with the malefic thing which had come from the night to take the coolie.

At dusk Ryall, Huebner and Parenti went to the carriage. They took with them rifles and ammunition, some cold food and beer, two hurricane-lamps. Huebner trimmed, filled and lighted the lamps: the carriage and the metal of the guns and the flesh of hands and faces were suffused with a pale glow. Dusk passed into nightfall. Ryall was quiet, still weak from malaria. Huebner talked effusively, the flow of words a betrayal of his tension. He was restive. The hands played on the mechanism of his rifle, rattled the empty beer tumbler. Parenti listened to the excitable voice, watched the siding from the window. After a time the German began to eat the remnants of his sandwich. Behind the sounds of those rapid jaws they could hear the murmur of the two coolies in the servants' compartment of the carriage.

The carriage was divided into two sections. The larger section was Ryall's police-station. In it were a table, three bamboo chairs, a padlocked chest containing arms and restrainers, a small chest-of-drawers for papers, a high berth and, opposite it, a low berth under a window. There was a door dividing the compartments: it was a sliding-door and, for reasons of security, could be bolted from Ryall's side of the carriage. At the opposite end there was a second sliding-door which afforded the only entrance. Below and outside the door were three wooden steps to the ground. The door ran, easily, on a brass runner.

At nine o'clock Ryall rose from his chair and peered from the window into the siding. The moon had risen and the station and the huts threw splinters of shadow which commingled with the yellow irradiation from the carriage. He could see nothing clearly on this tapestry of black and yellow patterns. He extinguished the lanterns and Huebner's swart face was lost momentarily in blackness and Parenti was a silhouette. Then the faces came again in contours of vagueness, pricked by the white of an eyeball or a tooth. Outside, the siding sharpened in a tide of glacial light. He could see the rib-cage of the dead coolie and a morsel of flesh trembling in wind.

There was no sound from the coolies in the small compartment. They were safe. They slept. The night would be divided into three watches of three hours each, Ryall told them. There was a good field of fire from the window above the berth and, therefore, the watch should sit with his back to the head of the berth, a rifle upright against the frame of the opened window. He himself would undertake the first watch. They agreed. Huebner climbed to the high berth. Parenti arranged his blankets on the floor. Soon both men were asleep. Ryall stared into the siding, the night wind cold on his fevered temples. Insects tapped in the shadows of the carriage. He could hear the German's stertorous breathing. The smell of the putrefying coolie came faintly on the wind. He half-closed the window. The fever was rising. Outside, the moon-pools were as enticing as water.

There was always movement in the siding; the dart of lizards on the timber, the sporadic run of rats which was like the progress of mechanical toys, even a jackal. It had crossed the track, breaking the luminous steel ribbons and drawing the eye. He had watched its wizened face turn into light and the nose point for the scent of carrion. He could not sit there with the jackal on the coolie's ribs and he rose, slung his rifle, went from the dark of the carriage to the bright white light of the siding.

The jackal ran. It was good in the siding, the wind cool on the flesh and the light aseptic and the ground crystalline where the moon struck. He could hear the tree-frogs in the scrub. The line curled toward Kiu, narrowing with perspective until the steels became one fragile needle of luminescence. He returned to the carriage, mounted the wooden steps. The sliding-door had closed and he pushed it back along its runner, held it, then released it. The door closed. He descended the steps, walked around the carriage, measuring its angles with his eye. The ground was not ballasted and there was a pronounced list. He climbed the steps again, opened the door. A wave of heat came from the compartment, touched with the smell of sleep, food and rifle-oil. He hesitated. Then he wedged open the door so that air would flow, went to his berth. Huebner and Parenti were still asleep. The fever throbbed and his body had begun to tremble. He lay full-length on the berth, closed his eyes. The attack would pass: then he would finish his watch. He slept.

Huebner awakened, later, to the stench of something so nauseous that he retched as he came out of sleep. The stench was evil. It filled the carriage. An old area of the mind recoiled seconds before his eyes adjusted and saw the lion. It stood within the doorway, the hindlegs on the lower steps and the head, chest and shoulders in the carriage. The face and mane were absolutely still. Then the head turned and the nostrils flared for the scent of men and the eyes had the pale, opaque bloom of a rabid dog. He screamed and the lion entered and, wheeling, dislodged the wedge. The door closed behind it and, with the scream, Ryall sat up.

Parenti, too, was shocked from sleep. The scream, the sense of peril, the enormous weight which compressed his chest and prevented him from rising, the blackness on his face were components of a nightmare. He would emerge and the terror would fade and there would be no fear or suffocating weight or impenetrable night and the carriage would come clean and silver from the blackness, the air sweet and this smell of dung and hide and urine which was the smell of a beast going into the limbo of the dream and the soft hot belly which his palms felt but could not move or press away and the knives of pain which were in his chest and in his belly and thrust with the weight blood-sticky against his lungs all this would pass, *must* pass . . . Staring from the high berth Huebner saw the great height of the lion, the vertical ridge of the spine, the lion standing now on Parenti's chest and the tail lashing and Parenti's hands pushing against the weight and the dark mass of genitals like a gourd above his face and, higher, the forepaws on Ryall's body. He saw it take out Ryall's throat and, with that, he was released from the cast of terror and he leapt from the berth lurching against the lion so that his face touched the hide and he smelled the fetid heat of it and his hands were on the door and behind the door the coolies were screaming and he felt the resistance of them, their strength on the door holding it against him, his strength against

270

their strength, and he could not *could* not open it and behind him the tufted tail swung against his calves and the flood of fear renewed the sinews of his arms and the door gave and slid and, then, he was through, into the compartment, into safety. . . . Parenti felt the hindpaws move and the weight move and his lungs fill and the nerves of his groin break under the claws into new excruciating centres of pain and, rolling from the pain, he was free from the lion and against the door where Huebner and the coolies were and fist-beating on the door and the lion still standing and tearing at Ryall and he beating beating beating and the door not moving and he pushing crying beating and, still, the door not moving . . . Huebner held the door the cries strident through the thin wood of the door and the panels bending under the fists and, feeling the fractional movement of the door, he tore the turbans from the coolies' heads and bound the handle of the door to the stanchion and the door, now, would not slide and nothing could enter, not Parenti or the lion or even the smell of death . . . Nothing could enter and sensing through his hands the ungiving immovability of it the strength left them and they were like empty hanging gloves and Parenti sank to his knees and in that moment of resignation the lion turned, blood-wet from Ryall's throat, and took Ryall from the berth inert and heel-scuffing to the exit door and the door was shut, shut like a trap, and the instinct for a trap rose in the lion and the big moon-grey body turned and the rabid eyes glowed like clouded glass and Parenti closed his eyes and waited, hearing, then, the frenzy of the lion in the carriage and the body hurling itself insensately into the wood the glass the furniture of the carriage the breaking carriage and the shattering glass and the berserk noises of the throat and the sound of Ryall's body swinging in the carriage like a limp rag doll. Then the movement stopped and he heard only the moaning of the coolies. He waited. Air rushed across his face and glass broke and timber rended. Death had not come. There was a feeling of emptiness, of vacated space. He opened his eyes. The lion and Ryall had gone. The window above the low berth was an aperture of splintered glass and wood. A sleeve of Ryall's jacket, some skin and membrane hung from the jags of glass. He could smell the oil from the broken

271

lanterns. He sat there, smelling the oil and the resinous wood and the fungus scent of the lion.

That was on the night of 6-7 June 1900. Three days later White-house returned from the Mau reconnaissance. He came rein-vigorated by the solitude of the forests. Without doubt he hoped to find that his problems were resolved; that any minor resent-ments caused by the new economy measures would, by now, have abated and that the man-eating lion of Kima was dead. The reality was different. The sullen but ordered protest he had expected had erupted into riots and strikes. Ryall was already buried in the Nairobi cemetery. The man-eater was alive and fifty miles of track were caught in an inertia of fear. And the Pathan police, bereaved by Ryall's death, were apathetic: there were new pockets of discontent in Kilindini, drunkenness and fighting.

Whitehouse was alarmed. The events of Tsavo had left an ineffaceable scar. Another crisis was in the making: only positive action could prevent it. He reprimanded Rawson for the failure in authority, restored the old order of perquisite and privilege, increased the wages of the police and made a few careful promotions. Mombasa relaxed again. He entrained for Nairobi.

He stopped at Kima. Robert Turk and the Suk and some hunters from Nairobi were there. Another coolie had died in the jaws of the lion. The lion was old, mad and degenerate, Turk told him. It was unpredictable. It came and went, sur-viving everything that was fired at it, disdaining the pits and the strychnine. He produced a scrap of tawny skin, edged with white hair and doubled over like a purse. He himself had shot off half its ear. This was unlikely to incapacitate the lion but, now, it was identifiable. Whitehouse walked around the station. Men worked under the rifles of guards. They stared at him with hatred. The fear was as tangible as the yellow heat and the ripped wooden doors. This was Tsavo again. Soon they would begin to talk of Kali. He examined the pits and the poisoned meat and the three cage-traps Turk had built. The scene was familiar.

In Nairobi the anxiety intensified. He waited for the telegraph messages that would proclaim another death, another mutiny.

Mail train on the Makupa Causeway

Mail train climbing Great Rift Valley. Mount Longonot is in the background

But nothing came. Then, because the inaction was unbearable, he prepared the draft of a handbill. Gone was the niggardly care with which he had investigated the Europeans' allowances. This was no time for parsimony. The bill, when drafted, offered £100 for the killing of the Kima man-eater; and, as a precaution against the existence of more than one man-eater, a sum of 200 rupees for the death of any full-grown lion shot within the Kima engineering division and in an area restricted to one mile on either side of the track. He had not forgotten the disastrous Tsavo handbill and its expensive consequences. The Kima rewards would not be so costly. There was no possibility of confusion and only a dead lion with one-and-one-half ears and, moreover, positively identified by Turk, Huebner and Parenti, would be a candidate for payment. The term 'full-grown' precluded men like Paul Verschoren from claiming on the death of cubs. And, deliberately, he had not defined the term. In practice only the most mature of adult lions would be considered. He borrowed the small Government press which Ainsworth used for official ordinances and printed a hundred handbills. Then he entrained them for distribution.

The telegraph came within a day of the circulation of the offer of reward. The lion had been captured and caged. It was there, alive, for inspection. The telegraph was signed by Turk: there could be no doubt. His first reaction was one of immense relief; his second a growing regret that he had been so precipitate. A delay of a day or so would, in effect, have enriched railroad funds by £100 and, equally important, have relieved him of the obligation of explaining so large a payment. He went to Kima.

The lion, which had walked blindly into the simplest of baited traps, was preserved in a small cage in the shadow of the station building. It was senile, broken-toothed, pimpled with colonies of ticks. The severed ear had suppurated. It was ugly and unclean, the chest and lower jaw congealed with old blood. It alternated, they told him, between periods of apathy and terrible frenzies in which it flung itself against the walls and roof of the cage. He had turned from it. It was a thing of pity, not of fear. The lion, he instructed, must be displayed for a week in order that all men might see it and satisfy themselves that the terror was gone. Then it must be shot.

He returned to Nairobi. Turk rode on the cowcatcher at the front of the locomotive. The cowcatcher, now, was an addiction. 'It was a strange sight (Dr Waters wrote) to see the engine approach around a bend and his great height spreadeagled on the bars . . . He liked to affix his boots between the bottom bars and, leaning backwards, grasp firmly the sides. The engine would sweep by and one would see his hair, which was as long as a woman's, streaming in the wind and the face staring at the unfolding panorama with a rapt and almost adoring expression . . .' Waters had gauged Turk's mood with his customary perceptiveness. For Turk the rides on the cowcatcher were revelations. It was as if this land he loved had, by a combination of speed and unfamiliar angle, been transmuted; as if the whole of Africa in all its infinite shape and colour had been joined and flung swiftly against his senses. It came out of a shaking horizon. It distilled patterns of colour through meshes of scintillating light. It was a painted land and the pigment of it flowed and was cut by this prow of a train, and was gone, and was replaced. He saw it all afresh.

Turk spent a night in Nairobi. Then, at sunrise, he rode on the Mombasa train to Kima. The sensuous pleasures of the cowcatcher were soon forgotten. A dozen coolies were assembled around the cage. They were prodding the lion with sharpened bamboo canes. When he parted them with his shoulder he saw the things they had done. The tuft had been chopped from the tail. There was smouldering straw in the cage and the flanks were burned. A broken ligature was knotted on the left foreleg and, by stretching the leg outward from the cage, they had managed to draw the claws. He stared at their faces. There was no self-disgust, no guilt, not even enjoyment. Suffering was an abstract. This was an enemy: they had punished it. He took the Winchester and shot it.

The steel for the viaducts that would ease the permanent way from the crest of the escarpment to the base of Kijabe Hill had not been delivered until February of 1901. There Ronald

Preston laboured to bring railhead to that point on the western flank where the track would poise before (he wrote) 'what might be considered the last section of the construction of the railway, for from here onwards the line steadily falls making a total drop of over 5,000 feet in less than 100 miles before reaching the Great Lake . . .' But the way up the Mau was hard. 'On leaving Njoro we entered heavy forest land cut up by deep ravines which necessitated the laying of a couple of reversing stations, and the building of temporary viaducts with timber[1] which was mostly cut from the neighbouring forests. One of these temporary viaducts was 450 feet long and another ran to 345 feet. The jagged nature of the country we experienced in passing over the Mau escarpment can be judged by the fact that to complete the permanent line over this section 27 viaducts had to be erected which varied from 156 feet to 881 feet in length, and from 37 to 111 feet in height. There are altogether 11,845 running feet of viaducts between Njoro and the further foot of the Mau. On the Njoro-Elburgon section the difficulties of construction were increased by the incessant downpour of rain. At the best of times the light forest loam would not make a good foundation for railway embankments, but now with the rain coming down in torrents, the sun when it did come out was partially obscured by the heavy forest which made our progress very slow indeed, in fact at times we had to suspend work altogether, for it was well-nigh impossible, owing to the boggy condition of the track, to keep our locomotives on the rails. Derailments were the order of the day, it was not an unusual thing to have as many as half a dozen derailments a day . . .'

Preston built his trestles down the Mau. Turk shot game and scouted the route. Nesbitt planned the cutting and the fashioning of timber and drew the shapes of timber bridges. Turner bent over the Morse-key. Sharaf Din scoured, cooked and ironed, trolleyed between the camps. These were their individual duties. But at night they were joined, sharing the heat of a fire or a draught of whisky or the silence of contentment. At these times Din was no longer a coolie and a servant. He came

---

[1] Later the American Bridge Company contracted to build permanent steel viaducts.

to the fire (when he could give them no more in the way of comfort), and they were ashamed that this man of devotion and dignity should sweep and scrub and do menial things for them. But the fire and the darkness were great levellers. The white beard leaned into firelight and went pink and the voice talked of a childhood and a village and the tiger which came nightly from the oak-woods and took his family one by one. They listened. Sometimes Preston talked of an Indian childhood which had been no less rigorous. Turk cleaned and oiled the Winchester and stirred his dysentery with tea-and-whisky and told them of the great caravans and James Martin, the Maltese master, and the slaves that stumbled for a thousand miles to stand, eventually, in the peacock glare of the Zanzibar market. Soon the last of the ivory caravans would leave Uganda for the last march to the Coast: soon the tusks would voyage on the deck of the *William Mackinnon* to Port Florence and be borne to the waiting trucks and the merchant would exchange his whip and his porters for a freight-ticket. A piece of African history was vanishing in the steam of trains.

Within this group of men Nesbitt and Turner formed a closer, more intimate tie. They were inseparable. Each bore a striking resemblance to the other; each of them fair-haired, youthful and as slender as a girl. They were quiet men, drawing on a shared well of silence and communicating with a glance or a touch or the wave of a pipe. Nesbitt wrote a nightly letter to a wife in England, holding the pad into the radiance of the fire, searching for words (or perhaps a face) in its incandescent heart. Turner was never excluded. Friendship and love came from the same spring. Sometimes Nesbitt passed him the letter and Turner read it, and smiled, and returned it, and there was no embarrassment.

Florence Preston was at the centre of the group. She was Preston's woman and, for the others, was indivisible from him. She had no part in this male world of rails and bridges and locomotives. She sought no part. But she was warm, generous and affectionate. She preserved an inviolable femininity; and, in so doing, she gave to all. She brought a scent of lavender-water, the rustle of a dress, a woman's laugh. They were grateful.

Billy Nesbitt was drawn to her. He was the youngest of the men, lonely and rather immature. He was enduring the pain of separation from a girl to whom he had not long been married. And the relationship of Ronald and Florence Preston, so innocently but obviously demonstrated in all its overtones of intimacy and affection, was a continuous goad to his nostalgia. Florence sensed this; and, in the rootlessness of that wandering camp-life, gave him a special and separate sympathy.

Robert Turk stood on the outer edge of the group. They trusted him. They would turn to him in crisis. But he was, perhaps, too grim, too isolate, too marked with the scars of old violences, too ruthless and wild to inspire tender sentiment. This was his condition. He could not give. He could not change.

The line crossed Mau Summit at an elevation of 8,300 feet. This was a world of creepered forests and resinous glooms where frost melted in the early sun. But there were spurs from where, men said, the Great Lake could be seen—if conditions were exceptional. This first sight of the Lake, from railhead, was something yearned for, carried like a thirst through the years that had passed since the rails left the coast. To see it was to attain it. There, at the limit of vision, would be an end to endeavour. Preston went daily to the outcrops, staring across the great panoramas of hill and plain, through the films of distance to where the Lake must be. But there was nothing. There was not even a horizon. Mist layered on mist. Brightness defined brightness. He went at dawn, when the land might shed its darkness and, in a second of clarity, reveal itself before the hazes of day came down. He went at sunset, when the redness might catch, and fire, and hold for a moment the mirror of water. But there was nothing. The Lake eluded him. Then, in the third week of the descent of the Mau, the viaducts cross-timbering the slope and the earthwork gangs breaking ground toward the valleys, he went with Turk, Nesbitt, Sergeant Turner and Sharaf Din to the spur that jutted like a platform above the crowns of trees. This was now an embittering ritual, the Lake withholding and the group of men on the rock assembled like pagans waiting for the sun.

On this day there was no observable sunrise. Rain-cloud engorged the sky. The light came slowly, bringing the forms of hills from a land thick with darkness. This would be a day of rain and heavy skies and Preston turned from this unrevealing drabness, feeling, then, in the act of turning, the touch of Turk's hand upon his shoulder. The barrel of the Winchester pointed from the spur. The quality of light had changed. The air was suddenly crystalline. There was still no colour in the day but the land had moved sharply into focus under the intensifying light. It was as finely-drawn as an etching: the hills, valleys and grasslands rolled in perfect detail to an edge of whiteness. The whiteness lay between the grey of land and the grey of sky. It had the lambent glow of distant water. It shimmered. Then the rain came and this beauty of water dissolved and went grey and was gone and there was nothing but the rain drawn across the vision like a curtain and the wall of sky near and smoking with mist.

They had embraced, grasped hands, savouring the moment of the Lake's unveiling, holding to this glimpse of the north-east tip and imprinting the glow of whiteness on the mind because it must not be blurred by all the other memories. Only the reaching of the Lake could now obscure it. The Lake was there. Every yard of track laid from here, the Mau, was now a part of the ending. They stood in rain until the spur of rock deluged water into the trees below and the junipers shook under the beat of it. The moment was gone. It could not be regained. They went down to the camp.

11. *The Three Hills of Nandi*

When Joseph Thomson returned from his East African expedition in 1884 he drew a route map and a geological map. Most of the route map is covered in a great wash of green. The green, he tells us, denotes Masai Country. It begins in the south at the mountains of Meru and Kilimanjaro and colours the map as far north as Lake Baringo. In the west it flows over the Mau Escarpment and almost to the country of the Lower Kavirondo. East of the Mau it crosses the Aberdares and the Lykipia Plateau to Mount Kenya. This, by any standards, is an enormous tribal territory. Thomson named his book *Through Masai-Land*; and for him the terms 'East Africa' and 'Masai-Land' are synonymous.

But the green on Thomson's map is not so much a territory as an area of wandering. The Masai gave nothing to the land except the scars of erosion. They were nomads: they took their herds to wherever the water and the pasturage were good. The herds were of immense significance. They were diet, inheritance, bridewealth, status. And when the land was stricken with the locust, the drought or the cattle-plague and the herds grew small, the Masai became predators. They raided. They recouped themselves. In short, they were cattle-thieves.

Too much has been written of the Masai. The red bodies ashine with clay and grease, the ochre-braided heads, the exotic diet, the killing of lions as a ritual proof of manhood, the strength and the fierceness—all this has become a cliché of East African literature. Beneath the exaggerations of three-quarters of a century lies only a thin substratum of truth. For, like all predators, the Masai preyed on the weak. Like all predators they were victors because the opposition was feeble. There were a dozen different clans. They produced, by tradition, an élite warrior-class. They raided over great areas, even as far as the coastal region or, as it was known then, Swahili-Land. When they were rich in cattle the clans feuded among themselves. To the early explorers and the pioneers the land rang with the clash of spears. The Masai, decked and ornamented for battle, were a fearsome sight. It was easy to invest them with a legend of invincibility.

Thomson entered Masai-Land with apprehension. Traders, he was assured, 'never dreamed of entering the Masai with less than 300 men.' The Masai, he confesses, were 'dreaded warriors that had been so long the subject of my waking dreams.' The warriors came; and 'seizing our guns in one hand, and a tuft of grass in the other, in token that we were prepared to fight, but meant peace, we proceeded outside to hear our fate . . .' But, of course, Thomson's guns were unnecessary. The rapacity of the Masai was leavened with a very proper caution; and the warriors, for all their pride, were more interested in a little *hongo*, or tribute, than in fighting a well-armed caravan. Much later in Thomson's journey the 'ferocious and arrogant warriors' of his imagination have been diluted into 'our savage friends.'

Thomson was never attacked by the Masai. But his book, with its careful details, its drawings and its descriptions of the Land of the Spear, was gratefully received by the novelists. Here was a fat and fertile seed from which would burgeon a hundred melodramas: here was an unknown land revealed; here were the villains to supplant the Zulus and the Matabeles of further south. The role of the Masai was cast. The myth grew.

Within East Africa the myth was advanced for different reasons. Neither the slaver nor the ivory-hunter wanted an influx of people and the inevitable edifice of law and regulation. And the trader, whether white, Asian or Arab, was, in the way of traders the world over, afraid of competitors. Stories of Masai barbarities were deliberately broadcast. They were believed. For a time they were effective. When the first men of God and the first administrators came they waited for treachery and massacre; but nothing happened. F. J. Jackson, who was Deputy-Commissioner of Uganda at that time, wrote: '. . . I began to suspect that the terrors and dangers of entering Masai-

Land were very grossly and purposely exaggerated by a small clique of traders . . . Their object was to keep the door closed as long as possible and their happy hunting-grounds free of poachers . . .'

The administrators and, of course, the missionaries, were more alarmed by the spectacle of naked breasts and uncovered sex-organs than by the brandishing of spears. Prudery was as militant in its way as the Masai legend. Sir Charles Eliot wrote indignantly of 'astonishing exhibitions of nudity.' Joseph Thomson, writing of a Masai preliminary to marriage, refers his reader to an appendix decorously translated into a camouflage of Latin —only the classically-educated, it seems, were fitted to learn that the tribe practised clitoridectomy upon its women. But Sir Harry Johnston's commentary was the best. He wrote, in relation to the railroad: 'The Indian coolie travelling through this land, not of nudity so much as of flagrant indecency, has brought home to the native the fact that his nudity is repulsive. There is probably no more decent land than India, and no more prudish person than the native of India. It is no exaggeration to say that one of the first objects of the Indian coolie has been to put his fellow-workman into breeches.'

Johnston's words are ludicrous. The first objective of the Indian indentured coolie was not to cover Africans' genitals but to preserve himself in a dangerous land. The dangers were four-fold: disease, accident, predatory animals and hostile tribes. This was Masai-Land: he entered it, when the railroad began its drive for the interior, as uneasily as Thomson fourteen years before him. Like Thomson he found that the Masai warriors were the least of the dangers. For five and one half years the rail thrust for the Lake and most of it passed through Masai territory. There is not a single recorded instance of an attack, not a suggestion of hostility, not the slightest pinprick from a Masai spear. The Teita and the Kamba attacked, and killed, when famine made them desperate. The Kikuyu skirmished when the line reached their country. But the Masai remained as docile as the antelope that grazed around the track. He watched the flood of colonists and settlers, of armies and police and merchant-traders —and did nothing. He offered no resistance to the British occupation or to the railroad which was an artery of that occupation. He executed treaties which denied him land and grazing which had been his for centuries. The legendary pride was never an impediment to his retreat. Nor did it prevent him from selling his women to the railroad camps.

But on the northern fringe of Masai-Land lay the country of the Nandi. Twenty miles due west of Lake Baringo the Mau Escarpment was hewn into the two great ranges of Kamasia and Elgeyo; and from Elgeyo the land began its fall to the Great Lake. A caravan, aiming for the Lake and crossing the head-waters of the Nolosegelli River, would, within six marches, light its fires in the centre of a vast, wind-combed sea of grass in the shadow of the Three Hills of Nandi. The Nyando River rose somewhere in these hills, flowed through a hot but pleasant valley to Ugowe Bay; and it was at Port Florence in Ugowe Bay that the railroad would find its terminus.

Tribal territories were always vaguely defined, fixed by natural landmarks and old rights of usage. The Nandi ranged a great area from where the ridge of the Elgeyo fell in the east, down across the plateau of Uasin Gishu to the verges of the Kavirondo Plain. The tribe was akin to the Masai. Like the Masai, and at an immeasurable distance in time, it had come from the valley of the Nile. The Nandi was the strongest of a group of Kalenjin-speaking tribes. It was a warrior-race. The men were cruel, dignified and savage, the women handsome and picturesque. They worshipped the sun, practised circumcision. They fought with poison-arrows and spears, and these they used with enormous skill. They lived from animal husbandry and killed their sheep by suffocating them with a hand over the nostrils. The wives of a dead chief were always buried at his side at the time of his dying—with a choice of being put to death or of entering the grave alive. Lugard had written of them during his 1890 expedition: 'To the north would lie the country of Nandi, whose people are reported to be excessively hostile and fierce, and no caravan, European or native, has ever yet dared to cross their hills . . .'

The Nandi were the supreme warrior-race in East Africa. Certainly they were the only tribe actively to oppose the British, the only tribe with the courage and the sense of heritage to match its arrows and its spears against the carbines, the Maxims and the Hotchkisses. When the steel of the railroad curled from the summit of the Mau to the great plain that lay between Victoria Nyanza and the Nandi Escarpment the Nandi warriors sharpened their weapons.

But the rail would not reach west of the Mau until March of 1901. Now, in the mid-year of 1900, the route from railhead in the Rift Valley to Port Florence was still a caravan-path. From the forests of the Mau the path followed the route which the railroad would take, that is through the valleys of Kedowa and Nyando. The Nandi Escarpment which joined the Mau at the head of the Nyando Valley and which Whitehouse had described as 'a particularly abrupt and deeply fissured descent of 2,000 feet' was thus avoided. The path forded the Kedowa River a mile above its union with the Nyando, then followed the Nyando to where it joined the Kibigori. The crossing at Kibigori was staked out at Mile 531. The Lake lay about fifty miles beyond.

The path was used by caravans carrying Army and railroad stores to Port Florence, by railroad survey-parties and the small gangs of telegraph engineers. The path did not, in fact, enter Nandi territory; but tribal boundaries were flexible and the Nandi had long regarded the path as an intrusion. In the beginning it was the Army that suffered. The Nandi were cunning in the techniques of ambush, adept at night-assault. They were incomparably brave—but they were not foolhardy. The powerful caravans—those with Swahili or Sudanese guards—were not molested. But the smaller columns were attacked with ferocity. The arrows, tipped with a venomous paste[1] brewed from the roots of trees, came out of the sun or from darkness. The spearmen followed. The Nandi were merciless. Survivors were mutilated or buried alive. Stores, merchandise and transport animals were borne away to the villages. The tribe grew wealthy, the warriors vain with triumph. The attacks intensified. Drums beat across the night of the scarp like the throb of fevers. War was in the air.

[1] There was no antidote. Injections of strychnine were used by the medicos of those days, but with no success.

When the first telegraph-parties came in the van of the rail-road they found themselves, as so often before, on a dangerous trail. This was isolated work, with none of the great concentrations of coolies which always followed the rail. In front was the wilderness and only the telegraph like thread caught and then drawn taut into the curve of hills to remind that men had worked and passed. There were stories of these men who, in isolation and in danger, planted the poles and unravelled the lines of communication. Africa was a land of messages; made urgent by the throat of a drum or the pad of feet on a forest path. The land was unstill with the messages; and, now, a new and wonderful messenger leapt across distance as swift as light. Some of the men who had made this wonder had died; of disease or bad water, from an arrow or a spear or the tooth of a snake. Their living was never as dramatic as those who rode the footplate or blasted the rock. The stories of their deaths sang once, above their graves in the wire they had joined; and were forgotten.

There were twenty men to a party and, to each party, two guards armed with Snider rifles. One of the European foremen wrote: 'They (the Nandi) left us alone at first and we on our part were careful to make ourselves inconspicuous. We always used the features of the natural landscape whenever possible, taking the wire through lonely ravines and nullahs and quiet woods. Later, when the railway was laid, we would have to re-route the telegraph to follow the track. But of course they had eyes like eagles and nothing escaped them for long. I wondered what went on in their minds when they saw men diligently uncoiling wire through the country at a height of twenty-five feet above the ground. Now there is one thing that sends a howling savage into transports of delight—and that is a length of wire line. They stole miles of it. At first they waited for us to lay it, descending at night and removing it. Then they saved themselves the trouble and conceived a plan of attacking the parties before the wire was uncoiled. The coolies were terrified. They ate their chop grovelling on their bellies in the undergrowth. One day we came on a dead Punjaubi up a pole near to the Kedowa Stream. They had filled him full of arrows and he was hanging there like a dead bird. After that the coolies refused to work until the district had been thoroughly scouted . . .'

There were many deaths, great losses of wire. The attempt to lay a line of communication between Londiani and Port Florence —a distance of some eighty miles—was abandoned. When the survey-parties came they found a country inflamed with war. The Nandi, a nation which at that time could find fulfilment only in battle, were exultant. They were fat from the spoils of a hundred victories. They had bought many cattle from their neighbours. The herds were thick around the Three Hills of Nandi. They had unified a number of the smaller Kalenjin tribes and, now, the armies moved down from the scarps and across the plains to the country of the Kavirondo.

Whitehouse reacted. Without the final surveys the line could not reach the Lake. Without a measure of protection the earth-work and the platelaying gangs would go no further than the summit of the Mau. In Nairobi he enlisted a company of rifle-men. It was a diverse band, scoured from the alleys of the town. There were ivory-hunters, slave-drivers from the old caravans, time-expired Sikh headmen, Baluchis, Swahilis, Zanzibaris, anyone who could use a rifle and would take a risk for a price. Many were drunks, some were degenerates. Typically, White-house gave them to Robert Turk. This, after all, was the kind of assignment for which the caravan-master had been engaged. Within a week they were assembled and equipped. Already they were known derisively as Turk's Militia. On the twentieth day of June the company left Nairobi on the railhead train. It would march from railhead to Mau Summit: there, and beyond, it would be available for the escort of the survey-parties.

The plan worked. Turk must have ruled that wild company (it was fifty strong) with remarkable resoluteness; and, in any event, self-preservation was a discipline in itself. There were skirmishes but, it seems, the militia were never exposed to serious attack. The Nandi were primitives. None of them had seen, or would even understand the function of, a railroad locomotive. Watching from cover the parties of red-necked men and the careful rituals of sextant, theodolite and quadrant they could never have known that this was the forerunner of a force which would destroy the warrior legend. And, at that time, the main Nandi attack was concentrated upon the Army formations based at Port Florence and Fort Ternan. The surveys were completed. In mid-July Turk marched at the head of the militia to the little port on the inlet at Ugowe Bay.

Port Florence was under the command of Colonel J. J. Evatt. Geographically Uganda was reached at an imaginary line drawn vertically down the waters of Lake Victoria. But for administrative purposes the Protectorate began at the Kedong Stream in the Great Rift Valley. Thus, Port Florence was garrisoned with a detachment of a battalion of the Uganda Rifles. There were several companies, composed mainly of Sikhs and Punjabis, enlisted in India. Colonel Evatt was a distinguished soldier whose service record had earned a marvellous embellishment in the previous year (June 1899) by his capture of the rebels Kabarega and Mwanga. Evatt was, if Turk's description is accurate, almost the prototype of every fierce, ruthless and indomitable C.O. to appear in the pages of fiction. He was (Turk says) 'brawny, thick and glaring, a bit grey and a face like an old walnut, running them all with an iron hand . . .'

Turk's impression, at that point in time, is probably reliable. Evatt was entitled to glare. The triumphs of 1899 were evaporating with every failure to repulse the Nandi. Already he had mounted two expeditions, infiltrating the Nandi country but never closing with an enemy which, always brave but seldom fanatic, would choose its own battlefield, its own time at which to fight. He had fired a few empty villages, confiscated a small kraal of cattle. But that was all. The warriors had vanished into the mists of the high land, regrouped and then descended again when the unit returned to garrison. It was humiliating. It was a check to personal advancement. Now, with the first exploratory feelers of the railroad reaching into the sector, the affair had become much more than a tribal war. It was political. Uganda waited for the railroad link. Westminster watched. There were critical notes; from London, from Military Command, from the Chief Engineer, from Hardinge and Jackson. Suddenly a great weight of responsibility sat upon his shoulders. When Turk entered Port Florence he found a man irascible and nervous, consumed by hatred of the Nandi and resentment at a providence which had placed him so conspicuously under the lens of sovereign power.

The advent of Turk's Militia (however distasteful that company was to an officer of Evatt's professionalism) provided an opportunity too good to be missed. He had suffered from the lack of men steeped in knowledge of the country. Now here was a band of men, admittedly plucked from the slums of Nairobi, with an exceptional tally of experience. Their leader was a hunter and a caravan-master of repute. And even the Suk tracker was a Kalenjin and a mixture of Nandi and Karamojon. But they were mercenaries. They could not be pressed into service under the colours. That night Evatt shared a bilious kettle of tea-and-whisky with Robert Turk. They came to an arrangement. In the morning Colonel Evatt mounted his third punitive expedition.

The marsh-green plain behind Port Florence was vaguely marked on Evatt's map as Kavirondo Flat. The ground lifted slightly with the march but there would be no appreciable rise until twenty miles beyond the port. This was the route to Fort Ternan, which lay nearly fifty miles deep into the Nyando Valley. The column would leave the route after Kibigori, strike upward to the escarpment.

With the marching and the rising of the ground the Lake revealed itself. The mists of sunrise lay low on the water and, lanced with sunlight, threw a white and luminous glow. There were creeks of papyrus and euphorbia. The steam-launch *Kenya*, small and carnival-painted like a toy, was tied at the jetty. Further out, beyond the shallows, was the *William Mackinnon*— that itinerant steamer which had spent its early life voyaging through the bush, in two thousand separate parts, on the backs of porters. At noon the storm came; and, on the fringe of it, they saw the Lake darken and move like oil and join with the cloud and the charge from the electric-storm yellow on the oil and the creeks defined as black as charcoal in the lightning. When the storm passed the column moved again and, now, the turbans, the fezzes and the tunics were vivid under the rainbow and the land was marzipan.

This was a strong column. There were one hundred and forty Indian troops, a section of Sudanese (the best, and most brutal, soldiers in East Africa), Turk's fifty riflemen and a platoon of Swahili askari. It was officered by Colonel Evatt, a captain and a lieutenant (both unnamed in contemporary accounts), Dr Sherlock, the Medical Officer; and a Sergeant-Instructor, seconded from the Royal Marines, named Ellison. But the strength of the column came not from numbers or from the quality of its men but from three canvas-covered objects carried by the Indians at the rear. These were Maxim machine-guns. Each gun, in that territory and used within the wrists of a trained man, was worth a company of infantry. Such a man was Sergeant Ellison. If Evatt, in his toughness, his relentlessness and his regimental hauteur, presented to the world a recognisable caricature, then Ellison was the reverse. This was no semi-literate, battle-calloused sergeant of Marines. Turk described him as 'young but silver-haired & a voice like tiny silver bells . . .' And, later, as 'very quiet, very clever with the guns, with hands like a woman . . .' It had been Ellison's task to explain to the soldiers of Port Florence and Fort Ternan the mysteries of the Maxim; and, it seems, to demonstrate its powers.

The expedition bivouacked by the Kibigori. By noon of the second day the plain had risen into pastures of white clover and trefoil, the rise of the ground felt in the thighs and the respiration and the taste of mist. They could not see the Lake. It was there, engulfed in mist, the light of it diffused by the mist and thrown in mackerel patterns on the sky above where the Lake would be. Ahead were the scarps, purple with height and distance and formless behind the mist. Now the steel of the carbines and the leather of equipment were veined with damp and the column was long and tenuous on the climbing land and lost in mist at its extremity. There had been no sign of the Nandi; not a drum or a pillar of smoke or the gleam of a spear. At dusk, after four forced marches, Evatt halted the column in the cover of a rock-face. This was the second bivouac. With night the mist turned to rain and the cold of the scarps came down and the fires died in the rain.

At sunrise Evatt took the column north-west toward the

forested clefts where the Nandi and the Mau Escarpments joined. This was a silent land of eagles and dripping rock. Distant was the range of Elgeyo, vaguely seen like a dark battlement behind the rain. At mid-morning Turk and the Suk left the column, striking laterally along the lower scarp. There were two Nandi villages under the scarp, each with an air of abandonment. Turk walked through them. They were forlorn. There had been no fires for many weeks. Rain ran in the thatch of the huts. Nothing lived in the huts except rats. Something had emptied the villages, perhaps plague or the pox. Or rinderpest had struck the herds and the tribe had moved. They followed the contours of the scarp, leaving the bamboo for the opening plain. At noon they saw the village. Smoke dissipated in the rain but only the young and the old moved through the rain or peered from the huts or sat under the narrow eaves of thatch like propped ebony dolls. The warriors had gone. Turk went deeper into the plain, turning, when the light of day weakened, on an arc that would take him south to the rendezvous. Night had come when he saw the fires of the column. Rain fell. The land was sibilant with running water.

Evatt was in a mood of savagery. He had lost two mules and their loads of rations on the scarp. The men were dejected, cold and wet. And not a Nandi had been killed. Ellison, too, was morose. The Maxims had not emerged from their canvas jackets. In three days only the British had been punished. That night, leaning into a fire which burned under a sheltering carapace of leaves and brush, Evatt devised a plan. The expedition would divide at dawn. Plainly the Nandi warriors must be concentrated around the hills where the river rose. One-third of the column, including Turk's Militia, would be led by Sergeant Ellison on a radial line direct to the Three Hills. He himself would lead the remainder of the column on a line circumscribing the opposite face of the hills and into the bowl formed by them. The Nandi force should lie somewhere between the closing pincers of the columns; between the power of the Maxims.

Evatt and his two officers and the Indians left before first light. The rain had not stopped and, when the light came, the land and the sky were ashen. Turk watched the column become small on the slope below. Only the oilskins brought livid-yellow colour to the greyness, the turbans white and the flesh of hands and faces like dark mahogany. Then the glimmer of the skins went in small points of yellow phosphorescence into the raining plain; and were lost. Turk and Ellison left the bivouac one hour after Evatt: theirs was a shorter, different route. The march was fast, across the grain of the scarp and down the plain to where the Three Hills lay behind the mist. At mid-morning the rain stopped and the mist parted and, with the sun, a flush of colour was decanted like pale wine across the pelt of the hills. The column halted. Tea was brewed and Turk took two big kettles of tea-and-whisky down the line of the Militia. The men were silent from the privations of the last three days and nights. He smelled the sourness of exhaustion and the dampness of their clothes. They filled their mess-cans from the kettles, gulping the liquid and holding their faces to the warmth of the sun. Most were bearded. All were marked with a common brutality. He topped the kettles with more of the cheap German whisky and refilled the cans. When they had drunk they cleaned the wetness from their rifles and oiled the mechanisms with the enormous care of men who respect nothing but a proven weapon. Ellison, too, was silent, but consumed with a strange nervous excitement. He had gone to the two Maxims that Evatt had permitted them, stripping the canvas from one of them and stroking the fat brass cylinder with his sensitive fingers as if the metal were as finely-textured and as satisfying to the touch as satin.

At an hour past noon the Three Hills of Nandi separated into purple cones. The grass was thick toward the river-valley and the wind combed it and gave it tones of green. Beyond the hills the pearl of the Lake's reflection was pendant again in the sky. Somewhere there, in the shadow of the hills, Evatt's men would be deployed. Ellison stopped the column. This country of hills and valleys and high grass could conceal a thousand warriors. Clearly the terrain must be scouted. Robert Turk and the Suk left the column, were lost in waving grass.

There were three villages around the base of the hills. All were empty of warriors. Children sat or ran in the thick red mud. Women leaned pap-swinging over the cooking-pots. The Nandi forces, it seemed, had gathered somewhere and were out on foray. Beyond the third of the villages the valley opened into plain. There, spread and linked in infinite permutations of hide and horn, was the greatest concentration of native cattle Turk had ever seen. The herds grazed from the valley and the gleam of river-water to where the grass became blue with distance. He could hear them now; that lowing sound which was as timeless as the sunlight and the patterns of wind in grass. He counted the spears of thirty herdsmen. There were no kraals or stockades.

He rejoined the column at four in the afternoon. Ellison was disappointed. Thirty tribesmen were hardly a test for the Maxims. But the cattle were interesting: such a herd must represent the wealth of half the Nandi nation. Perhaps it could be driven. The column moved. The sky was already darkening with the approach of evening when they reached the fringe of the herd. One half of the herdsmen were building pyramids of wood for the fires. The herd was closer-knit, as if the nearness of night had pressed it inward. Ellison deployed the riflemen along a periphery of two hundred paces. Then he uncovered the Maxims, stroked the barrels sensuously, set them on their tripods. He placed them with care so that they gained a maximum field of fire, checked the water-casings and the magazine-belts, swung the barrels on a slow pivot and stared through the sights at the herdsmen and the cattle. The first Maxim he gave to a sergeant of Sudanese. The second he took for himself. Watching, Turk saw that all this was an exciting ritual. The guns were more than weapons, more important than foot-soldiers. They were admired and respected like regimental flags. They were pampered in canvas, propitiated with oil and brass-polish and the touch of fingers. But when the Maxims began to fire they became perfect engines of death. The herdsmen fell in a long, easy progression, cut exactly through the midriffs and falling to the ground like puppets pulled by string. 'It was all too easy,' Turk wrote. 'My own repeater (the Winchester was twenty-five years old) seemed a poor thing after that . . .'

The noise from the Maxims, magnified in the casing, broke in waves against the herd. It began to ripple with movement, to plunge in fright. Four of the herdsmen had run into cover. Ellison's gun began to rake through the cattle and, staring along the moving arc of the brass, Turk saw the first line of beasts collapse into postures of injury and death and, the gun returning along its arc, the second line layered horn-swinging and leg-dragging on the first and, now, the Maxim of the Sudanese sweeping in from the flank, the cattle wheeling into the fire, then turning, then broken-legged and bloody-chested and the mouths bellowing in silence because he could not hear their pain above the violence of the guns. The herd was moving now from this terror of the guns, flowing in long undulations of rump, hide and horn into the blueing grass of evening and the riflemen, infected by this slaughter, began to fire into the rear of them, plucking them from the herd and arranging them in wounded cameos, they left in the sea of grass like flotsam from a retreating wave. The Maxims swivelled and fired, swivelled and fired until steam plumed from the boiling water in the casings. Then they were silent and Ellison's sensitive fingers fell from the grips and the face was sweating from the heat of the barrel. The riflemen lowered their guns and the pain of the cattle's dying broke on the silence and against the hills. No-one knew why the cattle had died and were dying. They were ashamed and they did not speak of the killing. Later they regrouped and went down into the valley.

In the morning they found the remnants of Evatt's column. The Nandi had attacked in the hour before sunrise. Burial-parties were digging in the soil and there were mounds of muti-lated bodies. Dead tribesmen lay in the grotesque attitudes of death. Everywhere were the slanted shafts of spears. Evatt walked murmuring around the graves, prayer-book in hand. Rain had begun and the leaves of the open book were wet. It had been a good day until the attack, Evatt told them. They had met and killed a small war-party. They had found a thousand head of cattle in the valley and these they were driving with some success toward Fort Ternan. Then the Nandi had come out of the darkness. He pointed to the spears and the bodies which lay in profusion under the broken wands of grass.

The attack had been launched with a terrible ferocity. Even at the height of the battle he had marvelled at the fury which brought them berserk and screaming on to the bullets.[1] Three-quarters of the column were dead or wounded. Dr Sherlock lay, dismembered, in twenty pieces. Only the Maxim had saved them from total annihilation. The Nandi had recovered their cattle. The expedition was at an end.

Evatt led the remains of the column to Fort Ternan. There, in the mess of the small fort in the Nyando valley, under the protection of a company of Sudanese infantry, he found a distinguished emissary from London. Sir Clement Hill was much more than a member of the Uganda Railway Committee: he was also the Permanent Under-Secretary of the Foreign Office. He came with delegated powers: at that moment he was the most powerful person in East Africa. The two men were immediately antagonistic. The colonel was dirty, limping, lacerated and blood-stained, burdened with the memory of cold, wetness, death and mutilation, conscious of failure. The diplomat was immaculate, suave, immensely dignified, fastidious and virulent of tongue. He was also cynical. He came, he told Evatt, bearing gifts of dispraise. This was the year in which the railroad was expected to reach the Lake; but now it could not even hang a coil of telegraph wire across the Nandi country. Her Majesty's Government could no longer tolerate a situation in which Imperial ambition was continuously thwarted by a tribe of savages. The railroad was slow and costly. It was deficient in many respects. It employed incompetents. But it could not fight a battle and, at the same time, lay the plates and build the bridges. It was entitled to protection. And protection was the responsibility of the armed forces of the Crown. In the Kavirondo district and its environs the duty of protection lay with the colonel; and the colonel could hardly claim that he had discharged it. The expedition was, by all accounts, a failure. And, moreover, during the absence of the colonel's forces the Nandi

[1] In fact the four herdsmen who had escaped Ellison's fire had reported the massacre of the cattle to a section of the main Nandi force. The killing of cattle was so gross an outrage that the news had brought down the warriors on Evatt's column.

had waylaid the Uganda mails near Eldama Ravine and had butchered an entire platoon of twenty Sudanese soldiers.

Colonel Evatt had listened in silence to the rebukes of that scathing tongue. Later, when he was bathed and changed and at less of a disadvantage, he had attempted a justification. It was, of course, the justification of every professional soldier under pressure. He had not enough men. They were thinly spread. They could not guard every gang and every yard of wire. And when the road was laid they could not guard that either. Perhaps, in defending himself, he had seen again the tattered scraps of Dr Sherlock's body. But Sir Clement was cold, aloof and unimpressed. Defeat was a fact, however unpalatable. But out of the ashes . . .

It was then that Evatt heard the soft and unmistakable accent of the appeaser. Her Majesty's Government, Sir Clement said, had only one objective; and that was an early announcement in the House that the Lake had been reached. Nothing else mattered: regimental honour, vengeance and retributive punishment—all these were unimportant. There was more than one way of subduing the Nandi. They were primitives. They liked goods and possessions. They could be bought. Gifts of merchandise and cattle would be a better assurance of the Crown's benevolent intentions than the bullets of Maxims. To this end, the suave voice said, the Commissioner in Uganda, Mr F. J. Jackson, would be instructed in an immediate policy of pacification. As for the Army, there would be no more sorties, no more machine-guns, no more confiscation of cattle and burning of villages. The Nandi would not be provoked.

The gifts were given and the honeyed words were said. The Nandi grew rich, the Army withdrew into its stockades and the Maxims were silent. The warriors were arrogant with triumph. They saw no reason to refuse these agreeable offerings: the spoils of war were merely gained without the battle. That was in the last half of 1900. Sir Clement returned to England. He was not the first, or the last, Foreign Office appeaser to find his policy construed as weakness.

12. Nyanza

The land was sodden with rain until the last quarter of 1901. The black-cotton soil sank under the plates. 'I have stood on the station platforms at Fort Ternan and Kibigori (Jackson wrote) and watched a train coming slowly and cautiously along, rocking from side to side, heaving gently up and down like a ship in a choppy sea-way, and squirting liquid mud for ten feet on each side of it from under the sleepers, after the manner of a water-cart . . .' Derailments were the danger. Preston commented: 'The railway embankments became so soppy that it was almost impossible to keep the engine from turning over on her side. So long as we kept the engine going she would keep to the rails, but no sooner the train stopped than the engine, the heaviest part of the train, would quietly, inch by inch, lean over . . .'

Then, in early September, the skies cleared. Heat grew and the soil of the plain hardened and the bloom of the Lake hung again on the sky in a half-pearl of brilliant light. Excitement touched the camps. Men stared at the glow as if it were a grail in the sky. The Lake was there. This enticement of light was actually the Lake. The Lake was reachable. Preston gathered his resources, drawing men and materials from behind the rail-head and poising them like an army at the head of the Nyando Valley. During this marshalling of power he trolleyed between the stations and the tented camps, standing on the trolley or the footplates of engines or the girders of bridges, sometimes black in silhouette against the lustre of the Lake, talking to the white turbans and the anonymous faces, talking of an end of effort, an end of wandering. The Great Lake could be reached by Christmas Day. This was his message: this was his promise.

He would never know if the persuasions and the pleadings, the bribes and the exhortations had kindled them. The faces were always impassive. These were coolies. There was no nobility in work. The goal of all effort was food in the belly, a handful of rupees, fornication. But the line drove from the valley and into the Lower Kavirondo plain at the rate of a mile a day. By the end of September more than 7,000 coolies were spread between Fort Ternan and the bay.

The camps, now, were carried on the railroad like open sores on a limb. The years had bred an acceptance of corruption. It was easier like that; easier to return those thousands of degenerating men to the camps at nightfall, to leave them circumscribed by darkness in their squalor and their degradation. These were pools of labour; nothing more. In the morning they emerged. The camps lay within the railroad zone: the law was enforceable by the railroad police. This was the theory. But, in practice, that small corps of men was spread too thinly to be of value, it was apathetic after Ryall's death and it did not care. The railroad authority was content to remain blinkered. Its business was the laying of track, not the exposure of vice.

But when the track entered the Kedong Valley it also entered the administrative area of the Uganda Protectorate. Sir Harry Johnston, its Special Commissioner (and the man who professed to be shocked by the spectacle of nudity), was curiously silent about the depravity of the camps. But not so his Deputy. Jackson was disgusted. He made many complaints to Whitehouse. The camps, he wrote, were 'astounding examples of incompetence on the part of those responsible for their conduct, and for maintaining even a mild form of discipline. There were two in particular I knew well, as they were more or less standing camps, between Lumbwa Station and the tunnel (Mile 526), and there was another near Fort Ternan. I passed them on foot, and that was enough; I never had the courage to walk through one. It was quite sufficient to view them from the line, well above, and only a few hundred yards away from them. Apart from the squalor, they were crowded with prostitutes, small boys and other accessories to the bestial vices so commonly practised by Orientals . . .' These were the men of whom Sir Harry had written: 'There is probably no more prudish person than the native of India . . .'

The Lumbwa and Nandi tribes, whose women and boys were inveigled into the camps, would have disagreed.

Johnston returned to England a few months before the line drove into the Kavirondo plain. He bequeathed to his successor a situation of developing danger.

There had been no war in the land since the visit of Sir Clement Hill in the third quarter of 1900; and, for more than a twelve-month, the Nandi herds grazed around the Three Hills and swelled with the gifts of the white man. The Uganda mails came with safety and free from ambush down the path from Eldama Ravine to Londiani. The Maxims at Port Florence and Fort Ternan remained in their canvas jackets. A temporary telegraph line crossed the plain to the Lake, looped its shores and reached Entebbe. A rough dirt road joined Lumbwa with the bay. All this was bought at a price. But Hill's peace of bribery could not last. The Nandi were not so covetous that their pride could be irretrievably mortgaged for a few hundred head of cattle and a cartload of beads and wire, nor the chiefs so reduced by wealth that they were prepared to surrender to the gathering invasion of men and machines. The peace had never been more than an intermission. And in any event the young warriors were nothing without war.

Tribally the Nandi women were treated with cruelty: they were given less care than the cattle. But they were not promiscuous. And they were never for sale. When the tents of the coolie camp at Fort Ternan began to grow in great fields of triangular white flowers and the young women of the villages disappeared, the warriors rose in anger. The camp was too large, too well-armed for frontal attack even by fighting men as formidable as the Nandi. But it was assaulted on the fringes. The arrows came by night. Coolies were taken, mutilated and hung on the thorn of the bomas. Fear spread. Gangs were caught in isolation, murdered, sometimes buried alive. By the end of October the country was inflamed again. The route between Fort Ternan and the Lake was perilous, the telegraph was down and the Uganda mails were endangered.

It was then that there began a strange vacuum in recorded

history. The Foreign Office, through its emissary Sir Clement Hill, had decreed a policy of pacification. There would be no war. The Nandi would be friends. The land would be quiet. And the rails would reach the Lake. This was the progression of events: nothing, not even fact, must interfere. Colonel Evatt at Port Florence and the commanding-officer at Fort Ternan were under no illusions about their own precarious situations. Theirs was the task of protection, theirs the duty of preserving this fictional peace. In the weeks that followed every skirmish was recorded as a 'parley,' every battle as a 'dispute,' every casualty or death as a loss to 'disease.' Turk's Militia was re-formed and entrained from Nairobi, engaged by the railroad as 'casual African labour' and joined with the military in the campaign. The Lumbwa tribe, who had lost their women and children to the coolie camps, found a common cause with the Nandi. This was war.

Whitehouse and Jackson watched from the wings. The camp at Fort Ternan was the obvious provocation (although, perhaps, it was little more than a pretext for a return to the heady delights of killing and looting). There could be no peace, certainly, so long as women were prostituted and boys abducted. But the District Officers could do nothing. The camp lay in the railroad zone: the railroad should cleanse. Whitehouse met Turk at Muhoroni. This was the last call he would make upon Turk before steam ran to the Lake, before Turk left for Mombasa. It was essential, he told Turk, that the camp be cleared of local natives. The trash from the Coast or from Nairobi could remain. But he wanted every Nandi, Lumbwa or Kavirondo restored to the tribe. Turk agreed.

Turk chose twenty militiamen and a small section of railroad police. Then he entered the camp. 'Went in middle of morning when Indos were out at work,' he recorded. 'Still hundreds of them there, so-called sick and scrimshankerers and hundreds with contracts up waiting to go home. Sick, it made *us* sick to see the filth they was living in. They living like filthy pigs . . . We went through that place with a comb, tent to tent, rousing out the whores, I never saw such a hareem of whores—from coffee to black as coal and done up to the nines . . . The Indos got mad when they see their tickly going & some of them got rough & we had to clobber a few. We leave them the muck, some eighty or ninety first-class Coast & Masai whores, and we take Nandi girls and some Lumbwa and Wa-kamasie and a whole lot of little boys and girls the Indos had been at, it made you cry to see them . . .' Turk and his little band waited by the camp that night. But there was no trouble. Darkness clothed the tents and the three thousand men. The stench of that festering place came on the wind, later the whining songs and the cooking-smells of India. 'They did not want trouble, only women,' Turk commented; and, with distaste: 'If the whores don't go round they have plenty of mules to fall back on . . .'

The return of the women and the children to the tribes had no effect. The violations had been done. And war was too exhilarating a potion to be tasted and forgotten. The warriors were drunk on it. And when the track drove deeper into the plain and the power of the railroad, its engines and its steam and its waggons and its great concentrations of men and its detritus of dumps and sidings and stores, was there for all to see and measure the chiefs took counsel with each other. The iron snake was plainly an enemy. It would bring soldiers and guns, stealers of cattle and of land and of the wood of the forests, legions of the Indian hyenas. It must be stopped.

There was a bridge across the Kibigori, not permanent but thrown hurriedly in timber across the stream to take the rail. This, the station of Kibigori, was the last before the Lake was reached. Beyond the duckboards and the shed and the stencilled name (which was all there was of a station) lay twenty miles of marsh and the water of the Great Lake. The earthwork gangs were well advanced into the marsh and with ballasting and the girdering of the softest places the rail should drive with a new and final momentum to an end. An end: that incredible, obsessional word, that taboo word carried in the mind but never spoken. Twenty miles: the last fractional piece to be fitted into the pattern of a vision. It could be walked from Kibigori. It could be ridden in a cart down the ruts of the dirt road. But no-one went; not Preston nor Florence nor Turk nor any of the engineers. They would go to the Lake under a head of steam and the engine would stop where the rails were truncated at the shore and they would climb from the train and put their hands in the water under the feathers of the papyrus. They would have this pathetic and childish ritual. This was the last week of November and the sky was metal and the sun white and the light of water like an immense flower above them.

But, then, it seemed that the lands of the Lake would deny them. The camps and their crowded communities moved further into the plain, that plain which, beneath the crust of drought, was waterlogged from the rains and the seepage of the Lake. The crust droned with a plague of flies. The camps dragged a trail of pollution, casting the waste of their mess-tins and their bodies into the soil and the water of the Kibigori. This was a perfect culture; and, soon, bacillary dysentery ran from railhead to the river, decimating the gangs and filling the tents with emaciated men. Then, the heat developing and the track still advancing and touching the fringes of the mosquito breeding-swamps, the fevers of malaria came. Now a great pullulating cell of sickness lay on the plain, growing larger with the hour, divided from the Lake by eighteen infinite and insuperable miles. Preston collapsed; and, for three days, lay immersed in the green aquatic light of his tent and shuddered and stared unfocused through films of delirium at the vee of the drawn tent-flap and a sky down which the sun slipped perpetually in a stream of burning white jelly. Florence was there, the plump face parting those moving veils, leaning, withdrawing, sometimes merging with the indistinguishable faces of Billy Nesbitt and Sergeant Turner. Then the delirium passed and his eyes unfilmed and the sky through the vee was the clear colour of soapstone and the hands of Sharaf Din sponged his body and even the dung smell of the beard was recognisable. This was reality again; the reality of the track and the impassable miles. Nesbitt and Turner were now lieutenants. 'Many a time when I was prostrated with fever (he wrote later, with gratitude) would these two obliging souls carry instructions from me to my workmen so that our progress might not be delayed.'

But the rail had lost momentum; and, on the day that Preston left his tent to walk weakly to the track, the Nandi struck to the rear of railhead. The attacks came at dusk, not against men or store-dumps or any of the camps but at the line itself. The warriors descended at seven different sectors between Kibigori and Fort Ternan, wrenching the lengths of fifty-pound rail from the earth, the bolts and the sleepers, retreating, then, with this harvest of steel to the hills. The Nandi were fine smelters of metal: many spears, arrowheads and weapons would be fashioned in the villages.

Preston detached three hundred platelayers from railhead camp, entrained them downtrack on the task of restoration. A line was imperative. Without it no materials could be delivered to the railhead. But for the Nandi this was a new and profitable kind of war. The enemy could be disrupted and, at the same time, furnish the steel for future weapons of attack. The assaults continued. Railhead crept with frustrating slowness across the plain. Turk and his militia were given a shunting-engine and four waggons and, soon, the patrol steamed slowly through the nights and the early dawns. This was dangerous work. At night a man clung to the cowcatcher and peered through the channel of yellow light flung from the locomotive's lamp and searched for the gap in the luminous twin ribbons which would signify a missing rail.

Derailment was not the only hazard. Preston was in continuous fear of collision. This was a danger common to all sectors of the single-track railroad. But other sectors were under telegraph control. There was a rigid system and no train moved without authority. But the Nandi had effectively stopped the telegraph at Muhoroni; and between Muhoroni at Mile 547 and railhead at Mile 564 there was no communication. Those seventeen miles were largely flat; but there were curves of wide radius, belts of scrub, a bridge-crossing at Kibigori partially obscured by trees, a few shallow rock-canyons. These were the natural hazards. In addition the Nandi might remove a rail or place a rock or tree-trunk across the track.

Muhoroni was a depot. It was a feeder to railhead. Two trains carrying rations, materials and drinking-water ran daily to Preston's camp. They ran at a prescribed interval and, as a safety measure, he had devised a simple tally system. The first train out from Muhoroni (usually at sunrise) would arrive at railhead, unload and await the arrival of the second. The dawn-train was forbidden to return until the drivers of both locomotives had exchanged the halves of a wooden tally. Thus, possession of the required tally was a guarantee of sole possession of the track. No train must leave Muhoroni without the signed authority of the Station-Master. This was the system. Like any system based on human action it was fallible. It presupposed the interrelation of two trains—and ignored the possibility of a third. On the evening of the first day of December 1901 the system failed.

That day the fever returned and Ronald Preston lay again in his febrile world of sweat and trembling limbs and green canvas walls. The commiserating hands were there, Din's beard and the swing of Turk's long hair, Nesbitt's face and then Turner's, the two melting and coalescing and bewildering the eye with their similarity. Then the tent was empty and the lizards ran again on the walls and the light changed with the advance of the afternoon and the bodies of the lizards were membraneous against the fierce red light of the dipping sun and, through his stupor of heat and delirium, he heard the sound of the Muhoroni train. It was a heavy panting sound like the respirations of his own fever and he listened and the sound went into distance and was gone and there was nothing but the pulse of blood in his temples and the scratch of the lizards. That was surely the second train. It would reach Muhoroni before nightfall. The second train.

It was in fact the first train. Darkness lay on the Kavirondo Flat when the second train left railhead for Muhoroni. It drew eight empty trucks: it carried the four men dearest to Preston. Sergeant Turner, restive because the Lake was near and inactivity was now intolerable, had chosen to go to Muhoroni on a vague mission 'to see what progress the telegraph party were making.' Billy Nesbitt went because they were inseparable and the night was humid and there would be a wind of moving air in the open trucks. Sharaf Din boarded it because, for him, a train-ride was the pinnacle of pleasure. And Robert Turk elected to go because there was no patrol that night and the train had need of a sentinel. When the train steamed from railhead Turk was spread-eagled on the cowcatcher, Sharaf Din stood on the footplate and Nesbitt and Turner sat in the truck immediately behind the tender.

From the cowcatcher Turk could see the tunnel of yellow light thrown from the big brass lamp that hung behind and above his head on the breast of the engine. The rails caught the light and the perspective of them ran through the yellowness and died in a distant wall of darkness. The train gathered speed and, now, the rails leapt from the wall in separate tracers of light and the sleepers blurred and the rails came like steel arrows fired from darkness and fell in perfect trajectories beneath his feet. He could feel the heat of the vizor on his neck, the great pulsations of power that were bred in the frame of the locomotive trans-mitting through the iron, through the spokes of the cowcatcher, through his hands and thighs, everything fleeting now, the ballast of the track coming like a brown wave and the steels flowing and the wall of darkness parting and flapping in black wings and the stars cascading out of the night-sky like a snapped necklace, everything faster, faster, drowning the senses in an ecstasy of motion, the wind, the scented African wind in the face and in the opened mouth and in the shirt and cold on the chest, everything rushing and this night of Africa splitting into purple cliffs and the tunnel of light gathering the trees and the rocks and the jackals' eyes and hurling them into the wells of black like fragments of pictures and the train faster and the exhaust-beats urgent and the fragments fusing and, now, another sound, another rhythm, another heart somewhere in the night and he alerting to this sound, this counterpoint, this pulse of danger. Standing, then, on the cowcatcher and leaning into the wind and staring through and beyond the yellow tunnel he saw a small ruby of light touch the darkness and expire like a spark, the darkness thick again and the pulse louder and nearer and the ruby beating in quick shutters of redness on the rock-walls. Then the yellow eye came from the thickness, suspended in it and growing in it and projecting its own tunnel of light so that the tunnels met and the rails and the track and the embankments were brilliantly revealed. He flung himself from the cowcatcher, into the wet grass of night, into the void.

Preston was awakened in the small hours by the sound of steam, the shouts of men. It was very dark. The lamp outside the tent had died. Every sense warned him of catastrophe. The fever had not left him and he draped his blanket around his shoulders, went down to the track. There were many men, circles of hurricanes, a hiss of steam from the small Kibigori shunting-engine. Two trucks with open sides lay behind the engine. Turk stood by the first of the trucks. The head was bandaged. He was drinking whisky. He gestured with the bottle to the interior of the truck and Preston went to it. Nesbitt and Turner and Sharaf Din were arranged on the floor. They had the look of broken toys left in a box. Turner and Din were dead, Turk's voice told him: Nesbitt was on the way. He bent over Nesbitt and the eyes showed recognition and the lips muttered something about the last bridge. Then he died.

Later he went to the tent which Turner and Nesbitt shared. The lamp still burned and he took it into the tent and set it on the folding-table. The two cots had been prepared by Sharaf Din. They were close, separated only by an upturned box which served as a table. On it were a tobacco jar, a few books and magazines, a bottle of lime-juice. Everything was shared. There was an unfinished letter on the central table and an envelope addressed to Billy Nesbitt's wife. He doused the lamp and stood in the blackness of the tent. Then he went back to the truck. They were as alike in death as they had been in life; the hands folded on each of the chests, the boots spread at an identical angle, the broken profiles turned to the opening of the truck.

The inquiry was held on 4 December in the station-shed at Kibigori. Heat flowed through the corrugated-iron and the papers dampened from contact with the hands. Baas was the President. He was assisted by Sandiford, the Loco Superintendent; Cruickshank, the Traffic Manager; and Goldney, the Assistant Police Superintendent. Nothing much emerged from the inquiry. Someone had blundered. A third train had steamed into the night from Muhoroni. That was all. Six more names were added to the mortality statistics. Baas wrote it all down in the careful, ugly jargon that was reserved for such occasions.

Short history of the case: The line upwards of Muhoroni Mile 547 was in the hands of Construction Engineers and the telegraph wire was not in use beyond that station. The rail-head train was working upwards of Muhoroni and in the face of this the ration train proceeded on from Muhoroni forwards without any line clear or written authority and at Mile 553 the ration train and railhead train collided and resulted in the death of the following viz:

R. B. Turner (Sergt. R.E.) Telegraph Signaller
William Nesbitt, Foreman Carpenter
Mohamed Ali (Cooly)
Sharaf Din (Cooly)
Rajabu, Swahili Porter
Abdulla Sadiki (No. 802) Swahili Porter

Findings: The accident was unquestionably caused by over-zeal on the part of the staff in attempting to push on the ration train to supply men at Railhead. . .

They did undoubtedly delude each other into the belief the instructions warranted it. Of course this is a delusion and we can only accuse them of being responsible for a rash and mad act in disregarding Rule 14, Clause 2, Para 2, viz: 'Traffic Engines are on no account to run beyond that Station (i.e. Railhead Station, see para 1) unless by special order of Traffic Manager at request of the Railhead Engineer.'

This was the epitaph preserved in railroad records. It was as inelegant as the crude stone slabs in the swamp by the track that marked the graves of Nesbitt and Turner. Fifteen days after the inquiry Ronald Preston laid 10,400 feet of line in a single day and brought the track to the edge of the Victoria Nyanza. That was at sunset of the nineteenth day of December 1901.

Railhead camp lay three miles back of the Lake. Whitehouse's special train left Nairobi at dawn the following day. The train was titivated with flags and streamers. The brass and the corselet of the locomotive gleamed in sun. There were three carriages, an assortment of Government and railroad officials. The Uganda Queen had regained its splendour. Game fled from the track before the rush of that exquisite engine. This was a day of festival. The sun had no malevolence and the wind was clean. But on the Mau the cold came and the crowns of trees went black and dripping into mist: the walls of the forest were felt like the sides of a trap and the men and the women were quiet in the carriages until the mists parted and sun suffused the valley of Nyando in a sudden benison of warmth.

The train stopped at Fort Ternan. Here, in a fold of the valley, was the escort. Turk's train, its ugly shunting-engine and its three open waggons, had waited on a loop of rail for three hours. Lizards ran on the wheels like small red-and-gold toys. Turk signalled from the footplate and the engines moved; out of the valley and into the country of the Nandi. This, now, was a land of oppressiveness. The carriages were silent again and, when the track curled, they saw the waggons and the beards and slouch hats of the militia and the aligned rifles.

At Mile 553 Turk slowed the engine. There, by the track, were the two wrecked locomotives and all the intricacy of disaster. Already rust reddened the metal: already the convolvulus climbed. The whistles sounded in homage and the sound was melancholy and a woman threw a flower into the iron carcases so that it caught and hung on the convolvulus.

They reached railhead camp at four in the afternoon. Lunch was eaten and speeches were made. Then the party, Whitehouse and Ronald and Florence Preston and the railhead engineers, boarded the train. The Uganda Queen went slowly and with great dignity to Port Florence. Preston was on the footplate, easing the engine until the waters of the Lake shone ten feet from the cowcatcher. This was the moment. They left the train, climbed down the slope of the last embankment and walked through the stems of sedge and papyrus to where the water rocked. The Lake was indigo and birds were scattered on it like white paper. Preston bent to the water, scooped a little of it into his hand, smelled it. He had waited five years for this; but, now, the moment was as sour as the water. The ending, the true ending, had come eighteen miles back where the graves were. But there was still something to be done.

Whitehouse led them to where the track finished. Florence was waiting, the hands gloved in white lace and a gay straw hat shielding the face. This was the planned and final ceremony, the driving of the last key into the last rail. He gave her the keying-hammer and Preston levered with a crowbar so that she might drive home the key with greater ease. The sound of the impacts ricocheted on the water of the Lake like flung stones and birds rose and the sounds sank in its mackerel sheen. Robert Turk left the party and, through the plumes and the uniforms and the khaki drill, Whitehouse watched him walk along the sleepers, the Winchester balanced in the crook of the arm and his shadow broken by the shadow of the Suk. The caravan-master turned where the track curved. The rifle waved in salute. Then he turned again and the figures grew smaller. The hair had the red sun of evening in it.

Epilogue

The Times of London printed a suitable leader in its issue of 21 December 1901. 'A telegram from Mombasa (it reported) announces that the laying of the rails of the Uganda Railway has been completed to railhead, having reached the shore of Lake Victoria Nyanza on Thursday last. Plate-laying began on August 5th, 1896, and thus within less than five years and a half of its inception this great and arduous undertaking has been brought to a successful conclusion. The railway is altogether 572 miles long,[1] but its mere length conveys no idea of the difficulties which had to be overcome in carrying the steel track up from the shores of the Indian Ocean to a great plateau of the Central African Lakes, more than 3,000 feet above the level of the sea, over intervening ridges of twice that altitude and more. The road had frequently to be cut through dense forests or hewn out of the rock, bridges had to be built over streams subject to the sudden rise and fall of tropical rains, in the lowlands malarial fever of a virulent type had to be reckoned with, and the attacks to which working parties were often exposed in the jungle from wild beasts, disturbed for the first time in their hereditary lairs, added a new and serious danger, certainly unprecedented on such a scale, to the task of railway construction . . .'

But, of course, much remained to be done. The rails had reached the Lake and a locomotive might steam from Mombasa to Port Florence. Two years would pass before the work of re-grading and re-alignment was complete; and, from that single-track beginning, a system of rail, harbour and inland waterways

[1] Actually, the length was 582 miles.

evolved which was to serve the 700,000 square miles of Kenya, Uganda and Tanganyika.[1]

The railroad itself could not fulfil its function until Port Florence was effectively joined with Uganda. The cargo steamboat *William Mackinnon* had already begun to ply (with the steamlaunch *Kenya*) from Ugowe Bay to Entebbe. But these were inadequate for the gathering flow of trade goods, the ivory, hides and horns, the grain and the cotton and the coffee. A period began in which many craft were built and launched. The old pictures catch the throat. It is not that they are exceptionally beautiful. Some, like the m.v. *Sybil* of 1904 and the s.s. *Nyanza* of 1907, are sturdy and functional. These are working ships: they will plough their way through the waters of the Great Lake and last for half a century. Others, like the s.s. *Usoga* of 1913, have long white bows and festoons of rigging and a thin high funnel near to the stern and are undeniably graceful. It is, perhaps, the setting that engages. The ships are perfect in their settings. The white paint, brilliant in sun, reflects in the water. There are turbans and a gleam of blackberry limbs on the decks and, you feel, a hundred yellowing tusks still bloody at the roots. Forests grow down to the shores: at any moment a fish-eagle will fly from the crowns or the mauve back of a hippo will turn in the water. Even the pictures of the ceremonial launchings, the white colonial uniforms and the lines of fezzed askari, have enchantment. It is all inimitably African. It is the old Africa of the Lake; of steamer-smoke and the slave-trade and the caravans.

With the passage of time the Nandi raids became more serious. Appeasement had brought the usual sorry aftermath and the tribe was openly contemptuous of British rule. It would not pay hut tax. It raided, robbed, burned and murdered. It amassed cattle—and iron from the railroad. It crossed the Mau and raided as far down as Njoro. Settlement in the Nyanza Province was almost impossible. By the end of 1904 the country was so inflamed that no train could run to the Lake during the hours

[1] The German line from Tanga, begun in 1893 (before the British effort) reached Korogwe, only 51 miles inland, in 1902. By then, the British railroad had covered nearly 600 miles to the Lake.

of darkness and the line through the Nandi territory and its environs was picketed with troops. It was not until September of 1905 that a powerful force of the King's African Rifles, drawn from Kenya, Uganda and Nyasaland, invaded the Nandi country, crushed the warriors, killed their Laibon, impounded the cattle and brought an uneasy but permanent peace to the land.

Nairobi grew, and, with its growth, aggravated its problems of health and sanitation. There were fifty deaths from plague between 1901 and 1902. The Indian bazaar was burned to the ground again. Dr Spurrier, the Medical Officer of Health, wrote of it: '. . . here is the opportunity to remark that in young Nairobi, with unlimited space around and with the breezes of the highlands of British East Africa blowing unhindered from every quarter, a state of things has arisen which reproduced the worst features of an old densely crowded city of the East. Damp, dark, unventilated, overcrowded dwellings on filth-soaked and rubbish-bestrewn ground housed hundreds of people of most uncleanly habits who loved to have things so and were so let. Here was the soil, the "good soil" for the reception and free propagation of the plague once introduced . . .'

Representations were made to the civil authority. It was not too late to rebuild the town on a different, higher site. Even Major J. W. Pringle, Inspector of Railways to the Board of Trade, supported the agitation. 'As a station site (he wrote in 1903) the level ground commends itself to a railway engineer. As the site of the future capital of East Africa and for permanent buildings for Europeans, the sanitary engineer and the medical expert condemn it. Under the circumstances I cannot but urge on His Majesty's Government the desirability of further considering the question before the construction of numerous buildings of a permanent type pledges them hopelessly to the adoption of a bad site . . .'

But the bazaar rose again; as squalid and as insanitary as the last. Dr B. W. Cherrett, the Medical Officer of Health in 1904, protested: '. . . the whole place is in a shocking insanitary condition, in fact it is a huge evil-smelling swamp due to escape of liquid refuse from the houses, drains and overflowing sumps . . .

not the slightest provision of drainage has been attempted on the part of the authorities.'

The pressure was sustained for the next two years. Then, in 1906, the campaign for the removal of the town was abandoned. The task was now too formidable, the trading and other interests too involved, the cost too high. Nairobi, like all true cities, formed in its own way, from its own seeds. The plague returned in 1911, 1912 and 1913. Even at that late date the cement courses were still discharging sewage near to the irrigation-channels; and open gullies brought latrine refuse down from the police-lines and the gaol and deposited it on to the land near to the Telegraph Store. Winston Churchill wrote an apt postscript: 'The ground on which the town is built is low and swampy. The supply of water is indifferent and the situation generally unhealthy. It is now too late to change, and thus lack of foresight and of a comprehensive view leaves its permanent imprint upon the countenance of a new country.'

The terminus at Port Florence was renamed Kisumu. And Ugowe Bay became the Kavirondo Gulf. But the little port was never a good choice. The water of the inlet was too shallow for the ships and the trade of the new century. The level rose significantly when the hydro-electric dam was built at Ripon Falls in the 1950s; but even then ships using Kisumu and other ports on Lake Victoria were designed to draw a shallow depth of water. The R.M.S. *Victoria*, entering service in 1961 and the largest of the Lake craft, is 261 feet long—and draws when fully loaded a maximum draught of only nine feet.

George Whitehouse was appointed a Knight Commander of the Order of the Bath in 1902. He deserved his knighthood. For all the vicissitudes of the Uganda Railway, its costs and its casualties and its bitter controversies, steam had reached the Lake: his had been the burden, his the responsibility. During that term of construction he had been bedevilled by politics, bombarded by cables and memoranda, subjected to pressure by the Uganda Railway Committee. They had wanted more than a first-class engineer, more than any engineer could give. Sir Frederick Jackson, who had been so closely associated with the railroad and the territories through which it passed, said of him:

'While up to his eyes in work and overburdened with local troubles and responsibilities, he was perpetually being pestered by cables urging him to push along, and get through to the lake, in order to save the committee from being pressed to "get a move on" by the Foreign Office, whose Parliamentary Under-Secretary was, in his turn, being constantly nagged at and baited in the House of Commons.' His lieutenants were not always of the highest standard. Here again Jackson observed: 'Whitehouse was undoubtedly badly served by many of his executive staff. When the line entered Uganda territory, i.e. the Kedong Valley, but more particularly when it reached Londiani, I knew several who ought to have been sacked and their places filled by Anglo-Indians . ·. .' Whitehouse later went to the Argentine where he was Manager, for a time, of the Central Line. He retired in 1910, became a Justice of the Peace for the county of West Suffolk and died in 1938.

Little is known of Colonel Patterson. He revisited East Africa early in 1906 and, as you would expect, went on a nostalgic trip to Tsavo. It was midnight when he arrived. 'I got out and prowled about as long as time would permit (he confesses), half wondering every moment if the ghosts of the two man-eaters would spring at me out of the bushes.' Patterson's book claimed by implication that these kills represented the entire man-eating lion population of the district of Tsavo. But he was a jealous man and regarded the hunting and killing of man-eaters as his own exclusive preserve. Without doubt there were other lions at Tsavo with an addiction to human flesh. Patterson would not admit to their existence or concede the claims of other men.

The Prime Minister of the time, Lord Salisbury, assured the lions of a place in history by referring to them in the House of Lords: 'The whole of the works were put a stop to for three weeks because a party of man-eating lions appeared in the locality and conceived a most unfortunate taste for our porters[1] . . .' Salisbury was hardly a man with an ear for the accuracies of language; but, presumably, the phrase 'party of man-eating lions' implies something more than a pair.

[1] Twenty-eight Headmen and coolies were killed. The deaths of Africans in the jaws of lions were not recorded.

Karamojo Bell wrote (in a digression on African lions):
'. . . When they take to man-eating they do it thoroughly, as, for instance, the two or three old lions which terrorised the coolie camps at Tsavo during the construction of the Uganda Railway . . .' Bell did not remain at Tsavo to see the climax to the story. He was interested in ivory and he was disgusted by creatures which he stigmatized as 'pig-eaters.' The phrase 'two or three old lions' was not intended to be an assessment of the number of man-eaters: it referred to those positively identified as such. Only three lions could be thus categorized; the two killed by Patterson and the old lion whose carcase Turk had burned in the south-west hills. Bell's comment must be read in the context of the paragraph. There, alluding to the Sikh bounty-hunter and his son, he writes: 'In nine months these two men claimed the reward on some ninety skins. On about forty-five the reward was actually paid . . .' There were other bounty-hunters at Tsavo, all of whom were killing lions. They killed without discrimination. Most of the animals killed were guiltless. But among them were surely many lions perverted to the eating of men.

The late J. A. Hunter, the white hunter of contemporary fame, believed that there was 'a considerable number of man-eaters in the area.' Dead coolies, he suggested, had been flung into the bush without burial; and, finding the corpses, the lions had acquired an appetite for human flesh. But this, as a theory, pre-supposed that there had been no man-eating at Tsavo before the advent of the coolie camps. This was not so. Ronald Preston wrote: 'All the old caravan leaders had disliked this camp . . . very few caravans passing through Tsavo without a couple of their porters being missed . . .' Some of those missing were of course deserters: but some were taken by lion. The tribes feared Tsavo. There was no recorded history: but the fear was buried deep in tribal consciousness. It was inherited, it was passed from mouth to mouth, and its basis was the killing of man by lion. There is an early reference, written at Rabai in 1888 by a missionary of the Church Missionary Society, to '. . . slaves who flee the caravans along the Tsavo River, preferring the teeth and claws of the lions to the halter and the whip . . .'

There is no accepted explanation of the continuous presence

of man-eaters at Tsavo. Some claim (without biological justification) that the soil and water of Tsavo produced a salt de-
ficiency in the lions' natural prey and that the lions compensated
themselves in human flesh and blood. Probably the root lies in
the trade and slave caravans that used the Tsavo path and
encamped by its river. Disease was never far and there were
always losses. Bodies were certainly left to the scavengers. From
these (as Hunter suggests was the case with the railroad coolies)
the lions learned a flavour. And perhaps, with time, the lions
learned from cubhood that the two-legged creatures were there
to stalk and eat.

But whatever the cause the chain was broken at Tsavo in that
year of 1898. Many lions were killed. The caravans died with
the coming of the rail and no men came to light their fires by the
river. And the game retreated from the noise and development
of the railroad and the predators followed. And after that the
sportsmen came (easily and quickly on the train) to kill those
which were left. Today there are lions in the Tsavo Royal
National Park; but the Game Department Reports reveal no
disposition to the eating of men. And even the Asian station-
masters have forgotten. Patterson died in 1947.

Ronald Preston remained in East Africa. This was a country
he loved; and the railroad had given him a deeply personal
concern in its development. He saw many remarkable changes
until his death in 1952. The Nyanza railhead of 1901 had been
the beginning of the true flow of history. He had played a
dominant part in that beginning. In return the country gave
him a home and the prosperity of successful business enterprises,
the blessings of children and grandchildren. But it denied him a
proper recognition. At the railroad's half-centenary celebration
on 11 December 1945 (calculated from Whitehouse's arrival in
Mombasa exactly fifty years previously) he was a frail and unnoticed figure on the Nairobi platform. And in the Official
History, a tome of 350,000 words, he is granted a single line of
reference. Even the name Port Florence (with its proud and
intimate association) had gone.

Robert Turk died in 1926. Like many of the wild things with
which he spent his early life he found it difficult to survive. After

the railroad there were no more caravans to lead. Those wonderful instincts, developed and nurtured in the wilderness, were useless in the competition with the Asian traders. The First World War and the skirmishings on the borders of German East released him for a few years into a world of danger and violence. But it was only an interval. He returned to a rapid decline in spirit and in health, to an ending in a room over a worm-eaten shop.

The statistics, perhaps, need grouping. The line was 582 miles long. It was begun on 5 August 1896 on the Mombasa mainland and it reached Port Florence on Lake Victoria on 19 December 1901. The capital cost was £5,502,592. The cost in lives was 2,493 Asians and 5 whites. 31,983 coolies were imported from India. Of these 6,454 were invalided back to India and 16,312 were repatriated or dismissed. 6,724 Indians remained in East Africa to become the main progenitors of the present Asian population. 43 stations were built and 22 construction locomotives worn out. The bridging included the Salisbury Bridge (joining the island of Mombasa to the mainland) of 21 spans of 60-foot girders, 35 viaducts on the Kikuyu and the Mau Escarpments; and 1,280 smaller bridges and culverts.

Sources

Through Masai-Land: JOSEPH THOMSON
To the Central African Lakes and Back: JOSEPH THOMSON
Travels and Missionary Labours in East Africa: L. KRAPF
The Rise of Our Empire in East Africa: F. D. LUGARD
Early Days in East Africa: SIR FREDERICK JACKSON
The Man-Eaters of Tsavo: J. H. PATTERSON
Permanent Way: M. F. HILL
My African Journey: WINSTON S. CHURCHILL
The Genesis of Kenya Colony: R. O. PRESTON
Descending the Great Rift Valley: R. O. PRESTON
Construction of the Uganda Railway (Serial in 'The Kenya Critic'): R. O. PRESTON
Kenya—From Chartered Company to Crown Colony: C. W. HOBLEY
John Ainsworth: F. H. GOLDSMITH
Soldiering and Surveying in British East Africa: J. R. L. MACDONALD
Eighteen Years in Uganda: BISHOP TUCKER
The East Africa Protectorate: SIR CHARLES ELIOT
With Macdonald in Uganda: H. H. AUSTIN
Three Years in Savage Africa: L. DECLE
The Great Rift Valley: J. V. GREGORY
British East Africa or B.E.A.: the work of The British East Africa Company: P. L. MCDERMOTT
The Work—Diary kept during employment with the Uganda Railway 1898-1901: CHARLES RUSSELL
The Wanderings of an Elephant Hunter: W. D. M. BELL
Lugard: the Years of Adventure: MARGERY PERHAM
Nairobi: Master Plan for a Colonial Capital; A Report prepared for the Municipal Council of Nairobi: L. W. THORNTON WHITE, L. SILBERMAN, AND P. R. ANDERSON
Nairobi: The Geography of a New City: R. WALMSEY
The Mombasa Road and the Old Caravan Track (article): A. T. MATSON

Pamphlets, Reports and White Papers:

Railway Survey to Victoria Nyanza: J. W. PRINGLE

Uganda Railway: F. L. O'CALLAGHAN

Uganda Railway: H. HENSMAN

Curiosities of the Uganda Railway: F. W. EMETT

To the Victoria Nyanza by the Uganda Railway: COMMANDER B. WHITEHOUSE

Uganda Railway: R. S. RAMSDALE

Reports relating to Uganda: SIR GERALD PORTAL

Report on the Progress of the Ukamba Province: JOHN AINSWORTH

Report on the Uganda Railway (1899): SIR GUILDFORD MOLESWORTH.

Report on the Uganda Railway (1901): COLONEL T. GRACEY

Africa No. 4, 1897

Africa No. 6, 1899

Africa No. 4, 1900

Africa No. 7, 1900

Africa No. 7, 1901

Africa No. 8, 1901

Africa No. 9, 1901

Africa No. 6, 1903

Africa No. 11, 1904: (final report of Uganda Railway Committee)

Magazines of the period: The Field, The Wide World, Pall Mall, Blackwood's